Chemical Carcinogenesis

(in two parts)

Part B

The Biochemistry of Disease

A Molecular Approach to Cell Pathology

A Series of Monographs

Series Editor

Emmanuel Farber

Temple University
Philadelphia, Pennyslvania

Chemical Carcinogenesis

(in two parts)

Part B

Selected Papers Presented at the
World Symposium on Model Studies in Chemical Carcinogenesis
Held at The Johns Hopkins Medical Institutions, Baltimore, Maryland
October 31—November 3, 1972

Edited by

Paul O. P. Ts'o

The Johns Hopkins University
Baltimore, Maryland

and

Joseph A. DiPaolo

National Cancer Institute
Bethesda, Maryland

MARCEL DEKKER, INC.   New York   1974

MARCEL DEKKER, INC.

270 Madison Avenue, New York, New York 10016

LIBRARY OF CONGRESS CATALOG CARD NUMBER: 73-84816

ISBN: 0-8247-6170-7

Current printing (last digit):
10 9 8 7 6 5 4 3 2 1

PRINTED IN THE UNITED STATES OF AMERICA

CONTENTS OF PART B

VI. VIRAL CARCINOGENESIS AS RELATED TO CHEMICAL CARCINOGENESIS

VIII. SUMMARY AND PREDICTION

CONTRIBUTORS TO PART B

N. G. ANDERSON, The Molecular Anatomy (MAN) Program, Oak Ridge National Laboratory, Oak Ridge, Tennessee, and The University of Tennessee, Department of Microbiology, Knoxville, Tennessee

HUGO A. ARMELIN, Department of Biology, University of California/San Diego, La Jolla, California

JOHN P. BADER, Chemistry Branch, National Cancer Institute, Bethesda, Maryland

R. W. BALDWIN, Cancer Research Campaign Laboratories, University of Nottingham, Nottingham, England

J. K. BALL, University of Western Ontario, Cancer Research Laboratory, London, Canada

A. BENDICH, Memorial Sloan-Kettering Cancer Center, New York, New York

JAMES BONNER, Division of Biology, California Institute of Technology, Pasadena, California

E. BORENFREUND, Memorial Sloan-Kettering Cancer Center, New York, New York

BRUCE C. CASTO, BioLabs, Inc., Northbrook, Illinois

E. H. Y. CHU, Department of Human Genetics, University of Michigan Medical School, Ann Arbor, Michigan

J. H. COGGIN, JR., The Molecular Anatomy (MAN) Program, Oak Ridge, Tennessee, and The University of Tennessee, Department of Microbiology, Knoxville, Tennessee

THOMAS L. DAO, Department of Breast Surgery and Endocrine Research Laboratory, Roswell Park Memorial Institute, Buffalo, New York

JOSEPH A. DIPAOLO, Cytogenetics & Cytology Section, Biology Branch, Division of Cancer Cause and Prevention, National Cancer Institute, Bethesda, Maryland

ROBERT R. FRIIS, Department of Microbiology, University of Southern California School of Medicine, Los Angeles, California

xi

W. H. HANNON, The Molecular Anatomy (MAN) Program, Oak Ridge National Laboratory, Oak Ridge, Tennessee, and The University of Tennessee, Department of Microbiology, Knoxville, Tennessee

MORGAN HARRIS, Department of Zoology, University of California, Berkeley, California

CHARLES HEIDELBERGER, American Cancer Society Professor of Oncology, McArdle Laboratory for Cancer Research, University of Wisconsin, Madison, Wisconsin

P. J. HIGGINS, Memorial Sloan-Kettering Cancer Center, New York, New York

FA-TEN KAO, Department of Biophysics and Genetics, University of Colorado Medical School, Denver, Colorado

HAJIM KATSUTA, Department of Cancer Cell Research, Institute of Medical Science, University of Tokyo, Tokyo, Japan

J. C. LEAVITT, The Johns Hopkins University, Department of Biochemical and Biophysical Sciences, Baltimore, Maryland

MAXINE LINIAL, Department of Microbiology, University of Southern California School of Medicine, Los Angeles, California[*]

H. V. MALLING, National Institute of Environmental Health Sciences, Research Triangle Park, North Carolina

W. S. MASON, Department of Microbiology, University of Southern California, School of Medicine, Los Angeles, California

J. A. MCCARTER, University of Western Ontario, Cancer Research Laboratory, London, Canada

LISELOTTE MEZGER-FREED, The Institute for Cancer Research, Fox Chase, Philadelphia, Pennsylvania

G. BARRY PIERCE, Department of Pathology, University of Colorado Medical School, Denver, Colorado

RICHMOND T. PREHN, The Institute for Cancer Research, Philadelphia, Pennsylvania, and Department of Pathology, University of Pennsylvania, Philadelphia, Pennsylvania

BERNARD PULLMAN, Institut de Biologie Physico-Chimique, Fondation Edmond de Rothschild, Paris, France

HERBERT J. RAPP, Biology Branch, National Cancer Institute, Bethesda, Maryland

---

[*]Present address: Department of Genetics, University of Washington, Seattle, Washington

UMBERTO SAFFIOTTI, Associate Director for Carinogenesis, Division of Cancer Cause and Prevention, National Cancer Institute, Bethesda, Maryland

GORDON SATO, Department of Biology, University of California/San Diego, La Jolla, California

L. M. SCHECHTMAN, The Johns Hopkins University, Department of Biochemical and Biophysical Sciences, Baltimore, Maryland

S. S. STERNBERG, Memorial Sloan-Kettering Cancer Center, New York, New York

E. H. STONEHILL, Memorial Sloan-Kettering Cancer Center, New York, New York

TOSHIKO TAKAOKA, Department of Cancer Cell Research, Institute of Medical Science, University of Tokyo, Tokyo, Japan

P. O. P. TS'O, The Johns Hopkins University, Department of Biochemical and Biophysical Sciences, Baltimore, Maryland

PETER K. VOGT, Department of Microbiology, University of Southern California School of Medicine, Los Angeles, California

ROBIN A. WEISS, Department of Microbiology, University of Southern California School of Medicine, Los Angeles, California[*]

JOHN A. WYKE, Department of Microbiology, University of Southern California School of Medicine, Los Angeles, California[*]

TAKASHI YAMADA, Division of Pathology, National Cancer Center Research Institute, Tsukiji, Tokyo, Japan

---

[*]Present address: Imperial Cancer Research Fund, Lincoln's Inn Fields, London, England

CONTENTS OF PART A

I. INTRODUCTION AND MEMORIAL LECTURE

II. CHEMICAL AND ENZYMATIC ASPECTS OF CHEMICAL
CARCINOGEN ACTIVATION AND METABOLISM

PREFACE

From October 31st to November 3rd, 1972, an International Symposium on "Model Studies in Chemical Carcinogenesis" was held at the Johns Hopkins Medical Institutions, Baltimore, Maryland, with the following four objectives:

(1) Scientists and scholars in chemical carcinogenesis had an opportunity to come together for the exchange of information and ideas with the expectation of finding new directions for future research by examination of past results.

(2) A closer relationship was promoted among the scientists in this field and between the sponsoring agencies of this symposium and the scientific community.

(3) The comprehensive reports and critical reviews presented on the current position and future prospects in the field of chemical carcinogenesis can now be published for use by government agencies, concerned organizations, and individual scientific and medical workers.

(4) The late Professors Antoine Lacassagne and N. P. Buu-Hoi were honored for their contributions to the field of chemical carcinogenesis.

This symposium encompassed a broad range of scientific disciplines, such as chemical physics, organic chemistry, enzymology, biochemistry, cell physiology and genetics, pathology and immunology. The five major areas of discussion were:

(1) Recent advances in chemical carcinogenesis with emphasis on polycyclic hydrocarbons; correlation of the physicochemical, organic, and biochemical studies of the basic mechanism of this abnormal biological process.

(2) Interrelations of chemical, physical, and viral carcinogenesis.

(3) Recent advances in cell transformation and cell mutagenesis.

(4) Prospects in anti-carcinogenesis, such as the nucleic acid repair process and the inhibition of metabolism of carcinogens.

(5) Recent advances in cancer biology, especially in the area of immunology as it relates to the problem of carcinogenesis and possible therapy.

The comprehensive scope of this symposium clearly indicates that advances in the research on chemical carcinogenesis and the solution to the cancer problem depend on a coordinated, multidisciplinary approach.

In 1968, the first international symposium on "Physicochemical Mechanisms of Carcinogenesis" was held in Jerusalem under the auspices of the Isreael Academy of Sciences and Humanities. It was especially appropriate that the second international symposium be held in the United States in 1972, the first year of the launching of the "Conquest of Cancer Campaign" in our country. We wish to acknowledge our gratitude to the National Cancer Institute and the Atomic Energy Commission, the two federal agencies most concerned with cancer, which jointly sponsored and financed this symposium (NIH-72-C-1074, AT(49-7)-3107). In particular, we appreciate the support and participation of Dr. Frank J. Rauscher, Jr., Director, and Dr. Umberto Saffiotti, Associate Scientific Director for Carcinogenesis, Division of Cancer Cause and Prevention, of the National Cancer Institute, and of Dr. James L. Liverman, Director, Division of Biomedical and Environmental Research, Atomic Energy Commission.

Assistance of staff members of the National Cancer Institute, Atomic Energy Commission, and the Johns Hopkins Medical Institutions are gratefully acknowledged. To Jean Conley, the symposium secretary, we are indebted for her dedication and most valuable assistance, and to the staff of Marcel Dekker, Inc. for their help and patience in the preparation of this publication.

Paul O. P. Ts'o
The Johns Hopkins University

Joseph A. DiPaolo
National Cancer Institute

Chemical Carcinogenesis

(in two parts)

Part B

IV
CELL TRANSFORMATION AND DIFFERENTIATION

Chapter 20

QUANTITATIVE ASPECTS OF IN VITRO CHEMICAL CARCINOGENESIS

Joseph A. DiPaolo

Cytogenetics & Cytology Section
Biology Branch, Division of
Cancer Cause and Prevention
National Cancer Institute
Bethesda, Maryland

An interest of long duration in our laboratory has been the utilization of mammalian cells in culture for the development of in vitro models for screening environmental factors that are potential carcinogens to humans. Three aspects of this problem are considered: (a) The evidence that supports the concept that cancer can be studied in vitro. (b) The basic biologic questions to be asked in in vitro chemical carcinogenesis. (c) The factors that influence transformation. Most of the data to be presented evolved from our studies with fresh Syrian hamster embryo cells at the National Cancer Institute.

Any discussion of in vitro chemical carcinogenesis must refer to Earle and his associates (1) who, in 1943, used mass cultures of mouse connective tissue to demonstrate that transformation occurred in the presence or absence of a chemical carcinogen. This led them to investigate the causes of spontaneous transformation, but studies involving the addition of chemical carcinogens came much later. It should be pointed out that certain cell lines never knowingly exposed to a carcinogen do acquire in vitro the ability to form disorderly morphologic patterns in culture and to produce tumors when injected into animals. In one of our studies (2), mass cultures of cells derived from mouse heart tissue, free of polyoma, underwent spontaneous transformation after being cultured for three months in medium supplemented with fetal bovine serum. Spontaneous transformation, however, occurs with a much lower frequency than induced transformation, particularly with hamster cells. If cells are cloned the incidence of transformation may be determined, and thus spontaneous transformation does not interfere with the study of chemically induced transformation.

443

In the sixties, a number of investigators independently demonstrated that mass cultures could be transformed in the presence of chemical carcinogen, whereas in most cases the controls failed to produce tumors. I refer specifically to the Japanese group, Kuroki and others (3), who found that 4-nitroquinoline-N-oxide transformed Syrian hamster embryo cells without any spontaneous transformation in the controls; to Berwald and Sachs (4), who showed that mass cultures underwent transformation in the presence of carcinogen but not in the absence of carcinogen; and to our experiments reported at the International Cancer Congress in Japan (5) that a variety of carcinogens could transform, whereas no transformation occurred without carcinogen. Heidelberger's experiments with mouse cell showed responses similar to those that utilized hamster cells (6).

All of these studies, as good as they were, suffered from a serious drawback in that the primary events associated with the target cell insult could not be separated from secondary events, such as toxicity, which interfere with early recognition of transformation. Thus the need was recognized for quantitative chemical transformation systems analogous to those in virology. Sachs provided the first system for use with chemicals (4, 7), but its relevance to in vivo study was not shown since information on the ability of cells from transformed colonies to produce tumors was not given. Huberman and Sachs demonstrated a model for in vitro quantitative transformation (8); ours is a modification of the one they first described (9). At that time, we were interested in developing systems with hamster cells primarily because control cells did not readily undergo transformation, because transformed mass cultures acquired a number of indices that are characteristic of transformation, and, most important, because transformed cells were known to produce tumors (10).

The quantitative system consists of mixed hamster embryo cells plated on an irradiated rat embryo feeder layer; some hours after seeding and attachment of the hamster cells, 6 to 24 hr post-plating, they were treated with a carcinogen for a period of time ranging from a half-hour to seven days. Usually by the end of eight days of growth, two types of colonies have formed: those that are oriented and those that are disoriented and show a criss-crossing of cellular elements. The latter are referred to as morphologically transformed colonies. Their cells are refractory and continue to undergo mitosis, whereas the normal nontransformed colonies have a finite area of growth. At 8 or 9 days, if [^{3}H]thymidine is added, rare regular division occurs in nontransformed colonies; but in transformed colonies there is active division as indicated by [^{3}H]thymidine incorporation.

The transformation may be expressed in several ways: the number of transformed colonies per dish; the number of transformed colonies per cells plated; or the number of transformed colonies per total number of colonies obtained. Some of these take into consideration toxicity; others do not. The use of the term <u>neoplastic transformation</u> implies that a cell line derived from a transformed colony is capable of producing tumors when injected into the appropriate host. The word <u>malignant transformation</u> denotes that the cells produce tumors at the site of injection and that metastasis also occurs. Thus, transformation, the formation of an altered colony, becomes relevant if it results in the production of a tumor; furthermore, transformation is significant because under the conditions of culture, it does not ordinarily occur in control cultures.

Another point concerning the relevancy of in vitro studies to in vivo studies concerns the quantitation of transformation. If one adds 0.04 µg of [^{3}H] 7, 12-dimethylbenz(a)anthracene/ml medium, 80-100% of the cells, depending upon their doubling time, will take up carcinogen within a period of 6 hr (11). This is very similar to results when the back of a mouse is painted. The carcinogen spreads over the back of the mouse yet the tumors are discrete. In vitro, all cells incorporate carcinogen; yet only a small percentage undergo transformation. With a series of polycyclic hydrocarbons, a positive correlation was obtained with in vivo results (9). Carcinogens in vitro showed a high positive correlation to the Iball index. Weak carcinogens were weak transforming agents and the potent carcinogens transformed a higher frequency of cells. The two noncarcinogens, pyrene and phenanthrene, at 20 µg/ml medium (twice the maximum used for any carcinogen), produced no transformants. Compounds regarded as weak in vivo carcinogens were slightly effective in producing transformants. Benz(a)anthracene treatment produced a 0.5-1.0% transformation. Similar results were also obtained with two other weak in vivo carcinogens, benzo(e)pyrene and dibenz(a, c)anthracene, which are analogs of strong carcinogens. Four compounds that are considered potent carcinogens were more toxic than the other compounds, as indicated by the decrease in cloning efficiency. The benzo(a)pyrene consistently was about ten times as effective as the benzo(e)pyrene in the number of transformants obtained. The dibenz(a, h)anthracene was five to ten times more potent than dibenz(a, c)anthracene in producing altered clones. Only half as much 3-methylcholanthrene (5 µg/ml) was required to obtain the same range of transformants as was obtained with the benzo(a)pyrene. This concentration of carcinogen was slightly less toxic than the benzo(a)pyrene (10 µg/ml), as indicated by the slightly greater cloning efficiency. The most potent in vivo polycyclic carcinogen, 7, 12-dimethylbenz(a)anthracene, was also the most toxic in vitro compound used. Concentrations that were effective with the other carcinogens in producing transformants were so toxic that the cloning efficiency could not be obtained nor could transformants be accurately scored. At a concentration of 0.1 µg/ml, the cloning efficiency with 7, 12-dimethylbenzanthracene was approximately half of that reported with solvent only, while the frequency of transformants, 16.9%, was the highest obtained. Thus, a very strong relationship exists between the in vitro results in terms of transformation and in vivo results.

These experiments provide valuable information as to whether the observed transformation is due to selection or induction. The cloning efficiency, the ratio of the number of colonies observed to the number of cells seeded, is reduced by approximately 50% and yet a significant transformation frequency is observed. This is the first step leading to the conclusion that transformation is an inductive phenomenon for this system which uses fresh hamster cells. If transformation had been due to selection, by analogy with microbial studies, the cloning efficiency would have been expected to have been reduced by approximately 99%. Furthermore, no transformation occurred in the controls, and since transformation with an acceptable level of toxicity did occur, this becomes prima facie evidence that transformation is inductive rather than selective. If the numbers of cells at risk is increased from 300-1000, the number of transformations also increases; but the frequency of transformation is constant, demonstrating that the transformation is independent of the number of cells used. If control plates that have the same number of colonies are matched with any of those obtained with carcinogen treatment, it cannot be concluded that the dispersement of the colonies of cells is involved in the formation of a transformed colony. This is additional evidence that selection is not responsible for transformation.

A series of structurally related derivatives of carcinogens, some of which are metabolic products of known polycyclic carcinogenic hydrocarbons and most of which are known to be less carcinogenic in vivo than the parental compound, were studied (12). These compounds do not necessarily occur as a result of the metabolism of the parental compounds. All compounds were used at 5 µg/ml except the 3-hydroxybenzpyrene (a gift from Dr. H. Falk) which was used at 2.5 µg/ml. This compound, which is related to the benzo(a)pyrene, does produce transformation. Why it is positive has yet to be determined. Whether the cells cannot conjugate it to detoxify it, or whether it is reconverted to benzo(a)pyrene is unknown. Nevertheless, it is a more active carcinogen than benzo(e)pyrene, but not as active as benzo(a)pyrene. The 3-hydroxymethylcholanthrene is from Dr. Simms who reported in 1967 that it produced almost as many tumors as 3-methylcholanthrene but with a much longer latent period (13); it was a less efficient transforming agent than 3-methylcholanthrene. Simms pointed out that if the metabolic formation of ketones of methylcholanthrene are involved in its activity, this compound must be operating by a mechanism different from that of other polycyclic hydrocarbons. Previously we reported that dibenz(ah)anthracene was a potent carcinogen in vitro and that dibenz(ac)anthracene was weak; of the two analogs of dibenz(ah)anthracene tested, 5, 6-dihydrodibenz(ah)-anthracene is a weak transforming agent and 5, 6-dihydrodibenz(aj)-anthracene is a potent transforming agent. These results parallel those obtained from painting the compounds on the skin of mice.

The most potent in vivo polycyclic hydrocarbon carcinogen is 7, 12-dimethylbenz(a)anthracene, which is the most toxic and potent transforming compound that we have used in vitro. A series of compounds related to 7, 12-dimethylbenzanthracene were used at a level 200X that of 7, 12-dimethylbenzanthracene (14). Two hydroxy compounds, 7-hydroxymethyl-12-methylbenzanthracene and 12-hydroxy-methyl-7-methylbenzanthracene, were less toxic than 7, 12-dimethyl-benzanthracene and one-third to one-half as active as 7, 12-dimethylbenzanthracene in terms of transforming ability. The partially hydrogenated derivatives of 7, 12-dimethylbenzanthracene, 5, 6-dihydro-7, 12-dimethylbenzanthracene and 8, 9, 10, 11-tetrahydro-7, 12-dimethylbenzanthracene, are strongly carcinogenic and have produced sarcomas in 11 of 30 and 15 of 30 mice, respectively. In vitro, they are less toxic than the hydroxy compounds and one-fourth to one-third as potent as 7, 12-dimethylbenz(a)anthracene in capacity to induce transformation.

The ability to test compounds that belong to different classes is important for both the study of carcinogenesis and the development of screening techniques for potential carcinogens in the environment (14). Other known carcinogenic compounds are active when used directly on cells in vitro. For example, aflatoxin B_1 from Aspergillus flavus is a potent transforming agent. Methylcyclopenta(a)phenanthrene (a gift from Coombs), structurally related to a steroid, but not identifiable from natural sources, is a potent mouse skin carcinogen and a fairly active transforming agent. N-2-fluorenylacetamide (FAA) and its metabolites, the subject of recent discussions, are all toxic since they reduce cloning efficiency equally; but in terms of transforming ability, FAA and N-OH-FAA result in rare transformations while acetoxy-FAA is extremely effective. The mutagenicity of FAA and its derivatives, indicated as 8-azaguanine resistant colonies of Chinese cells (V-74-4), increased with concentration and degree of reactivity of the FAA derivative (16). It is concluded that a parallelism exists between mutagenicity and transformation.

When urethane, hydroxyurethane, or diethylnitrosoamine were applied directly to cells, no transformations were observed. As a consequence, a host-mediated in vivo-in vitro assay was developed (15) that differs in having one additional step added: The pregnant

animals are treated transplacentally with the carcinogen. As in the
standard procedure, the fetuses are removed two or three days later
at 13 days' gestation, processed in the same way, and then plated
out from a secondary culture. This procedure results in a cloning
efficiency of treated cells that is higher than the control as well as
in a significant transformation frequency; however, the increased
transformation frequency probably includes the multiplication of the
primary event that occurred in vivo. The list of carcinogenic chemicals that are positive after transplacental treatment also include,
e. g., a number of carcinogens that are effective when applied directly
to cells in culture. In screening for carcinogens the ability to mini-
mize false negatives is essential.

As indicated, a number of laboratories had established that mass
cultures were capable of being transformed, and that the transformed
cultures produced tumors. The question remained: If a transformed
colony were isolated, would cells from it be capable of producing
tumors? This important question was resolved when tumors of diverse
morphologies grew in hamsters injected with transformed cell lines
from isolated transformed colonies (17, 18). Some were clearly fibro-
sarcomatous, with interlacing bundles. Others were anaplastic, while
some were what have sometimes been called carcinoma because of
their epithelial-like cells; at this stage we prefer to call everything
sarcomatous. From the tumors, it is possible to derive tumor lines
in culture. Furthermore, primary tumors induced by carcinogenic
polycyclic hydrocarbons in Syrian hamster had, after being cultured,
many of the characteristics observed following in vitro transformation
(19). It can be concluded therefore that morphologic transformation
observed in vitro is relevant to the process of carcinogenesis in vivo.

A number of important conclusions can be drawn from dose-response
experiments. As the amount of carcinogen used increases, the transformation frequency increases; but with the hamster cells used, cell
survival, as indicated by cloning efficiency, decreases until only
25% of the colonies that were obtained in the absence of carcinogen
remain. After all cells sensitive to carcinogen are killed and only
resistant cells remain, transformation continues to increase. Consequently, it can be concluded that transformation is independent of
toxicity. If this data, as well as that of other experiments, are considered, transformation can be demonstrated to fit a Poisson distribution; furthermore the transformation phenomenon is found to be
consistent with the one-hit hypothesis (20). If the transformation
frequency is calculated on a per cell basis (number of cells initially
at risk), the problem of toxicity is not considered. With increasing
doses of carcinogen, the transformation frequency again increases.
The plotting of these data on a semi-log scale resulted in a linear
relationship with dose over a range within statistical practicability.

Even though there is a problem of solubility, selectivity would have resulted in a curve that would have plateaued, indicating that all the transformed colonies had been selected. This is finite evidence that transformation results from induction rather than selection.

It is our position that with this particular system, transformation is both inductive and direct since there is no indication of viral activation. First of all, the cells used have been tested for 18 different viruses, ranging from Reo virus, whose function is unknown, to known oncogenic viruses, such as polyoma, SV-40, and the adenos, all of which transform hamster cells. The remaining test to be completed involves virus rescue. The addition of simian virus 40 or the LLE 46 strain of adenovirus 7 to hamster cells previously transformed by 3-methylcholanthrene resulted in cells with additional transformation properties that are ordinarily associated with virus (21). The hamster cells are negative for these as well as for the hamster leukemia virus; also, Dr. Gallo recently demonstrated that cells are negative in terms of his test for reverse transcriptase. Thus, the evidence presented demonstrates that transformation with the hamster embryo system is direct and is not due to selectivity.

Although evidence has been presented to show that toxicity and transformation are independent phenomena, the question remains whether the prevention of toxicity and the rescue of cells would eliminate transformation. Protection by 1,2-benzanthracene, i.e., inhibition of 7,12-dimethylbenzanthracene-initiated cell lysis, cell division, and DNA synthesis, was first reported in 1968 (22, 23). When the cells were protected from the toxicity normally associated with a polycyclic hydrocarbon carcinogen, the transformation was enhanced (24). Low or high doses of α-naphthoflavone were given singly or every other day (three times) in association with one treatment of benzo(a)pyrene, or 3-methylcholanthrene. Treatment with a flavone or benz(a)anthracene 24 hr before the addition of a potent carcinogen, benzo(a)pyrene or 3-methylcholanthrene, enhanced the transformation of Syrian hamster cells seeded to form colonies. 7,8-Benzoflavone and benzo(a)anthracene prevented the cytotoxicity by the carcinogens, while 5,6-benzoflavone did not. The results clearly indicate that it was possible to dissociate the transforming from the toxic metabolic properties of benzo(a)pyrene and 3-methylcholanthrene. However, the enhancement obtained with 3-methylcholanthrene was not as great as that obtained with benzpyrene. These results, which indicate the complexity of the metabolism and activation of a polycyclic hydrocarbon, probably are due to the differences in metabolism of 3-methylcholanthrene and benzo(a)pyrene.

Because of the difficulties encountered in the transformation of human cells with chemical carcinogen, we have been interested in the combined action of chemicals with viruses, or radiation in the transformation of hamster cells. Consequently, studies of the interaction of chemicals with virus SA7 have been undertaken in collaboration with Casto (25). The following comments are limited to experiments in which hamster cells were pretreated with X-irradiation, cloned, and, at varying intervals, treated with benzo(a)pyrene (26). No transformation was observed with X-irradiation only. The time relationship between various irradiation doses and subsequent treatment with either 2. 5 or 10 μg benzo(a)pyrene/ml of medium was determined by adding carcinogen at 6, 12, 24, 48, and 72 hr after irradiation. The proportion of transformed to total colonies was calculated for irradiated and unirradiated cells at each time interval; the ratio of the two represents the enhancement factor. The overall shapes of the curves obtained by plotting the enhancement factor against the radiation doses were similar for both 2. 5 and 10 μg benzo(a)pyrene/ml medium. The addition of benzo(a)pyrene 6 or 12 hr after the plating of irradiated cells resulted in an enhancement of approximately 3. 5- to 4. 5-fold and 2. 9- to 3. 7-fold at 250 and 500 rad, respectively, with either low and high dose of benzo(a)pyrene. The number of transformed colonies observed with benzo(a)pyrene at 6 and 12 hr with and without irradiation were unexpectedly large, relative to the total colonies counted, indicating that although the plated cells had attached, they had not completely adapted to substrate and had been either eliminated or were physiologically more prone to transformation. Adding benzo(a)pyrene to cloned cells 24 hr after irradiation further increased enhancement in the range of 3. 5- to 4. 5-fold for doses of 250 and 500 r. Results similar to those obtained by adding benzo(a)pyrene at 24 hr, but with maximum enhancement of greater than eightfold, occurred with 250 rad when benzo(a)pyrene was added 48 hr after irradiation. Increase in the radiation dose beyond the 250–500 rad range or delay in the addition of carcinogen until 72 hr after plating increased the enhancement of transformation very little or not at all. Transformation increased on a per cell basis, indicative that induction rather than selection was responsible for the transformation, as had been found with chemicals alone. The data were again consistent with a one-hit hypothesis. The sensitivity to transformation rose during the first two days after irradiation and subsequently fell to normal or subnormal levels. This highly significant transitory increase in enhancement among irradiated cells can be taken as evidence that irradiation did not cause selection of cells more likely to be transformed by benzo(a)pyrene because of a radiation-resistant state. Selection of radiation-resistant cells would have produced a relative increase in the fraction of transformed colonies among the surviving colonies. Furthermore, the multiplication of resistant cells would have resulted in maintenance of a relatively high enhancement factor. As a result of experiments carried out in transformation with radiation and chemicals, some of the concepts of radiobiology will have to be altered.

After several years of examining chromosomes of tumor cells and transformed cells in our studies of carcinogenesis, we had concluded that chromosome changes appeared to be random (10, 18). With [^{3}H]3-methylcholanthrene, the label was concentrated in the nucleus of hamster cells with no specific chromosome localization (27). Preparation by conventional procedures of chromosomes from cells transformed by polycyclics may reveal new acrocentrics or metacentrics and new marker chromosomes, but no specific changes occur. With new techniques for chromosome bands, it has been possible to definitely identify each pair of Syrian hamster chromosomes (28). The technique has made possible the accurate identification of numerical changes in chromosome groups and of chromosomes with uncommon banding pattern that occurred subsequent to neoplastic transformation.

Thus far we have formed the following tentative conclusions: Similar banding patterns in transformed cell lines and tumor lines derived from them may occur, providing conclusive evidence that the transformed cells were responsible for tumors obtained. Different carcinogens may produce transformation associated with a specific marker but not all transformed lines have the same marker even with the same chemical. The increase in chromosome number does not involve a specific chromosome group. In some rearrangements heterochromatin may be involved. The significance of the changes observed is debatable but probably reflects secondary alterations (29).

The correlations between normal and transformed Syrian hamster cells in vitro are presented in Table 1. The correlation between these indices is high but not universal. The most significant characteristic to date, since chemically transformed cells do not have highly specific common antigen markers, is malignancy, the ability to produce tumors. Not all virally transformed cells are immortal. Sublines derived from Balb/3T3 cells, which appear to be immortal, are aneuploid, exhibit a normal heterochromatin pattern (30), and produce tumors only after being transformed (31); BHK, which is contact inhibited, may produce tumors (32). Still to be determined are the characteristics important for transformation and the characteristics essential for the development of tumors. Events leading to the formation of transplantable cells after treatment with chemicals of fresh cells may differ to a certain extent from the events occurring in the transformation of permanent lines such as Balb/3T3. Since permanent lines have already undergone a permanent hereditary change, the number of primary events may be the same. Whether any of the specific phenotypic differences between euploid and aneuploid

TABLE 1

Characteristic Differences between
Syrian Hamster Parent and Transformed Cultures

Characteristics	Parent euploid cells	Carcinogen-induced transformants
Karyotype	Euploid	Aneuploid
Life expectancy	Finite	Immortal
Malignancy	0	+
Plating efficiency	< 1%	20 – 50%
Glycolysis		Increased
Surface properties		
Contact inhibition of movement and growth	+	0
Maximum population density per cm^2		Increased
Growth in suspension	0	+
Arrangement of fibroblasts in packed culture	Ordered	Random
Morphologic changes in individual cells		+
Colony formation in agar	0	+

transformation determine the biologic characteristics of malignancy has yet to be established.

In conclusion, the observations that transformation can be quantitated, that it follows a linear relationship with dose, that transformed colonies do produce transformed lines with attributes of neoplastic cells, including the production of tumors, and that in vivo activity correlates with in vitro activity provide evidence that chemically induced carcinogenesis can be studied in vitro.

ACKNOWLEDGMENTS

The individuals involved in the in vitro studies in our laboratory are gratefully acknowledged. Mr. Donovan and Mr. Nelson have been with us from the start. Dr. Evans has been associated with guinea pig studies primarily, as well as with the hamster problem.

Dr. Takano and Dr. Oshiro collaborated on the Balb/3T3 problem and Dr. Popescu, a visiting scientist from Bucharest, has contributed to the chromosome analysis.

REFERENCES

1. W. R. Earle and A. Netleship, Production of malignancy in vitro. V. Results of injections of cultures into mice, J. Nat. Cancer Inst., 4, 213 (1943).
2. J. A. DiPaolo, In vitro spontaneous neoplastic transformation of mouse heart tissue, Nature, 213, 932 (1967).
3. T. Kuroki, M. Goto, and H. Sato, Malignant transformation on hamster embryonic cells by 4-hydroxyaminoquinoline N-oxide in tissue culture, Tohoku J. Exptl. Med., 91, 109 (1967).
4. Y. Berwald and L. Sachs, In vitro transformation of normal cells to tumor cells by carcinogenic hydrocarbons, J. Nat. Cancer Inst., 35, 641 (1965).
5. J. A. DiPaolo, Morphological and growth response of hamster cells to carcinogenic hydrocarbons in vitro, IX Intern. Cancer Congress, Abstracts of Papers, Oct. 23-29, 1966, Tokyo, Japan, p. 100.
6. T. T. Chen and C. Heidelberger, In vitro malignant transformation of cells derived from mouse prostate in the presence of 3-methyl-cholanthrene, J. Nat. Cancer Inst., 42, 915 (1969).
7. Y. Berwald and L. Sachs, In vitro cell transformation with chemical carcinogens, Nature, 200, 1182 (1963).
8. E. Huberman and L. Sachs, Cell susceptibility to transformation and cytotoxicity by the carcinogenic hydrocarbon benzo(a)pyrene, Proc. Nat. Acad. Sci., 56, 1123 (1966).
9. J. A. DiPaolo, P. J. Donovan, and R. L. Nelson, Quantitative studies of in vitro transformation by chemical carcinogens, J. Nat. Cancer Inst., 42, 867 (1969).
10. J. A. DiPaolo and P. J. Donovan, Properties of Syrian hamster cells transformed in the presence of carcinogenic hydrocarbons, Exptl. Cell Res., 48, 361 (1967).
11. D. I. Connell, L. A. Riechers, and J. A. DiPaolo, Radioautographic analysis of 7,12-diethylbenz(a)anthracene-^{3}H incorporation and cell survival of Syrian hamster embryo cells during exposure to nucleic acid inhibitors, J. Nat. Cancer Inst., 46, 183 (1971).

12. J. A. DiPaolo, P. J. Donovan, and R. L. Nelson, Transformation of Syrian hamster fetal cells in vitro by chemical carcinogens, Proc. Amer. Assoc. Cancer Res., 12, 65 (1971).
13. P. Sims, The carcinogenic activities in mice of compounds related to 3-methylcholanthrene, Intern. J. Cancer, 2, 505 (1967).
14. J. A. DiPaolo, R. L. Nelson, and P. J. Donovan, In vitro transformation of Syrian hamster embryo cells by chemical carcinogens of diverse classes, Nature New Biol., 235, 278 (1972).
15. J. A. DiPaolo, R. L. Nelson, P. J. Donovan, and C. H. Evans, Host mediated in vivo-in vitro combination assay system for chemical carcinogenesis, Arch. Pathol., 95, 380-385 (1973).
16. E. Huberman, P. J. Donovan, and J. A. DiPaolo, Mutation and transformation of cultured mammalian cells by N-acetoxy-N-2-fluorenylacetemide, J. Nat. Cancer Inst., 48, 837 (1972).
17. J. A. DiPaolo, R. L. Nelson, and P. J. Donovan, Sarcoma producing cell lines derived from clones transformed in vitro by benzo(a)pyrene, Science, 165, 917 (1969).
18. J. A. DiPaolo, R. L. Nelson, and P. J. Donovan, Morphological, oncogenic, and karyological characteristics of Syrian hamster embryo cells transformed in vitro by carcinogenic polycyclic hydrocarbons, Cancer Res., 31, 1118 (1971).
19. J. A. DiPaolo, R. L. Nelson, and P. J. Donovan, Characteristics of primary tumors induced by carcinogenic polycyclic hydrocarbons in Syrian hamsters, J. Nat. Cancer Inst., 46, 171 (1971).
20. J. A. DiPaolo, P. J. Donovan, and R. L. Nelson, In vitro transformation of hamster cells by polycyclic hydrocarbons: Factors influencing the number of cells transformed, Nature New Biol., 230, 240 (1971).
21. J. A. DiPaolo, A. S. Rabson, and R. A. Malmgren, In vitro viral transformation of chemically transformed cells, J. Nat. Cancer Inst., 40, 757 (1968).
22. L. J. Alfred and J. A. DiPaolo, Reversible inhibition of DNA synthesis in hamster embryo cells in culture: Action of 1, 2-benzanthracene and 7, 12-dimethylbenz(a)anthracene, Cancer Res., 28, 60 (1968).
23. L. J. Alfred, P. J. Donovan, M. S. Baker, and J. A. DiPaolo, Protection of cultured hamster embryonic cells from DMBA cytotoxicity and the induced synthesis of aryl hydroxylase, Cancer Res., 29, 1805 (1969).
24. J. A. DiPaolo, P. J. Donovan, and R. L. Nelson, Transformation of hamster cells in vitro by polycyclic hydrocarbons without cytotoxicity, Proc. Nat. Acad. Sci., 68, 2958 (1971).
25. B. C. Casto, W. J. Pieczynski, and J. A. DiPaolo, Enhancement of adenovirus transformation by pretreatment of hamster cells with carcinogenic polycyclic hydrocarbons, Cancer Res., 33, 819-834 (1973).

26. J. A. DiPaolo, P. J. Donovan, and R. L. Nelson, X–irradiation enhancement of transformation by benzo(a)pyrene in hamster embryo
cells, Proc. Nat. Acad. Sci. , 68, 1734 (1971).

27. J. A. DiPaolo and M. Banerjee, Autoradiographic demonstration of
H^3 methylcholanthrene labeling to nuclear components of Syrian
hamster cells in vitro, Proc. Nat. Acad. Sci. , 58, 123 (1967).

28. N. C. Popescu and J. A. DiPaolo, Identification of Syrian hamster
chromosomes by acetic-saline-Giemsa (ASG) and trypsin techniques, Cytogenetics, 11 (1972).

29. J. A. DiPaolo, N. C. Popescu, and R. L. Nelson, Banding patterns
of Syrian hamster chromosomes from cells transformed by chemical carcinogens, 11th Annual Mammalian Cell Genetics Conference, January 1973, p. 25.

30. N. C. Popescu and J. A. DiPaolo, Heterochromatin, satellite DNA
and transformed neoplastic cells, J. Nat. Cancer Inst. , 49,
603 (1972).

31. J. A. DiPaolo, K. Takano, and N. C. Popescu, Quantitation of
chemically induced neoplastic transformation of Balb/3T3 cloned
cell lines, Cancer Res. , 32, 2686 (1972).

32. V. Defendi, J. Lehman, and P. Kraemer, "Morphological normal"
hamster cells with malignant properties, Virology, 19, 592 (1963).

Chapter 21

CELL CULTURE STUDIES ON THE MECHANISMS
OF HYDROCARBON ONCOGENESIS

Charles Heidelberger

American Cancer Society Professor of Oncology
McArdle Laboratory for Cancer Research
University of Wisconsin
Madison, Wisconsin

In our laboratory we have long been interested in the cellular and
molecular mechanisms whereby polycyclic aromatic hydrocarbons (PAH)
initiate the process of oncogenesis (1, 2). It appeared that in order
for significant progress to be made in this field, it was necessary to
develop a cell culture system in which critical quantitative experiments could be carried out. In this report, I shall only discuss the
work done in my laboratory.

Following the reports of Lasnitzki (3) that PAH produced striking
histologic alterations of pieces of mouse prostate grown in organ
culture, I studied in her laboratory and then repeated her work in
organ culture using liquid medium and the prostates from inbred C3H
mice. Although we obtained histologic changes suggestive of
malignancy and implanted such pieces into isologous mice under a
variety of conditions, no tumors were induced (4). Thus, we had not
succeeded in obtaining oncogenesis in these organ cultures. However,
when the prostate pieces treated in organ culture with PAH were taken
into cell culture, lines were obtained that did produce tumors upon
inoculation into mice (5).

It was then possible to develop permanent aneuploid contact-
inhibited lines of cells derived from adult C3H mouse ventral
prostates that had a very low incidence of spontaneous malignant
transformation and produced no tumors even when 10^7 cells were
inoculated into irradiated C3H mice (6). When such cell lines were
treated with methylcholanthrene (MCA), their growth properties were
altered such that they piled up into an irregular multilayer, their

saturation density was increased, and they produced fibrosarcomas on inoculation of as few as 1000 cells subcutaneously into nonirradiated adult C3H mice (7).

The system was then made quantitative. One thousand cells were plated, treated one day later with PAH, and allowed to grow to a monolayer. The control cells stopped growing, and treated cells formed distinct piled up colonies that gave rise to fibrosarcomas on inoculation, and could easily be scored by fixing and staining the dishes (8). There was a good quantitative relationship between the oncogenic activity of a series of PAH and the number of transformed colonies they produced in this system. Moreover, there was no direct relationship between toxicity and transformation (8).

In order to determine whether the PAH transformed nonmalignant to malignant cells, or somehow selected for preexisting malignant cells, we treated single cells in individual dishes with MCA and in some cases obtained 100% of transformed clones. Recloning experiments demonstrated that all the progeny of those single cells were potentially transformed (9). Thus, selection was ruled out and it was concluded that the PAH do directly transform the cells.

Since individual PAH-induced sarcomas have individual cell-surface transplantation antigens, we wished to examine whether individual transformed clones had the same properties. It was found that the clones transformed in culture were antigenic and non-cross-reacting (10); less malignant variants lost these antigens (11). Moreover, using techniques of colony inhibition by immunized lymphocytes and by indirect immunofluorescence we succeeded in demonstrating non-cross-reactivity of 19 transformed clones all derived from a single clone. We also found that spontaneously transformed clones were not detectably antigenic (12).

At the same time we studied the metabolism of PAH in these cells, particularly with respect to the formation of water-soluble derivatives, and found that transformable cells had a higher rate of metabolism than did transformed cells (13). We also investigated the binding of a series of PAH to DNA, RNA, and proteins in these cell lines, and were not impressed with the correlation between binding to DNA and oncogenic activity (14).

At this juncture Grover and Sims produced evidence suggesting that epoxides of PAH might be metabolically activated proximal or perhaps ultimately oncogenic forms of PAH. In collaboration with them we compared with several series of PAH the ability of the parent hydrocarbon, the K-region epoxide, the cis and trans dihydrodiols, and the phenols to produce oncogenic transformation in cultures of mouse prostate and hamster embryo fibroblasts. In all cases the epoxides were considerably more active than any of the other compounds, suggesting that they were indeed metabolically activated products of the original PAH (15). More extensive studies in the mouse prostate system showed that not all epoxides produce transformation. The epoxides of phenanthrene, chrysene, and a non-K-region epoxide of benz(a)anthracene did not transform these cells (16). Transformation by MCA was greatly enhanced when the microsomal mixed-function oxidases were induced in the cells and when the cells were plated on feeder layers of metabolizing cells. Moreover, inhibition of these enzymes systems by α-naphthoflavone abolished transformation by PAH (17). These data all support the concept that PAH must be microsomally activated in order to transform mouse prostate cells. Similar findings were obtained with hamster embryo fibroblasts, in which the epoxides were the most active compounds in the series (18).

In biochemical and metabolic studies, we demonstrated that the epoxides are bound covalently to DNA, RNA, and proteins to a much greater extent than the parent PAH or other derivatives (19). We had previously partially purified from mouse skin a protein to which PAH were specifically and covalently bound in direct relation to their oncogenic activities; we termed this the h-protein (20). We also demonstrated that PAH and, to a greater extent, epoxides bind specifically to this protein in transformable (but not transformed) cells in culture (21).

In an examination of the relationship between oncogenic and mutagenic activities, we found that most oncogenic compounds were not mutagenic to T4 bacteriophage. However, chemically reactive metabolites, such as N-acetoxyacetylaminofluorene, did produce specific mutations in this system (22). We also studied the mutagenesis produced in cultured Chinese hamster cells by PAH and their derivatives. Although the PAH were inactive, as were the dihydrodiols and most phenols, the epoxides were very highly mutagenic (23). Thus, when the metabolically activated forms of chemical oncogens are recognized and tested, they are generally mutagenic. This, however, does not prove that the mechanism of oncogenesis involves a somatic mutation.

We have also developed another system of lines of very highly contact-inhibited cells from C3H mice. These cells, which we term 10/T1/2, can also be transformed and have some distinct advantages. Their properties were described and compared with those of the mouse prostate cells (24). The epoxide of 7,12-dimethylbenz(a)anthracene (DMBA) has been synthesized in our laboratory, but it is not significantly active in transforming 10/T1/2 cells, whereas the parent DMBA is (25).

It has been contended by some that chemical oncogens act by "switching on" latent C-type viruses. We have studied this possibility in a number of nontransformed and transformed clones of 10/T1/2 and prostate cells derived from three strains of mice. In C3H mice, viral gs antigens could not be detected by immunofluorescence of cells, whether or not they were transformed. In various clones derived from AKR mice, the gs antigens were present, whether or not the cells expressed the transformed phenotype. In cells from C57B1/6 mice the results were equivocal. Thus, our preliminary conclusion based on these experiments is that the genome of the cell determines whether the viral antigens will be expressed, regardless of the nontransformed or transformed phenotype of the cell (26).

Finally, when 10/T1/2 cells were synchronized by deprivation of arginine or isoleucine followed by addition, a short-acting oncogen such as MNNG only produced significant transformation when added at the time of release of the block, prior to DNA synthesis (27). This very specific cell cycle dependency of transformation will be explored further.

In conclusion, it seems that cell culture systems of chemical oncogenesis represent useful models of in vivo oncogenesis and can provide a variety of information relevant to mechanisms that cannot be obtained by experiments in animals.

REFERENCES

1. C. Heidelberger, Studies on the cellular and molecular mechanisms of hydrocarbon carcinogenesis, Europ. J. Cancer, 6, 161 (1970).
2. C. Heidelberger, Chemical carcinogenesis, chemotherapy: cancer's continuing core challenges, G. H. A. Clowes Memorial Lecture, Cancer Res., 30, 1549 (1970).
3. I. Lasnitzki, Growth pattern of the mouse prostate gland in organ culture, and its response to sex hormones, Vitamin A, and 3-methylcholanthrene, Natl. Cancer Inst. Monograph, 12, 381 (1963).
4. M. R. Röller and C. Heidelberger, Attempts to produce carcinogenesis in organ cultures of mouse prostate with polycyclic hydrocarbons, Intern. J. Cancer, 2, 509 (1967).
5. C. Heidelberger and P. T. Iype, Malignant transformation in vitro by carcinogenic hydrocarbons, Science, 155, 214 (1967).

6. T. T. Chen and C. Heidelberger, Cultivation in vitro of cells derived from adult C3H mouse ventral prostate, J. Nat. Cancer Inst., 42, 903 (1969).

7. T. T. Chen and C. Heidelberger, In vitro malignant transformation of cells derived from mouse prostate in the presence of 3-methylcholanthrene, J. Nat. Cancer Inst., 42, 915 (1969).

8. T. T. Chen and C. Heidelberger, Quantitative studies on the malignant transformation of mouse prostate cells by carcinogenic hydrocarbons, in vitro, Intern. J. Cancer, 4, 166 (1969).

9. S. Mondal and C. Heidelberger, In vitro malignant transformation by methylcholanthrene of the progeny of single cells derived from C3H mouse prostate, Proc. Nat. Acad. Sci., 65, 219 (1970).

10. S. Mondal, P. T. Iype, L. M. Griesbach, and C. Heidelberger, Antigenicity of cells derived from mouse prostate cells after malignant transformation in vitro by carcinogenic hydrocarbons, Cancer Res., 30, 1593 (1970).

11. S. Mondal, M. J. Embleton, H. Marquardt, and C. Heidelberger, Production of variants of decreased malignancy and antigenicity from clones transformed in vitro by methylcholanthrene, Intern. J. Cancer, 8, 410 (1971).

12. M. J. Embleton and C. Heidelberger, Antigenicity of clones of mouse prostate cells transformed in vitro, Intern. J. Cancer, 9, 8 (1972).

13. E. Huberman, J. K. Selkirk, and C. Heidelberger, Metabolism of polycyclic aromatic hydrocarbons in cell cultures, Cancer Res., 31, 2161 (1971).

14. T. Kuroki and C. Heidelberger, The binding of polycyclic aromatic hydrocarbons to the DNA, RNA, and proteins of transformable cells in culture, Cancer Res., 31, 2168 (1971).

15. P. L. Grover, P. Sims, E. Huberman, H. Marquardt, T. Kuroki, and C. Heidelberger, In vitro transformation of rodent cells by K-region derivatives of polycyclic hydrocarbons, Proc. Nat. Acad. Sci., 68, 1098 (1971).

16. H. Marquardt, T. Kuroki, E. Huberman, J. K. Selkirk, C. Heidelberger, P. L. Grover, and P. Sims. Malignant transformation of cells derived from mouse prostate by epoxides and other derivatives of polycyclic hydrocarbons, Cancer Res., 32, 716 (1972).

17. H. Marquardt and C. Heidelberger, Influence of "feeder cells" and inducers and inhibitors of microsomal mixed-function oxidases on hydrocarbon-induced malignant transformation of cells derived from C3H mouse prostate, Cancer Res., 32, 721 (1972).

18. E. Huberman, T. Kuroki, H. Marquardt, J. K. Selkirk, C. Heidelberger, P. L. Grover, and P. Sims. Transformation of hamster embryo cells by epoxides and other derivatives of polycyclic hydrocarbons, Cancer Res., 32, 1391 (1972).

19. T. Kuroki, E. Huberman, H. Marquardt, J. K. Selkirk, C. Heidel-
    berger, P. L. Grover, and P. Sims, Binding of K-region epoxides
    and other derivatives of benz(a)anthracene and dibenz(a, h)-
    anthracene to DNA, RNA, and proteins of transformable cells,
    Chem. -Biol. Interactions, 4, 389 (1971/72).
20. J. G. Tasscron, H. Diringer, N. Frohwirth, S. S. Mirvish, and C.
    Heidelberger, Partial purification of soluble protein from mouse
    skin to which carcinogenic hydrocarbons are specifically bound,
    Biochemistry, 9, 1636 (1970).
21. T. Kuroki and C. Heidelberger, Determination of the h-protein in
    transformable and transformed cells in culture, Biochemistry, 11,
    2116 (1972).
22. T. H. Corbett, C. Heidelberger, and W. F. Dove, Determination
    of the mutagenic activity to bacteriophage T4 of carcinogenic
    and noncarcinogenic compounds, Mol. Pharmacol., 6, 667 (1970).
23. E. Huberman, L. Aspiras, C. Heidelberger, P. L. Grover, and P.
    Sims, Mutagenicity to mammalian cells of epoxides and other
    derivatives of polycyclic hydrocarbons, Proc. Nat. Acad. Sci.,
    68, 3195 (1971).
24. C. A. Reznikoff, J. S. Bertram, and C. Heidelberger, Cancer Res.,
    in press.
25. N. Kundu, C. A. Reznikoff, and C. Heidelberger, in preparation.
26. U. Rapp, R. C. Nowinski, C. A. Reznikoff, and C. Heidelberger,
    in preparation.
27. J. S. Bertram and C. Heidelberger, Cancer Res., in press.

Chapter 22

CELLULAR HETEROGENEITY OF CANCERS

G. Barry Pierce

Department of Pathology
University of Colorado Medical School
Denver, Colorado

We have heard about chemicals and viruses that cause cancer, and about the molecular nature of their interactions with cellular components. My interests center around what develops from carcinogenic reactions.

The real consequence of carcinogenesis is a new tissue composed of parenchymal cells with supporting stroma. Many of the phenotypic traits of "normal tissue" are retained by the neoplastic parenchyma, some are absent, and others are added. The net result is a mass that has been described variously — lawless — autonomous — dedifferentiated — cells proliferating without control. These are misconceptions that misdirect research efforts.

The point of departure for this discussion is this neoplastic mass with reconsideration of observations known to most of you. Much of the work has been published and much of it comes from other investigators; the objective is to order some of the phenomena of neoplasia along developmental lines. A developmental concept of neoplasia may not be particularly useful to molecular biologists at this time, but it suggests types of experimentation at the cellular level and the possibility of experimental therapeutic approaches.

The basic observation is recognition of the importance of the cellular heterogeneity found in most tumors. There are variations in the organization of tumor cells, their cytology, function, and proliferative activity.

Structural heterogeneity of tumors is well illustrated in spontaneous adenocarcinomas of the breast of mice. Some of the tumor cells are arranged in glandular acini, whereas others are disorganized. Electron microscopy illustrates the degrees of cytologic differentiation

463

of these tumor cells. While some of the cells lack the ultrastructural machinery usually associated with the production of differentiated luxury molecules, others are well-differentiated cells containing secretory granules and numerous profiles of rough endoplasmic reticulum or smooth membranes of Golgi complexes. This type of heterogeneity raises interesting questions.

Some investigators, although rapidly diminishing in number, believe that the undifferentiated and differentiated elements are unrelated and probably represent different degrees of dedifferentiation of stem lines. Makino (1) isolated numerous clonal lines from a mouse leukemia, each of which was identifiable by a particular chromosomal marker that was faithfully passed from one generation of cells to another. This type of cellular heterogeneity can be obviated in experimental systems by cloning, but the developmental significance of neoplastic stem lines was not recognized until recently. Investigators who think developmentally would suggest that the undifferentiated cells could undergo differentiation and organization to form the well-differentiated cells of the acini (2). Berenblum (3), on the basis of his studies in chemical carcinogenesis of skin, was an early proponent of this notion. The final possibility would be that the differentiated cells might give rise to the undifferentiated ones, but there is no evidence in support of this idea.

One of the most extreme examples of heterogeneity is found in teratocarcinoma. In the male, these tumors usually occur in the gonads and are extremely malignant, causing destruction of more than 50% of their hosts within two years. The tumors are composed of a heterogeneous collection of any of the somatic tissues of the individual, and include teeth, brain, bones, glands, muscle, intermixed with a highly malignant tissue named "embryonal carcinoma" because of its resemblance to primitive embryonic epithelium (4). Human teratocarcinoma did not grow as heterotransplants or in tissue culture, so we decided to study the mechanism responsible for cellular heterogeneity in transplantable testicular teratocarcinomas of strain 129 mice — first described in 1954 by Stevens and Little (5).

In testing whether embryonal carcinoma was a multipotential stem cell capable of differentiating into the somatic tissues of the tumor, a method was developed for the isolation of embryonal carcinoma cells, and it was found that about 11% of single embryonal carcinoma cells, when transplanted intraperitoneally in a mouse, could give rise to a teratocarcinoma containing a dozen or more differentiated tissues. In all, 42 clonal lines of this tumor were developed and although they varied in their rates of growth and numbers and kinds of tissue produced, each contained elements representing the three germ layers and was therefore a teratocarcinoma (6).

Thus, it was determined that embryonal carcinoma was multi-potential and capable of differentiating into a broad spectrum of tissues. When the mode of differentiation was studied, embryonal carcinoma proved to be the equivalent of embryonic epithelium (7, 8). It differentiated first into a covering of endoderm, then mesenchyme developed from the embryonal carcinoma and lay between the endo-derm and embryonal carcinoma. The final differentiation then took place from each of the germinal layers. Thus, a teratocarcinoma appeared to be a caricature of embryogenesis. This notion was sup-ported further by the observation that embryonal carcinoma cells under certain circumstances differentiated and organized themselves into structures reminiscent of early stages of embryogenesis, which were called "embryoid bodies" (8). The most completely developed embry-oid bodies of this neoplastic system closely resemble the appearance of a mouse embryo $8\frac{1}{2}$ days postfertilization.

A method for the mass production of embryoid bodies was de-veloped (7). It turned out that if the teratocarcinoma were converted to the ascites, embryoid bodies in the thousands were produced. The embryoid bodies floated freely in the ascitic fluid and varied from large cystic structures measuring 6 mm or more in diameter to ones visible only with the microscope. Tissue culture studies and direct observations indicated that the small embryoid bodies developed into the large ones. Extremely large embryoid bodies were composed of an overlay of endoderm with supporting mesenchyme, but they lacked viable embryonal carcinoma. When transplanted in mice, they did not give rise to teratocarcinoma, rather to the equivalent of benign dermoid cysts so commonly found in the human ovary. This presented an opportunity to observe the biologic behavior of tissues derived by differentiation from embryonal carcinoma. Were these tissues benign or malignant? Cystic structures allowed to reside in the subcutaneous space of mice for six months, or about 25% of the life span of the animal, did not grow or show any of the biologic attributes of malig-nancy. These cystic structures contained a broad spectrum of well-organized derivatives of each of the embryonic germ layers, and it was concluded that embryonal carcinoma cells were multipotential and capable of differentiating into benign tissues. However, data were not available to say whether these tissues were normal — merely benign. This led to the conclusion that the dogma, once a cancer cell always a cancer cell, was incorrect. The notion that malignant cells could eventuate benign progeny was sufficiently important to require confirmation.

Confirmatory experiments were performed upon a chemically induced squamous cell carcinoma of an Irish rat, first isolated by Dr. Katheryn Snell. The tumor was composed of large masses of

undifferentiated cells surrounding so-called "squamous pearls, "
which were composed of well-differentiated squamous cells each
with a central nidus of keratin. In the first experiment, an effort
was made to identify cells synthesizing DNA (9). A pulse of tritium-
labeled thymidine was administered to hosts that were killed after
2 hr, and the tumors were examined by autoradiography. It turned
out that whereas many of the cells in the undifferentiated portion of
the tumor were synthesizing DNA, those of the pearls were not.
When an interval of 96 hr was allowed to elapse after the administration of the pulse, many labeled cells were found in the pearls (9).
This suggested, in confirmation of the experiments of Frankfurt (10),
that undifferentiated cells migrate into pearls and presumably differentiate into squamous epithelium. The experiments were repeated
using autoradiography with the electron microscope. The cells outside of the pearls were found to be extremely undifferentiated, lacking
the ultrastructural appearance of squamous cells. Their cytoplasm
contained the organelles for the production of cell cytoplasm. The
labeled cells that had migrated into the pearls were well-differentiated
squamous cells with desmosomes and tonofibrils, numerous profiles
of rough endoplasmic reticulum, membrane-lining granules, and a
paucity of polysomes. Thus, it was concluded that the undifferentiated cells migrated into the pearls and differentiated. Once again,
we were confronted with the problem, "Are the differentiated cells of
the pearls benign or malignant? " It was suspected that they were
benign because of their histologic appearance and inability to incorporate tritium-labeled thymidine. In support of this notion, pearls
were dissected from the tumors using a dissecting microscope and
transplanted subcutaneously in animals. For a control, bits of
undifferentiated tissue of approximately similar size were selected
from between the pearls and transplanted into animals. None of the
transplanted pearls gave rise to a tumor, whereas approximately one-
third of the transplants of undifferentiated tumor formed squamous
cell carcinomas (9). Thus, it was concluded that a squamous cell
carcinoma was a caricature of tissue genesis and that the squamous
cells observed in the pearls, although derived from malignant cells,
were benign. The cellular heterogeneity of this tumor was a reflection
of the ability of various stem lines to differentiate.

Thus a tumor is a developing system with malignant undifferentiated stem cells on one hand, which through processes of maturation
give rise to progeny some of which no longer express the malignant
phenotype on the other. The understanding of cancer therefore becomes
the problem of understanding the biology of malignant stem cells.

There are implications in these observations for carcinogenesis.
Reconsider the well-known observation that a tumor is a mass of tissue composed of cells. Since all other cells of the body arise by the

process of differentiation, it would seem reasonable to suppose that the mechanism of carcinogenesis should parallel in large part the mechanism of differentiation. The essential components of a differentiation are a precursor stem cell that responds to a particular stimulus evolving a new tissue with stable heritable characteristics which differ from those of the progenitor (11). The mechanism of differentiation is believed to be the result of sequential activation of various parts of the genome. If the mechanism of carcinogenesis parallels differentiation, then it is axiomatic that the target cells be undifferentiated, contain the genetic information compatible with expression of the malignant phenotype, and, as the result of carcinogenesis, have a capacity for proliferation and differentiation. The latter has been reviewed in this paper.

First, consider the origin of malignant stem cells. Several bits of information are useful in considering this problem. It is known that tumors arise only in organs capable of cell division. It is also known that when an oncogenic virus is added to a plate of fibroblasts a fibrosarcoma develops, not an adenocarcinoma, not a brain tumor, but a fibrosarcoma. Similarly, when chemical carcinogen is applied to the skin, the tumor that develops is a skin tumor, not a brain tumor nor a bone tumor. Thus, it would appear that the target cell in carcinogenesis is one capable of mitosis and determined for a particular differentiation (12). The only cells that fulfill these definitional requirements are the cells of normal tissues responsible for tissue maintenance and renewal (13). It would make good sense biologically if carcinogenesis were to reorder intracellular controls allowing for expression of fetal antigens, the production of hormones by tumors of nonendocrine tissue, alteration of the degrees of proliferation and differentiation, and other manifestations of the neoplastic phenotype.

If the hypothesis that carcinogenesis parallels the process of differentiation is to survive, then the attributes of malignancy need be encoded in the normal genome. These include the ability of the tumor to usurp the metabolic resources of the host at the expense of the host, the capacity of many tumor cells to proliferate with little evidence of differentiation, and the abilities of tumors to invade and metastasize. It turns out that each of these attributes of malignancy is a feature of normal embryonic development. The conceptus in utero has preferential treatment at the expense of the maternal organism, and will grow even when the maternal organism is starving or ill. The fertilized ovum achieves a sizable number of undifferentiated cells before overt manifestations of differentiation appear in it. The attributes of invasion and metastasis with all of the aggression that the terms imply are a reflection of our preoccupation with cancer — the disease. Invasion is the equivalent of migration. The cells of

the reticuloendothelial system invade the vasculature and metastasize to their adult sites. The germ cells of birds develop outside of
the embryo, invade the vasculature and metastasize to the gonad.
Thus, with the exception of particular antigens that might be induced
in cells as the result of the incorporation of a viral genome and that
have never been shown to be essential in the mechanism of malignant
transformation, it would appear that normal stem cells contain all of
the information required for the production of malignant stem cells
(14).

This then introduces the concept that a neoplasm is akin to a
postembryonic differentiation; or if you are disease oriented, it is
an "aberration" of cell and tissue renewal (12, 14).

If the aberration is a postembryonic differentiation, it follows
that the stability of the process would be the result of the stability
of the controls of a differentiation. Obviously, little is known about
this type of control, but the results of nuclear transplantation experiments indicate that cytoplasm plays an important role in the control
and stability of genome. When the nucleus of a differentiated gut
cell of an embryo is transplanted into the cytoplasm of an enucleated
fertilized egg, development is in accord with the state of development of the recipient cytoplasm (15). Similarly, the nucleus of a
renal cell carcinoma of the frog, believed to be induced by a virus,
when transplanted into the cytoplasm of an enucleated fertilized
ovum results in a facsimile of embryonic development. This development is not normal, but at least it is not a mass of malignant cells
that continue to proliferate until the yolk of the egg is consumed (16).

It has been amply established in these volumes that chemical
carcinogenesis is mediated by potent electrophiles that can react
with DNA, RNA, or protein. The stability of the neoplastic change
has led many to favor the possibility that interaction with DNA will
ultimately be shown to be the mechanism of carcinogenesis. Since
the stability of the neoplastic change may be explained on the basis
of alteration of existing stable cellular control processes, it is
conceivable that reaction of carcinogen with RNA or protein may be
the mechanism.

There is another implication in cancer biology stemming from the
recognition of heterogeneity in tumors. Mendelsohn found that 45%
of the cells in spontaneous breast carcinoma of the mouse did not
synthesize DNA during five days of observation, and postulated that
these malignant stem cells were arrested in G-0 (17). Since fully
differentiated cells presumably do not synthesize DNA, we wondered
if the nonproliferating population of cells might be extremely well-
differentiated, end stage senescent cells (18). Accordingly, animals

bearing spontaneous adenocarcinomas of the breast were perfused for
five days with tritium-labeled thymidine administered through an
intraperitoneal catheter attached to a pump. At the conclusion of the
experiment, the tumors were analyzed by autoradiography with the
electron microscope and attention was paid to cells that did not
synthesize DNA during the 5-day interval. These cells were scored
for their degrees of differentiation, taking into account the ultrastructural manifestations of differentiation described by Porter (19)
and Waddington (20). In each of the three tumors examined there
was a significant population of extremely well-differentiated cells
that did not synthesize DNA. In order to determine the state of differentiation of cells capable of synthesizing DNA, another tumor
was pulsed with tritium-labeled thymidine and examined by autoradiography. With few exceptions, it turned out that cells categorized
as well differentiated did not synthesize DNA. Thus, it may be concluded that a significant number of cells in this adenocarcinoma did
not synthesize DNA because they were senescent and well differentiated (18). It is not known whether these cells might ever be stimulated to return to the proliferative pool. Harris has shown that the
nonfunctional nucleus of a normoblast can be stimulated to synthesize
DNA by hybridizing the normoblast to an L-strain fibroblast (21).
Thus, it might be argued that postmitotic cells might be induced to
synthesize DNA if the appropriate stimulus could be identified. Although this is theoretically possible, the evidence indicates that
modulatory effects are usually mediated through cells capable of
division and not from terminal elements. For example, the glandular
metaplasia that occurs in squamous epithelium in the presence of
vitamin A appears to originate in the stem cells of the system after
the differentiated squamous elements deteriorate (22). There is no
evidence that senescent cells in vivo can be reactivated to synthesize DNA. The presence of large numbers of G-0 stem cells in
spontaneous adenocarcinomas suggests that tumor cells may not be
as "autonomous" and unresponsive to growth-controlling stimuli as
many have believed. Although it has been established that tumors
may lose responsiveness to systemic controls such as endocrines,
that is not the type of control to be considered now. What is to be
considered is an intimate type of control mediated by cells adjacent
to each other. The G-0 stem cells of these tumors were usually sur-
rounded by partially or completely differentiated tumor cells. This
suggests the possibility that the environment created by differentiated
cells is not an ideal environment for neoplastic stem cells. Herein
may lie the explanation for the phenomena of dormancy and of latent
tumor cells. It has been established that optimal numbers of cells
are necessary for tissue genesis to occur. Grobstein and Zwilling
demonstrated that whereas one-eighth of a head primordium of a chick

embryo, when suitably cultured in vitro, could form a head, one-sixteenth could not (23). In addition, there appears to be an optimal concentration of cells necessary for the establishment of a tissue culture. These observations all suggest that threshold numbers of like cells are required to create the optimal intimate environment for tissue genesis, whether neoplastic or normal. It is likely that the optimal requirements for malignant and benign cells differ.

It is conceivable that when normal stem cells are converted to malignant stem cells by carcinogenesis, they're separated from each other by normal cells in an environment unsuited for the optimal proliferation, growth, and behavior typical of malignant cells. When enough of these cells are aggregated together they create their own optimal micro-environment and express the clinically malignant phenotype.

These data suggest that individual malignant cells are not necessarily as autonomous and lawless as we have been led to believe. It would appear that tumor cells respond to controls that differ significantly from those of normal cells, but the fact that they respond should encourage us to pursue the notion that direction of the spontaneously occurring differentiation present in most tumors is a logical therapeutic alternative to the usual attempts at destruction of malignant cells.

ACKNOWLEDGMENT

This work was supported in part by Grant ET-1N from the American Cancer Society and Grant AM15663 from NIH.

REFERENCES

1. S. Makino, Further evidence favoring the concept of the stem cell in ascites tumors of rats, Ann. N. Y. Acad. Sci., 63, 818 (1956).
2. G. B. Pierce, "Teratocarcinoma: Model for a Developmental Concept of Cancer, " in Current Topics in Developmental Biology, Vol. 2 (A. A. Moscona and A. Monroy, eds.), Academic, New York, 1967, pp. 223-246.

3. I. Berenblum, "The Study of Tumors in Animals, " in General Pathology, 4th ed. (Lord Florey, ed.), Lloyd–Luke, London, 1970, Chap. 23, p. 744.

4. F. J. Dixon, Jr., and R. A. Moore, Testicular tumors — a clinico-pathologic study, Cancer, 6, 427 (1953).

5. L. C. Stevens and C. C. Little, Spontaneous testicular teratomas in inbred strain of mice, Proc. Nat. Acad. Sci., 40, 1080 (1954).

6. L. J. Kleinsmith and G. B. Pierce, Multipotentiality of single embryonal carcinoma cells, Cancer Res., 24, 1544 (1964).

7. G. B. Pierce and F. J. Dixon, Testicular teratomas. I. The demonstration of teratogenesis by metamorphosis of multipotential cells, Cancer, 12, 573 (1959).

8. G. B. Pierce, F. J. Dixon, and E. L. Verney, Teratocarcinogenic and tissue forming potentials of the cell types comprising neoplastic embryoid bodies, Lab. Invest., 9, 583 (1960).

9. G. B. Pierce and C. Wallace, Differentiation of malignant to benign cells, Cancer Res., 31, 127 (1971).

10. O. S. Frankfurt, Mitotic cycle and cell differentiation in squamous cell carcinomas, Intern. J. Cancer, 2, 304 (1967).

11. C. Grobstein, "Differentiation of Vertebrate Cells, " in The Cell, Vol. 1 (J. Brachet and A. E. Mirsky, eds.), Academic, New York, 1959, pp. 437–496.

12. G. B. Pierce, Differentiation of normal and malignant cells, Fed. Proc. Fed. Amer. Soc. Exptl. Biol., 29, 1248 (1970).

13. C. P. Leblond and C. E. Stevens, The constant renewal of the intestinal epithelium in the albino rat, Anat. Rec., 100, 357 (1948).

14. G. B. Pierce and L. D. Johnson, Differentiation and cancer, In Vitro, 7, 140 (1971).

15. J. B. Gurdon, Nuclear transplantation in amphibia and the importance of stable nuclear changes in promoting cellular differentiation, Quart. Rev. Biol., 38, 54 (1963).

16. T. J. King and M. A. DiBerardino, Transplantation of nuclei from the frog renal adenocarcinoma. I. Development of tumor nuclear-transplant embryos, Ann. N. Y. Acad. Sci., 126, 115 (1965).

17. M. L. Mendelsohn, Autoradiographic analysis of cell proliferation in spontaneous breast cancer of C3H mouse. III. The growth fraction, J. Nat. Cancer Inst., 28, 1015 (1962).

18. C. V. Wylie, P. K. Nakane, and G. B. Pierce, Degree of differentiation in nonproliferating cells of mammary carcinoma, Differentiation, 1, 11 (1973.

19. K. R. Porter, "The Ground Substance: Observations from Electron Microscopy, " in The Cell, Vol. 2 (J. Brachet and A. E. Mirsky, eds.), Academic, New York, 1961, Chap. 9, pp. 621–675.

20. G. H. Waddington, Ultrastructure aspects of cellular differentia-
    tion, Symp. Soc. Exptl. Biol., 17, 85 (1963).
21. H. Harris, Nucleus and Cytoplasm, Clarendon Press, Oxford,
    1968, p. 97.
22. A. B. Fell and E. Mellanby, Metaplasia produced in cultures of
    chick ectoderm of high vitamin A, J. Physiol. London, 119,
    470 (1953).
23. C. Grobstein and E. Zwilling, Modification of growth and dif-
    ferentiation of chorio-allantoic grafts of chick blastoderm pieces
    after cultivation at a glassclot interface, J. Exptl. Zool., 122,
    259 (1953).

Chapter 23

MALIGNANT TRANSFORMATION OF RAT LIVER PARENCHYMAL CELLS BY CHEMICAL CARCINOGENS IN TISSUE CULTURE

Hajim Katsuta and Toshiko Takaoka

Department of Cancer Cell Research
Institute of Medical Science
University of Tokyo
Tokyo, Japan

Takashi Yamada

Division of Pathology
National Cancer Center Research Institute
Tsukiji, Tokyo, Japan

In this paper we would like to describe our work concerning chemical carcinogenesis in tissue culture, which has been carried out for the last 12 years in our laboratory.

In most of the experiments of malignant transformation in culture done by other workers, only sarcomas were produced on back-transplantation of treated cells. However, most human tumors are carcinomas rather than sarcomas, and liver carcinoma has a high frequency of occurrence in our country. This was the reason why we tried to culture liver cells to transform them in tissue culture.

In the early stage, we could maintain the survival of rat liver cells for a long time, e. g., for several months or more, but could not obtain their growth (1). When they were treated, however, with $1\gamma/ml$ dimethylaminoazobenzene (DAB) for the first 4 days of the primary culture, the proliferation of liver cells was abruptly initiated 7 to 10 days after the treatment (2). We have obtained many cell strains this way, but all the strains did not give rise to tumors upon back-transplantation. Various second treatments given to these proliferating cells did not transform them into malignant cells (3).

Later we found a way to grow liver parenchymal cells and have established many cell strains from normal rats (4, 5). These have been used for our experiments (Fig. 1).

473

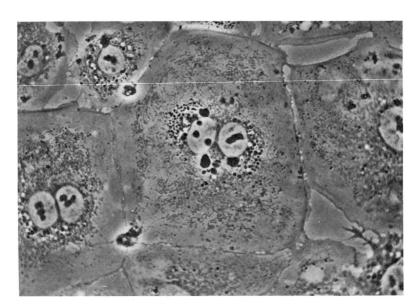

FIG. 1. Phase-contrast photomicrograph of the strain RLC-1 of liver parenchymal cells derived from a normal rat.

When we cultured the liver strains in culture tubes with flattened surfaces that were kept at an angle of 5° in stationary culture, we noticed an interesting finding. The culture medium was renewed routinely twice a week; however, when the cells were not subcultured for a long time, e. g., one to several months, tremendous changes appeared in morphology of the cells scattering on the zone nearest to the air-liquid interphase, named Nagisa, with no addition of carcinogens. The changes consisted of marked pleomorphism and atypism of cytoplasm and nucleus, fragmentation of nuclei, endomitosis, endoreduplication, and multipolar mitosis, as confirmed by cinemicrography. We eventually obtained several mutant strains by this Nagisa culture. The transformed cells closely resembled hepatoma cells in morphology and dynamic behavior. They produced nodules in hamster pouches, which regressed later, but did not kill animals on back-transplantation into rats (4). These findings suggest that mutants are produced at a higher rate in Nagisa zone and those mutants capable of growing under given conditions are selected. It should also be adaptable to the case of tumor production in man.

In some experiments, we treated the cultures of liver cells with DAB after Nagisa culture. This was very effective in obtaining mutant strains; in fact, mutant cells were produced in all the culture tubes.

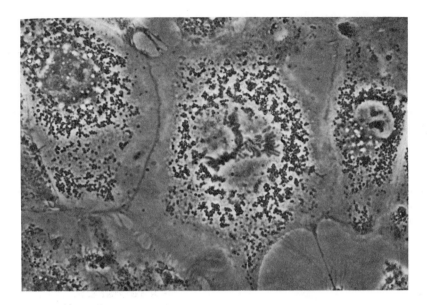

FIG. 2. Phase-contrast photomicrograph of the strain Culb TC. 4NQO-treated cells were inoculated intraperitoneally into rats, and the tumor cells produced in the ascitic cavity grew readily and rapidly when transferred to tissue culture. This photograph shows the morphology of the cells thus established by re-culturing.

It was also interesting that they were all different from each other in cell properties, especially in the sensitivity to DAB: Some strains completely metabolized 20 γ/ml DAB within 4 days, and others grew without any consumption of DAB under the same conditions (5).

4-Nitroquinoline-1-oxide (4NQO) has been known as a very active carcinogen. By the administration of this chemical into animals, no tumors were produced in liver tissue. We tried, however, to transform rat liver cells in culture by this carcinogen. Cells were treated with 3.3×10^{-6} M 4NQO one to several times, each time for 30 min. The treatment for 30 min was employed because it proved to be the most efficient time length in which cultures given [^{3}H] 4NQO attained the maximum radioactivity in their acid-insoluble fraction (6).

Malignant transformation of liver cells was obtained in all of five experimental series. In one of them, after one single treatment cells were transformed about 3.5 months later. The tumor cells produced in animals by back-transplantation grew readily and rapidly when transferred to tissue culture (Fig. 2). The control cultures were found to have undergone spontaneous transformation by the 17th month (7). The

TABLE 1

Examinations of Rat Liver Cell Strain [RLC-10(2)] after a Single Treatment with 3.3×10^{-6} M 4NQO; Growth in Soft Agar Medium, Cytoelectrophoretic Mobility, Chromosome Pattern, and Back-Transplantation into Rats

Days	Soft agar	Cyto-elec. phoresis	Chrom. analysis	Back-transplantation
0	Treated with 3.3×10^{-6} M 4NQO for 30 min			
6	o(-)			
10		o		
14		o		
21		o		
27	o(-)			
28		o		
45		o		5×10^{6}/rat I. P.
46			-------------------------------o	3-day-old F41 JAR-1 rats
51		o		Cont: 1/2 (246 day)
65		o		Exp: 2/2 (213 day)
76		o		(285 day)
90		o		
114		o		
135		o		5×10^{6}/rat I. P.
150			-------------------------------o	7-day-old F1 JAR-1×JAR-2
154		o		Cont: 2/2 (231 day)
182	o(-)			(243 day)
205		o		Exp: 2/2 (151 day)
				(178 day)
217			-------------------------------o	5×10^{6}/rat I. P.
223	o(-)			27-day-old F41 JAR-1 rats
233		o	o Cont: 42	Exp: 2/2 (147 day)
			Exp: 43	(151 day)
297		o		
321		o		5×10^{6}/rat I. P.
366	o(-)			2-day-old F1 JAR-1×JAR-2
370			----------------------------o	Cont: /2
				Exp: /2

transformed strains lost one or two chromosomes in the modal number, and they did not agglutinate with concanavalin A.

The cytobiologic examinations of rat liver cells, including back-transplantation into animals, cytoelectrophoretic mobility, growth in

TABLE 2

Growth of RLC-10(2) in Soft Agar Medium
(Number of Cell Colonies)[a]

RLC-10(2) (untreated)

	360	3600	36,000	360,000 cells/dish
1 week	0/3	0/3	0/3	0/3
3 weeks	0/3	0/3	0/3	0/3

6 days after 4NQO treatment

	6250	12,500	25,000	50,000 cells/dish
1 week	0/3	0/3	0/3	0/3
3 weeks	0/3	0/3	0/3	0/3

27 days after 4NQO treatment

	15,000	30,000	60,000	120,000 cells/dish
3 weeks	0/3	0/3	0/3	0/3

182 days after 4NQO treatment, simultaneously, JTC-16: Ca 50%[b]

	3500	35,000	350,000 cells/dish
3 weeks	0/3	0/3	0/3

223 days after 4NQO treatment

	45,000	450,000 cells/dish
3 weeks	0/3	0/3[c]

[a]Method (Yasumura): 10% CS + MEM (Nissui, × 2 AA & V); Agar (Difco, Bacto-) base layer 0.5%, over layer 0.33%.

[b]Strain JTC-16 cells, rat ascites hepatoma AH-7974, were simultaneously inoculated in a soft agar medium to confirm the reliability of the technique. These, however, produced colonies with the frequency of 50%.

[c]After 24 days, cells were transferred to ordinary culture (proliferated).

a soft agar medium, and chromosome pattern, were carried out in parallel with another experiment after a single treatment with 3.3 × 10^{-6} M 4NQO (Table 1).

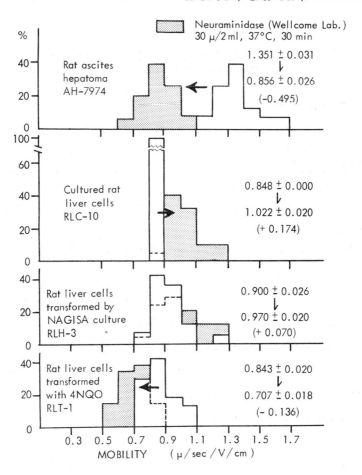

FIG. 3. Effects of neuraminidase treatment on electrophoretic mobility of cells (8).

Among the examinations employed, malignant transformation was demonstrated first by back-transplantation. It was confirmed by the transplantation 46 days after the treatment, but spontaneous transformation was found in the control cultures as well. The survival time of rats, however, was shortened month by month in the treated cultures, while it did not change in the control culture. Both have not been grown in a soft agar medium by repeated trials over 14 months (Table 2). The modal number of chromosomes did not change in the control culture but it was shifted to 43 in the treated cultures.

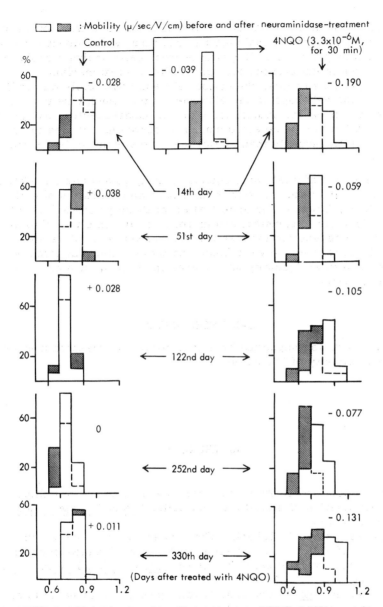

FIG. 4.   Cytoelectrophoretic patterns of RLC-10(2), rat liver cells after 4NQO treatment.

    In cytoelectrophoretic mobility, we previously found some difference between normal liver cells and hepatoma cells, especially changes after the treatment with neuraminidase (Fig. 3) (8).   In the case of back-transplantation, we could confirm the malignant transformation by tumor death of the animals after a long time, e. g., about 8 months after the transplantation. The cytoelectrophoretic analysis could reveal that the transformation took place after back-transplantation; probably because of this, the number of transformed cells was still limited in the cell population. However, it took much time to confirm the result of back-transplantation (Fig. 4). Consequently, malignant transformation may be detected earlier by surveying changes in cytoelectrophoretic mobility than by waiting for the result of back-transplantation.

In the case of viral carcinogenesis, many parameters have been proposed for the demonstration of malignant transformation of cells. Our findings, however, indicate that all of these parameters could not be adaptable to chemical carcinogenesis (9). This was also found in the back-transplantation tests, which are very closely related to immunologic reaction between hosts and tumor cells. Too much pronounced hetero-antigenicity may instead invite no growth of tumor cells in animals.

ACKNOWLEDGMENT

This work was supported by a grant for cancer research from the Japanese Ministry of Education.

REFERENCES

1.   H. Katsuta and T. Takaoka, Carcinogenesis in tissue culture. I. Cultivation of normal rat liver cells, Japan. J. Exptl. Med., 33, 265 (1963).
2.   H. Katsuta and T. Takaoka, Carcinogenesis in tissue culture. II. Proliferation-inducing effect of 4-dimethylaminoazobenzene on normal rat liver cells in culture, Japan. J. Exptl. Med., 35, 209 (1965).
3.   H. Katsuta and T. Takaoka, Carcinogenesis in tissue culture. III. Effects of the second treatments on DAB-induced proliferating liver cells of normal rats in culture, Japan J. Exptl. Med., 35, 231 (1965).
4.   H. Katsuta, T. Takaoka, Y. Doida, and T. Kuroki, Carcinogenesis in tissue culture. VII. Morphological transformation of rat

liver cells in Nagisa culture, Japan. J. Exptl. Med., 35, 513 (1965).

5. H. Katsuta and T. Takaoka, "Cytobiological Transformation of Normal Rat Liver Cells by Treatment with 4-Dimethylaminoazo-benzene after Nagisa Culture," in Cancer Cells in Culture (H. Katsuta, ed.), Univ. Tokyo Press, Tokyo, 1968, p. 321.

6. T. Andoh, K. Kato, T. Takaoka, and H. Katsuta, Carcinogenesis in tissue culture. XIII. Binding of 4-nitroquinoline 1-oxide-^{3}H to nucleic acids and proteins of L·P3 and JTC-25·P3 cells, Intern. J. Cancer, 7, 455 (1971).

7. H. Katsuta and T. Takaoka, Carcinogenesis in tissue culture. XIV. Malignant transformation of rat liver parenchymal cells treated with 4-nitroquinoline 1-oxide in tissue culture, J. Nat. Cancer Inst., 49, 1563 (1962).

8. T. Yamada, T. Takaoka, H. Katsuta, M. Namba, and J. Sato, Carcinogenesis in tissue culture. XX. Electrokinetic changes in cultured rat liver cells associated with malignant transformation in vitro, Japan. J. Exptl. Med., 42, 377 (1972).

9. H. Katsuta and T. Takaoka, "Parameters for Malignant Transformation of Mammalian Cells Treated with Chemical Carcinogens in Tissue Culture," in Topics of Chemical Carcinogenesis, Proc. of the 2nd Intern. Symp. of the Princess Takamatsu Cancer Research Fund (W. Nakahara, S. Takayama, T. Sugimura, and S. Odashima, eds.), Univ. Tokyo Press, Tokyo, 1972, p. 385.

Chapter 24

CELL CULTURES AS MODEL SYSTEMS FOR THE STUDY OF GROWTH CONTROL

Hugo A. Armelin and Gordon Sato

Department of Biology
University of California/San Diego
La Jolla, California

INTRODUCTION

Mammalian cell cultures can provide interesting model systems for the study of growth control mechanisms at the cellular or molecular level. While many variables inherent in culture procedure affect growth, it is likely that many of the factors that are important in culture play a lesser physiologic role in the intact animal. The object of our present work is to study physiologic growth regulatory mechanisms utilizing the methodologic advantages of cell culture. We have elected to concentrate our efforts on known hormones and serum growth factors. As a consequence we have found it necessary to develop cell lines from target tissues of known hormones and to develop techniques for producing culture media deficient in hormones or serum growth factors.

This chapter describes our recent observations. The practical approach to developing suitable cell lines is briefly described. Extensive study with an ovarian cell line recently developed in our laboratory is also presented. Our results suggest that model systems in cell culture may contribute significantly to basic studies in cell growth control mechanisms. These systems might also be useful for the assay of carcinogenic agents and for the study of their mechanisms of action.

EXPERIMENTAL RESULTS

The data and descriptive material below refer to experiments described in Figs. 1-7. One of the hormones used was LH, an impure preparation of bovine luteinizing hormone and bovine prolactin (Fig. 2), which were provided by NIH (NIAMD, Hormone Distribution Program). Pure steroid hormones were purchased from Nutritional Biochemicals Corporation. Insulin (Fig. 2) is a pure hormone commercially available. Medium ChCS was made up of 90% DME (Dulbeco's Modified Eagles Medium from GIBCO, but with 1.2 g/liter sodium bicarbonate plus 0.015 M of HEPES buffer from Calbiochem) plus 10% charcoal-extracted calf serum. The charcoal extraction procedure consisted of extracting serum (without heat inactivation) with 10 mg/ml of Norit A (Sigma Co.) and 1 mg/ml of Dextran T40 (stock suspension in neutralized physiologic saline) for 30 min at 55°C. The serum used throughout this work, when not charcoal extracted, was routinely heat inactivated for 30 min at 55°C. Calf serum was purchased from Flow Laboratories, Inc.; fetal calf serum and horse serum were obtained from GIBCO. Cell number was routinely assayed in a Coulter Counter. After trypsinization, the cells were suspended in Ca^{2+}-Mg^{2+}-free phosphate-buffered physiologic saline and counted in the range of 200 to 10,000 cells/ml. Routinely, 5-cm plates received 5 ml of medium and 10-cm plates received 10 ml. Each point on the growth curve is the average of two measurements made on separate replica plates. The range of each measurement is indicated by the bar. This general procedure was used in the experiments described in Figs. 1-7.

Fibroblastic Cells

3T3, an established line of mouse fibroblasts, shows a high dependence on serum for growth in culture (1). Under appropriate conditions, we have observed that the growth of these cells can be stimulated by pituitary extracts. The graphs in Fig. 1 show that impure LH preparations can stimulate the growth of 3T3 cells growing in 10% ChCS media[1,2] (charcoal-extracted calf serum has especially low growth promoting activity). Steroids (mainly hydrocortisone) enhanced the effect of LH but had no activity alone. The growth-promoting activity in LH preparation is not dialyzable, and its stability suggested that it is independent of LH activity. Growth-promoting activity was also found in pituitary extracts that had no LH activity. Virus-transformed 3T3 cells did not show a response to pituitary extracts. These results suggest that pituitary factors and steroids might play a role in the growth control of fibroblast; a full report of these data is presented elsewhere (9).

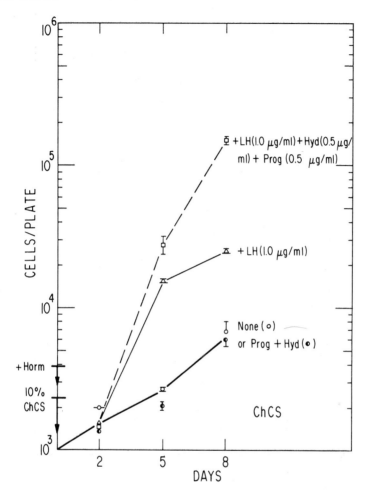

FIG. 1. Growth of 3T3 cells in ChCS; growth-promoting activity of a pituitary extract. 3T3 cells were plated in 5-cm Falcon plastic dishes. Hormones were added on the day of plating at the concentrations indicated in the graph.

Mammary Cells

Hormone-dependent, experimentally induced tumors in laboratory animals have been known for a long time (2-4). These transplantable tumors represent interesting starting material from which to develop cell lines whose growth in culture might be stimulated by hormones. We have established clonal cell lines in cultures from a rat mammary tumor developed by Dr. R. Iglesias. The growth of these cells is

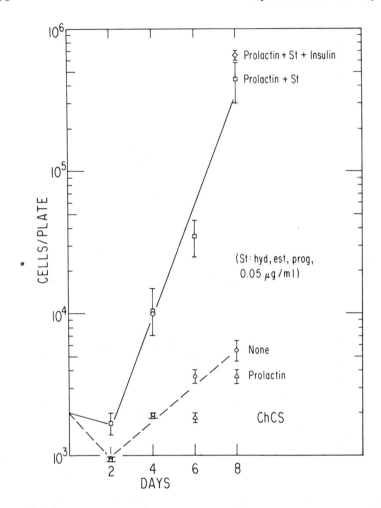

FIG. 2. Growth curves of clonal cell line obtained from a hormone-dependent mammary tumor of AC rats. Cells of mammary clone 1 were plated in ChCS in 50-mm plates. Hormones were added only on the day of plating. The concentrations of each hormone were as follows: 1 μg/ml prolactin, 1 μg/ml insulin, 0.05 μg/ml progesterone, 0.05 μg/ml estradiol, 0.05 μg/ml hydrocortisone.

strongly stimulated by steroid and protein hormones. Figure 2 presents growth curves of a mammary cell clone growing in 10% charcoal-extracted calf serum (a steroid-free serum). Cells growing without hormone addition or with prolactin alone had a doubling time of approximately 60 hr, whereas with the addition of steroids, prolactin,

TABLE 1

Growth of Ovarian Cells (uncloned population); Development of Colonies in Different Serums[a]

	Plating medium	24 hr later shifted to:	Colonies/plate, total	Maximum colony size, mm	Number of colonies = or > 1 mm
Experiment 1. 7 days' growth; plated 100 cells/plate	10% ChCS	FCHS + hormones	84 ± 14	2	42 ± 3
	FCHS + hormones	FCHS + hormones	100 ± 15	2	65 ± 5
	10% ChCS	10% ChCS	1 in 4 plates	0.2	—
	FCHS + hormones	10% ChCS	40 ± 5	0.2	Majority under 0.1 mm
Experiment 2. 9 days' growth; plated 150 cells/plate	10% ChCS	FCHS + hormones	134 ± 3	4	128 ± 4
	FCHS + hormones	FCHS + hormones	163 ± 8	4	160 ± 3
	10% ChCS	10% ChCS	10 ± 2	0.5	Majority under 0.3 mm
Experiment 3. 9 days' growth; 80 cells/plate	10% ChCS	FCHS + hormones	52 ± 4	4	—
		FCHS	56 ± 1	4	—
		10% CS	24 ± 1	1	—
		10% CHCS	4 ± 3	0.5	—

[a] Cells were plated in 9-cm plastic culture dishes in the indicated medium and shifted to another or the same medium according to the procedure described in Fig. 3. Each value in the table represents the average of four plates (fixed with formalin and stained with crystal violet).

and insulin, the doubling time observed was 18 hr. A complete report on these systems will be published elsewhere (8). These results suggested that it is possible to establish in culture mammary cells exhibiting variations of the growth control mechanisms that operate in vivo. There are several types of mammary tumor lines available, and these tumors are a potential source of cell variants.

Ovarian Cells

Clark et al. (5) established an ovarian cell line whose growth is stimulated by steroid and protein hormones. We observed that these cells have a low capacity for growth in calf serum medium and even less in charcoal-extracted calf serum medium. The data collected in Table 1 show how colonies developed from isolated cells plated at low density. In 2.5% fetal calf plus 12.5% horse serum medium, 100% of the cells developed colonies. Addition of hormones only slightly increased the size of the colonies. In order to determine whether deficient media can support cell survival for prolonged periods, cells were plated initially at low cell density in deficient media and then had their media replaced by one that supports 100% plating efficiency. If the cells could survive without growth, then the number of colonies ultimately formed after transfer to complete medium would be equal to the number of colonies formed by cells that were only plated in complete medium and had not spent the initial period after plating in deficient medium. It was determined that cell attachment was equally efficient in the two types of media. Initial plating in 10% ChCS medium for the initial 24 hr decreased the number of colonies developed to 80% of cells plated. In 10% ChCS, 5% of the plated cells developed colonies, but these colonies were of very small size. In 10% calf serum medium, a higher number of colonies was observed, 30% of the cells initially plated. Charcoal extraction of fetal calf and horse serum (FCHS) diminished the ability of these sera to support growth. These results indicated that according to the activity to stimulate colony development the sera are ordered as follows: FCHS > ChFCSHS > CS > ChCS. The highest plating efficiency is achieved in FCHS medium (100%) and the lowest in ChCS medium (practically 0%). Two points are worthy of comment at this juncture. First, although the calf serum growth-promoting activity for 3T3 is diminished by charcoal extraction, the plating efficiency for 3T3 in calf serum with or without charcoal extraction is the same. Close to 100% of the plated cells are able to initiate colonies either in CS or ChCS medium. This is a clear-cut difference between the behavior of the 3T3 and the ovarian cells. The second point that we wish to emphasize is that the ovarian cell line in these studies is a population of cells that was not cloned and has been in culture for about two

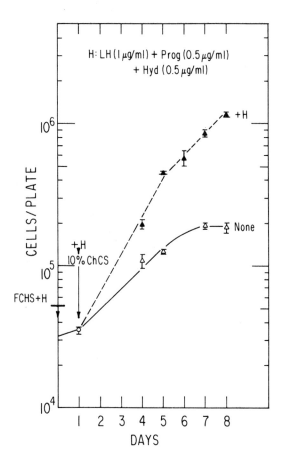

FIG. 3. Growth curves of the uncloned population of ovarian cells: shift from FCHS to ChCS. Ovarian cells were plated in FCHS (2.5% fetal calf serum + 12.5% horse serum + 85% DME) plus hormones in 9-cm plates. Twenty-four hours later, the medium was removed by aspiration, the adherent cells rinsed once with 3 ml ChCS medium, and the medium replaced with either ChCS medium or ChCS medium plus hormones.

years. Therefore, this cell population might contain several cell types with different hormonal responses. This expectation is reinforced by the fact that two epithelial types, morphologically distinguishable, are present in the culture.

Details of the ovarian cell growth pattern are presented in Figs. 3 and 4. Figure 3 shows that the growth of cells plated in FCHS

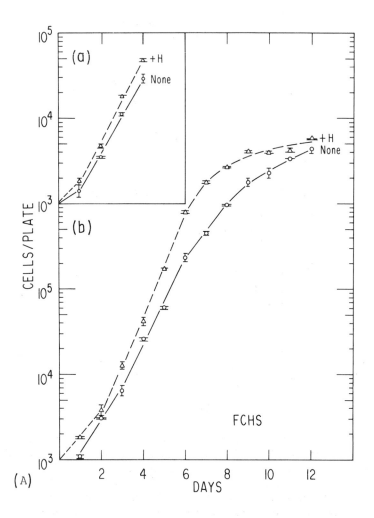

FIG. 4. Growth curves of the uncloned population of ovarian cells in FCHS and ChCS. Cells were plated in media containing hormones at the following concentrations: 1 µg/ml LH, 0.5 µg/ml progesterone, and 0.5 µg/ml hydrocortisone. (a) and (b) are two independent experiments with the same batch of 2.5% FC, 12.5% HS medium; (c) and (d) are two independent experiments with the same batch of 10% ChCS medium. Platings were made in 9-cm petri dishes.

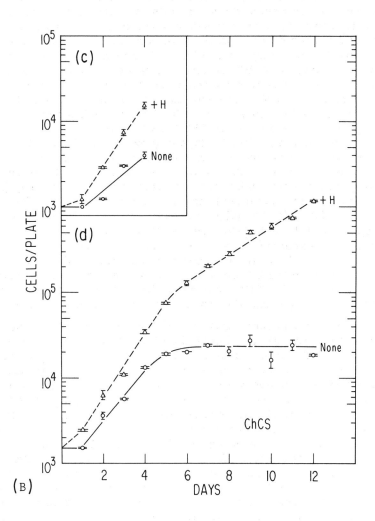

FIG. 4(B).

medium and hormones stopped completely five days after shifting to
ChCS medium. However, the same cells in ChCS medium and hormones kept growing, and after seven days, there were about 10 times
more cells per plate in the presence of hormones. A closer view is
offered by the growth curves in Fig. 4. Hormones had a slight effect
on the cell growth in FCHS medium. A small difference in the slope
of the log phase curve was observed, but the cells grew to the same
final density [Fig. 4(b)]. The doubling time of the cell population in
FCHS medium and hormones was 14 hr (from two independent experiments [Figs. 4(a) and (b)]). In ChCS medium, the cells grew to only
a very limited extent. After 12 days of growth, the plates with ChCS
medium plus hormones had 60 times as many cells as ChCS medium
plates without hormones [Fig. 4(d)]. The growth in ChCS medium plus
hormones is biphasic, indicating two rates of growth. Initially (between the first and fourth day), the doubling time was 19 hr (two experiments [Figs. 4(c) and (d)]). After the sixth day, the doubling time
was approximately 38 hr [Fig. 4(d)] or 43 hr (Fig. 3). The hormones
used in these experiments were: an impure LH preparation (1 μg/ml),
progesterone (0.5 μg/ml), and hydrocortisone (0.5 μg/ml). The
growth activity in the LH preparation is not dialyzable and is more
heat stable than LH. This greater stability and the fact that pure
LH is inactive imply that the growth activity is not identical with LH.

Addition of hormones singly to ChCS medium stimulated the development of colonies from isolated cells. Used singly, LH was less
effective than the other hormones. In order to analyze the heterogeneity of the hormonal response of different subsets of the population,
several series of clones were isolated in a selective way: From
colonies growing in ChCS plus LH (series L), ChCS plus progesterone
(series Pro), and ChCS plus hydrocortisone (series Hy). Another
series of clones were isolated in a nonselective way, that is picked
randomly from colonies growing in FCHS (series C). A limited number
of these clones were tested for growth requirements: 1 L, 4 Pro, 2 Hy,
and 2 C clones. A possible outcome of such an experiment is that
clones isolated from LH medium could be responsive to LH and not to
steroids while clones isolated in steroid medium would be responsive
to steroids and not to LH. No qualitative differences were found. All
clones were responsive to LH, progesterone, and hydrocortisone,
independent of the series to which they belonged. The differences
observed were only in the degree of responsiveness. Growth curves
for one of these clones (Pro 4), in ChCS medium, are presented in
Fig. 5. Growth of cells from clone Pro 4 is stimulated by progesterone
or hydrocortisone (same intensity) and inhibited by testosterone or
estradiol. LH alone also stimulated growth, but its activity in ChCS
medium appears to be limited.

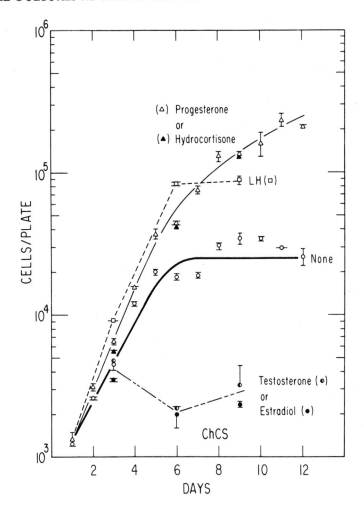

FIG. 5. Growth curves of the clone Pro-4 of ovarian cells. Hormones were added only at the day of plating at the following concentrations: 1 µg/ml LH and 0. 5 µg/ml for each steroid.

FUdR Effect in Ovarian Cells

FUdR is an agent that selectively kills dividing cells and can be used with mammalian cells for selection purposes (6). We observed that FUdR can irreversibly change the growth properties of the ovarian cell line studied in this work. Colonies of ovarian cells growing in

TABLE 2

Effect of FUdR on Growing Population of Ovarian Cells[a]

FUdR concentration (uridine was added at 10X the FUdR concentration), μg/ml	Surviving colonies/plate; 10 days' growth after FUdR treatment
0 (control)	137 ± 3
0. 5	17 ± 5
1. 0	9 ± 5
5. 0	0
10. 0	0
20. 0	0

[a] One hundred fifty cells of the uncloned ovarian line were plated in FCHS medium + hormones in 9-cm plates. After six days' growth, the number of colonies per plate was 133 ± 8 and the maximum colony diameter was 1 mm. On the sixth day, 5-fluordeoxyuridine (FUdR) was added at the concentrations indicated for 36 hr. After FUdR treatment, the medium was changed to FCHS medium + hormones + 10^{-5} M thymidine, growth was allowed to continue for an additional 10 days, and the surviving colonies were fixed and stained. The values in the table are averages from six plates. Control plates were plates treated in the same way except for FUdR addition. Surviving colonies was defined as those colonies with a diameter of at least 1. 5 mm.

FCHS medium plus hormones are completely killed if an adequate amount of FUdR is added to the cultures (see data in Table 2). When the cells are transferred to ChCS medium, growth slows, the efficiency of FUdR killing decreases, and a "modification effect" can be observed in the survivors. The protocol followed in this type of experiment is described in Table 3. Six survivor clones (series F) were isolated after the FUdR treatment. Five of them showed a morphologically different type of cell that is never observed in the stock population of ovarian cells (see Fig. 6). These modified cells have the tendency to grow in three-dimensional masses while the normal cell type grows in monolayer. Colonies of modified cells are easily distinguishable from colonies of normal cells in stained plates (Fig. 6).

TABLE 3

FUdR Effect on Ovarian Cells after Shift to ChCS Medium[a]

Day of culture	Sequence of procedure
0	200 cells/plate inoculated in FCHS + LH (1 μg/ml)
8	Shifted to 10% ChCS; colonies/plate 170 ± 10, maximum size 2 mm, majority 1 mm
10	Added FUdR (20 μg/ml) plus uridine (200 μg/ml) for 36 hr
11.5	Shifted to FCHS + hormones + 10^{-5} M thymidine
16	Six growing colonies were picked randomly: clones "F"
22	Cells fixed and stained; number of surviving colonies: 273 colonies per 15 plates; maximal size 7 mm, representing 10% of the total colonies

[a] This table summarizes the experimental procedure that gave rise to "F" clones.

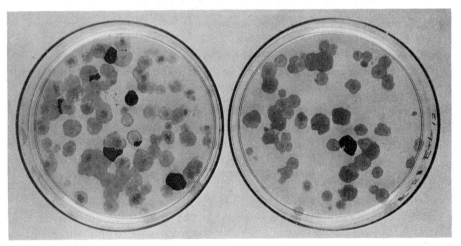

FIG. 6. Stained plates of F-1 and F-5 clones of ovarian cells. Cells of F-1 and F-5 clones (obtained in the experiment described in Table 3) were plated (200 cells/plate) in FCHS and after 15 days' growth, the plates were fixed with 10% formalin and stained with crystal violet. Darkly stained colonies and darkly stained areas of colonies are due to the presence of modified cells.

TABLE 4

Frequency of Modified Cells in F Clones[a]

Clone	% of modified colonies[b]
F-1	7
F-2	4
F-5	1
F-6	0[c]

[a] Cells from clones F-1, F-2, F-5, and F-6 were plated at 100 cells/plate. After approximately 10 days of growth, the colonies were stained and counted. The values in the table represent the average of four plates.

[b] These frequencies represent the upper limit of cells affected by FUdR during treatment. The plating efficiency for modified and normal cells in each clone seems to be the same as shown by the data in Table 5.

[c] In this clone "modified cells" were never detected. This experiment to estimate the frequency of modified cells was performed 10 days after the treatment with FUdR.

Within the same clone, modified and normal cells grow excluding each other. The frequency of modified cells in F clones were estimated 10 days after FUdR treatment, and the data are presented in Table 4. The surviving colonies in stained plates (see description of experiment in Table 3) were examined for modified cells, and about 90% of the large colonies contained at least some morphologically modified cells. Modified cells of clones F-1, F-2, and F-5 were capable of efficient growth in ChCS and were not stimulated by LH, progesterone, or hydrocortisone. Subclones of modified (named MF2) and normal (named NF2) cells from clone F-2 were isolated. The growth properties of modified MF2B cells and normal NF2A cells were studied in detail, and the results are presented in Table 5. NF2A cells were unable to develop colonies in ChCS, but were able to initiate colonies in ChCS with LH, progesterone, or hydrocortisone. MF2A (the modified type) cells developed colonies as efficiently in ChCS medium as in FCHS medium (Table 5). The growth curves in Fig. 7 indicate that the modified MF2A cells grow in ChCS medium to a high density with a doubling time of 26 hr. In FCHS medium, the doubling time observed was 13 hr and hormones had no effect on growth rate in either ChCS medium or FCHS medium. We believe that the results presented above are a clear indication that FUdR, under the conditions

TABLE 5[a]

Serum	Hormones	Number of colonies/plate	Range size of 70% of the colonies, mm
		Growth of MF2B cells: development of colonies	
FCHS	None	60 ± 6	3 - 4
	LH + Prog + Hyd	61 ± 4	3 - 4
ChCS	None	60 ± 2	1.0 - 1.5
	Hyd	53 ± 5	1.0 - 1.5
	Prog	57 ± 5	1.0 - 1.5
	LH	51 ± 5	1.0 - 1.5

Serum	Hormones	Number of colonies/plate	Maximum colony size, mm
		Growth of NF2A cells: development of colonies	
FCHS	None	62 ± 1	2.5
	LH + Prog + Hyd	59 ± 4	2.5
ChCS	None	Zero	—
	LH	12 ± 1	0.2
	Prog	30 ± 2	0.5
	Hyd	25 ± 5	0.5

[a] MF2B and NF2A are subclones of "modified" and normal cells of clone F-2 (see Table 3), respectively. Plating efficiency was determined after eight days of growth. Nine-centimeter plates in various media supplemented and unsupplemented with hormones. Values in the table are averages of four plates. Hormones were used at the same concentrations as described in Figs. 3, 4, and 7.

described, modifies the growth activity of the hormones used in this work. The mechanism of action of FUdR at the cellular or molecular level cannot be inferred from the previous results. Further experimentation on this subject is needed and may shed light on how drugs can affect the control of cell growth.

A last bit of information must be mentioned. The ovarian cell line is not able to develop tumors in Fisher rats (the rat strain of origin of these cells). Since the FUdR-modified cells showed alterations in growth control, we made preliminary tests of the ability of

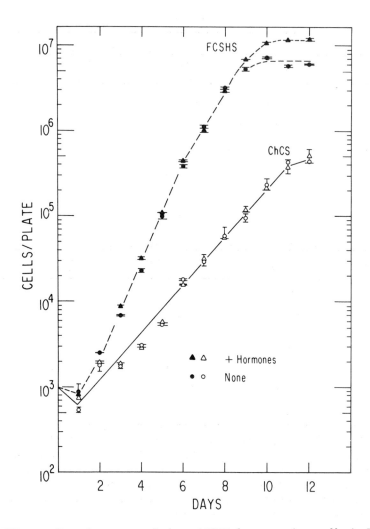

FIG. 7. Growth curves of clone MF2B from ovarian cells in FCHS and ChCS. MF2B is a subclone of "modified cells" isolated from clone F-2 of ovarian cells (see Table 3). Hormones were added only at the day of plating at the same concentrations used in the experiment of Fig. 4.

these cells to make tumors in the animal. MF2A cells were injected (10^7 cells per animal) subcutaneously in normal rats. No tumors have been observed after four months. Therefore, these cells are not highly tumorogenic, at least under our test conditions.

CONCLUDING REMARKS

Our observations in cell cultures indicate that pituitary extracts stimulate growth of different cell types: fibroblasts (9), ovarian cells (5), and mammary cells (8). Circumstantial evidence suggests that these growth-promoting activities might be different from the known pituitary hormones. Consequently, the pituitary gland could be a source of growth factors in vivo. This is a working hypothesis with immediate practical possibilities and deserves careful attention.

In order to assay or to study mechanisms of action of growth factors, it is highly essential that a minimal medium that supports survival of cells without growth be defined. Since serum is the probable source of these factors, one must develop techniques for removing these factors from sera. The charcoal extraction of the serum was intially designed to obtain steroid-free serum. This procedure extracts steroids efficiently, extracts thyroxin poorly, and does not extract proteins significantly (10). Charcoal also extracts fatty acids efficiently, as has been reported in the careful studies of Chen (7). The charcoal extraction procedure has proven very useful, since it provides reasonable survival conditions and has low growth-promoting activity. However, it is not practical to identify each of the components extracted by charcoal. Consequently, a more specific extraction procedure must be designed and eventually used in combination with charcoal extraction. One possibility is the elimination of macromolecules by affinity chromatography. This approach has already been used in our laboratory (5) with good results and promises to be of general utility.

We have not presented systematic procedures for developing target cells of trophic hormones. Our results only indicate that it is possible to do so. Hopefully, general procedures will be forthcoming. Undoubtedly, a good deal of selection is taking place during the isolation of cell strains and the strain ultimately established in culture may be quite different from the cell of origin. As long as the growth response to effector substances is retained, we feel that this is of little consequence since ultimately the intimate mechanisms of action of these effectors should be identical in the in vivo and in vitro situation.

NOTES

1. Media are designated by their serum component as this is the important variable. The synthetic part of each medium is Dulbecco's modified Eagles Medium. Thus, 10% CS medium is composed of

10% v/v of calf serum and 90% DME, and 10% ChCS medium is
10% v/v calf serum that has been extracted with charcoal.
2. List of abbreviations: LH — luteinizing hormone, ChCS — charcoal-
extracted calf serum, FCHS — fetal calf and horse serum, ChFCHS —
charcoal-extracted fetal calf and horse serum, CS — calf serum,
FUdR — 5-fluorodeoxyuridine.

ACKNOWLEDGMENT

This work was supported by the U.S. Public Health Service
(GM17019) and the National Science Foundation (15788GB). Protein
hormones for these studies were kindly supplied by the Hormone
Distribution Program NIAMD of the National Institutes of Health.
One of us (H.A.A.) is on leave from the Instituto de Química, Uni-
versidade de São Paulo, São Paulo, Brazil. He is supported by the
Fundacão de Amparo A Pesquisa Do Estado de São Paulo (FAPESP),
and a grant from the Alfred P. Sloan Foundation.

REFERENCES

1. G.J. Todaro, G.K. Lazar, and H. Green, The initiation of cell
division in a contact-inhibited mammalian cell lines, J. Cell
Comp. Physiol., 66, 325 (1965).
2. J. Furth, "Hormones and Neoplasia, " in Thule International
Symposia, Vol. 2, Cancer and Aging (A. Engel and T. Larsson,
eds.), Norkiska Bokhandelns Förlag, Stockholm, 1968, p. 131.
3. H. Kirkman and F.T. Algard, Characteristics of an androgen/
estrogen-induced, dependent leiomyosarcoma of the ductus
deferens of the Syrian hamster, Cancer Res., 25, 141 (1965).
4. R. Iglesias, "Transplantable Endocrine Tumors, " in Oncology,
1970, Proceedings of the Tenth International Cancer Congress,
Vol. I (R.L. Clark, R.W. Cumley, J.E. McCay, and M.M.
Copeland, eds.), p. 300.
5. J.L. Clark, K.L. Jones, D. Gospodarowicz, and G.H. Sato,
Growth response to hormones by a new rat ovary cell line,
Nature New Biol., 236, 180 (1972).
6. R.E. Pollack, H. Green, and G.J. Todaro, Growth control in
cultured cells: selection of sublines with increased sensitivity
to contact inhibition and decreased tumor-producing ability.
Proc. Nat. Acad. Sci., 60, 126 (1968).

7. R. F. Chen, Removal of fatty acids from serum albumin by charcoal treatment, J. Biol. Chem., 242, 173 (1967).

8. H. A. Armelin, in preparation.

9. H. A. Armelin, Pituitary extracts and steroid hormones in the control of 3T3 cell growth, Proc. Nat. Acad. Sci., 70, 2702 (1973).

10. H. A. Armelin, unpublished results.

Chapter 25

NATURE OF HORMONAL INFLUENCE IN CARCINOGENESIS: STUDIES IN VIVO AND IN VITRO

Thomas L. Dao

Department of Breast Surgery and
Endocrine Research Laboratory
Roswell Park Memorial Institute
Buffalo, New York

In hormone-regulated tissues, it is often considered axiomatic that hormones capable of stimulating excess growth and hyperactivity are potential carcinogens by virtue of such capabilities. Estrogen has been shown to induce mammary cancers in some strains of mice and rats just like chemical carcinogens such as 3-methylcholanthrene (3-MC) and 7, 12-dimethylbenz(a)anthracene (DMBA) (1-4). Can we then equate estrogen to chemical carcinogens insofar as induction of mammary cancer is concerned? How does estrogen exert its carcinogenic effect? These questions are yet to be answered.

Mammary tumorigenesis in mice has been intensively investigated. Nandi, Bern, and DeOme (5, 6) considered multiple factors including viral, genetic, and hormonal ones in mouse mammary tumorigenesis and concluded that hormones most likely play a "permissive" role, rather than an inductive one. Their experiments disclosed that in a genetically susceptible virus-infected mouse, hormones supporting normal gland development may result in the emergence of "precancerous" lesions; hormones maintaining such hyperplastic lesions may result in the emergence of tumors. According to these authors, hormonal factors involved in the development of a "precancerous" lesion may be no more than milieu concerned with the normal development of the mammary gland.

Some in vivo studies from our laboratory have given rather convincing evidence that initiation of carcinogenesis of the mammary gland requires the presence of ovarian hormones (7). In these experiments, it appears that the hormonal influence may be more than just promoting tumor growth: it may as well be involved in the inductive

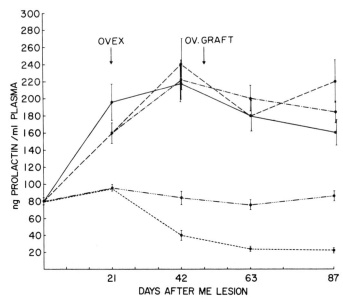

FIG. 1. Effect of median-eminence (ME) lesions, ovariectomy, and ovarian graft on plasma prolactin levels in rats. Each point on the graph represents the mean of prolactin values from five rats at different time intervals. $\cdots\cdots$, control (intact); $---$, ovariectomy (ovex); $-\cdot-$, rats with median-eminence lesions; $\underline{\hspace{1em}}$, ovariectomized rats with median-eminence lesions; $---$, ovariectomized rats with median-eminence lesions and ovarian (Ov) grafts. [Reproduced from Cancer Res., 33, 411-414 (1973), by permission from the publishers.]

process. The hormone(s) may be playing the role of a control mechanism regulating the interaction between a carcinogen and its target cell. In this sense, the ovarian hormones must necessarily be considered as playing an essential role in the inductive process even if ovarian hormones themselves are not specific inducers of the neoplastic transformation. The knowledge of exact hormonal role in the pathogenesis of mammary cancer is a sine qua non to an eventual prevention of breast cancer in humans.

RELATIONSHIP BETWEEN PROLACTIN AND ESTROGEN IN MAMMARY TUMOR GROWTH

It may be logical to presume that the role of hormones in the early phase of mammary carcinogenesis is to enhance the replication of the already transformed cells to grow into a tumor. Hormones that are mitogenic are apparently effective in accelerating tumor growth. It has generally been accepted that peptide hormones from the pituitary and steroid hormones from the gonads play a major role in the maintenance and stimulation of mammary tumor growth. There is now abundant evidence to show that prolactin and estrogen are the hormones regulating the growth of the mammary tumors. Several experiments seem to suggest that prolactin can promote the growth rate of mammary tumors in the absence of ovarian hormones (8-11). We, on the other hand, have observed that estrogen enhances tumor growth apparently without increasing the release or secretion of prolactin from the pituitary (12). Recent experiments from our laboratory disclose that estrogen influences tumor growth not only by increasing pituitary prolactin release and secretion but probably also by a direct action on the tumor cells to "sensitize" them for the action of prolactin (13). It was demonstrated conclusively that high levels of prolactin alone fail to stimulate mammary tumor growth in the absence of ovarian hormones.

In these experiments, mammary tumors were induced in female Sprague-Dawley rats by a single intravenous injection of an emulsion containing 5 mg of 7,12-dimethylbenz(a)anthracene. When the tumors were palpable and measured 1 cm in diameter, lesions were produced in the median eminence (ME) of the hypothalamus of some of these rats by using a Stoelting stereotaxic instrument. Placement of electrolytic lesions in the median eminence of the tuber cinereum enhances only prolactin release and secretion by the pituitary by inhibiting the pituitary inhibitory factor (PIF), whereas the secretion of all other pituitary hormones is inhibited (13). The control groups are sham lesioned rats bearing DMBA-induced mammary tumors. Blood prolactin levels were determined at regular intervals by radioimmunoassay (13). Tumor diameters in each rat were measured with a vernier caliper once a week. At the end of the 90-day experimental period, the rats were killed and tumors, endocrine organs, ovarian grafts, and brains from the ME lesioned rats were fixed and sectioned for histologic examination.

Figure 1 shows that the plasma prolactin level in rats rises rapidly above that of the control after placement of ME lesions. Ovariectomy in intact female rats induces a significant decrease of plasma prolactin level, but it fails to alter the levels of plasma prolactin in rats having electrolytic lesions in the median eminence. Grafting a pair of ovaries into the ovariectomized and ME lesioned rats likewise has no effect on the levels of plasma prolactin. These results demonstrate conclusively that the prolactin secretion and release are no longer affected by the presence or absence of ovarian hormones once ME lesions are induced in these rats.

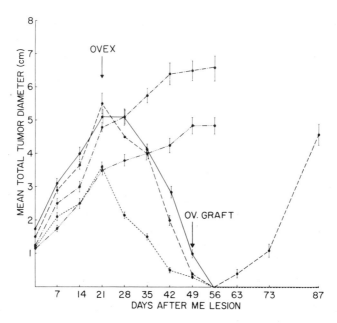

FIG. 2. Effect of median-eminence (ME) lesions, ovariectomy (ovex), and ovarian (Ov) grafts in mammary tumor growth. The experimental groups and the animals are the same ones used for prolactin assays in Fig. 1. The curves are the measurements of tumor growth rate as expressed in mean total tumor diameter. The symbols are the same as in Fig. 1. [Reproduced from Cancer Res., 33, 411-414 (1973), with permission of the publishers.]

The placement of ME lesions greatly enhances tumor growth rate pari passu with the rise of plasma prolactin level (Fig. 2). Ovariectomy brings about a rapid regression of tumors in rats in the control group as well as those in the ME lesioned groups. Interestingly, we find that the plasma prolactin remains unchanged at a significantly higher level than that in the control rats (Fig. 2). We then grafted a pair of ovaries into rats in one of the ME lesioned-ovariectomized group when their tumors became nonpalpable. We observed that shortly thereafter (within 14 days), the tumors resumed their growth, which continued throughout the experimental period. Radioimmuno-assays showed no change of plasma prolactin after the rats received a pair of ovaries. Examination of the ovarian grafts removed at the end of the experiments revealed that surviving grafts consisted mainly of follicular cysts with well-developed thecal cells, but there was no active corpus luteum. The uterine weights decrease significantly after ovariectomy in both control and ME lesioned rats, but grafting a pair of ovaries in the ME lesioned-ovariectomized rats causes a significant rise of uterine weights to values comparable with those in rats having ME lesions only.

These observations conclusively demonstrate that a high plasma prolactin level in the absence of ovarian hormones is unable to sustain or enhance the growth of mammary tumors. Other investigators have observed tumor regression after ovariectomy in rats with ME lesions (14). They attributed this to a lesser prolactin secretion due to estrogen withdrawal since estrogen is known to stimulate pituitary prolactin secretion. That this is not the case is clearly shown by the data presented here. We demonstrate that prolactin secretion does not decrease after ovariectomy in ME lesioned rats.

Results from these in vivo studies demonstrate the interaction between prolactin and estrogen (and progesterone?) in regulating the growth of mammary cancer, although the mechanism(s) by which estrogen enhances the action of prolactin is not clearly understood. The following explanations may be plausible: (a) estrogen and progesterone are required to initiate DNA synthesis and, henceforth, cell proliferation. Prolactin acts synergistically with ovarian hormones to augment growth activity. Prolactin is unable to initiate or maintain the mitogenic activity (15), whereas estrogen and progesterone can both initiate and maintain cell mitosis; (b) estrogen or progesterone act directly on the tumor cells by an interaction with a specific macromolecular species leading to an increased nuclear macromolecular synthetic capacity. Prolactin exerts its optimal effect on the already stimulated mammary cells, and (c) ovarian hormones may be required for making prolactin available to the mammary tumor cells. The decreased vascular flow to the mammary gland as a result of ovariectomy may indeed decrease the supply of prolactin to the mammary tumors. These possible mechanisms are being investigated.

IN VITRO STUDIES OF MAMMARY CARCINOGENESIS

Elucidation of the mode of action of hormones in the pathogenesis of mammary cancer requires a suitable in vitro system in which the role of individual principles can be evaluated.

We reported earlier a method for "long-term" organ culture of mammary gland tissue from the rat (16). We investigated the effects of various hormones on mammary explants grown in organ culture and the influence of DMBA on the mammary gland explants.

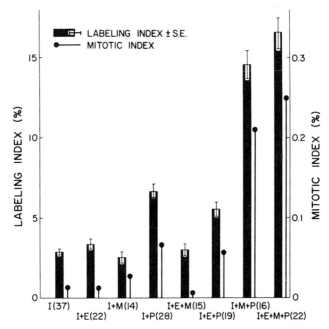

FIG. 3. Labeling and mitotic indexes in mammary gland explants
cultured in media containing various hormone combinations. The dose
of hormones used in any of the combinations is as follows: insulin (I)
5.0 μg; prolactin (M) 5.0 μg; estradiol-17β (E) 0.001 μg; and progesterone (P) 1.0 μg. All of these doses were added per milliliter of
medium. Numbers in parentheses are the number of mammary explants
examined. [Reproduced from J. Nat. Cancer Inst., 48, 1671-1680
(1972), with the permission of the publishers.]

    Mammary glands from adult female Sprague-Dawley rats were
cultivated for 6 to 12 days in a synthetic medium supplemented with
insulin, estrogen, cortisol, progesterone, and prolactin, singly or in
different combinations. The technique for organ culture has been described in detail in that paper (16). We found that insulin was essential for maintenance of the explants in culture. Of all the other hormones studied, progesterone greatly stimulated the growth of mammary
explants as measured by labeling and mitotic indexes. The labeling
and mitotic indexes reached a maximum level when insulin, estrogen,
prolactin, and progesterone were combined (Fig. 3). The increased
DNA synthesis resulting from the hormonal stimulation, however, did
not alter the duration of DNA synthesis. These data suggest that the
parallel increase in labeling and mitotic indexes after culturing with
progesterone and prolactin was due to the increased number of cells

TABLE 1

Duration of DNA Synthesis (T_S) as Measured by
the Double Labeling Method[a]

Hormone combinations	^{14}C nuclei (a)	^3H nuclei (b)	a/b	T_s, hr
I + M + P	187	20	9.4	18.8
	136	15	9.1	18.2
	142	17	8.4	16.8
	140	16	8.8	17.6
	130	13	10.0	20.0
			Mean	18.3
I + P	116	13	8.9	17.8
	148	15	9.9	19.8
	134	20	6.7	13.4
	104	14	7.4	14.8
	105	12	8.8	17.6
	135	14	9.7	19.4
			Mean	17.2
I	68	11	6.2	12.4
	44	5	8.8	17.6
	66	6	11.0	22.0
	83	10	8.3	16.6
			Mean	17.2

[a]Reproduced from J. Nat. Cancer Inst., 48, 1671 (1972), by permission of the publishers.

engaged in DNA synthesis rather than a shortening of the S phase (Table 1).

When DMBA was added in excess of 1 µg/ml of medium, it caused toxicity to the mammary epithelial cells. Degenerative changes, tissue necrosis, and cell death were observed with regularity when a dose of DMBA 5 µg/ml of medium was used. We observed a significant increase in the labeling indexes in explants cultured in the presence of DMBA 1 µg/ml of medium when compared with those of the controls. Interestingly DMBA can induce DNA synthesis in the mammary gland explants cultured in medium containing only insulin. The presence of other hormone combinations has only an additive effect on the labeling index in the mammary epithelial cells.

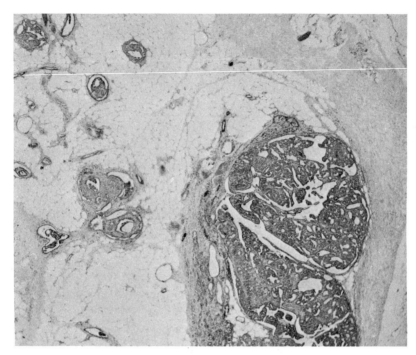

FIG. 4. Papillary adenocarcinoma developing in mammary explant cultured nine days in chemically defined medium containing combination of hormones and DMBA and transplanted into isologous host (X 35).

The successful culture of mammary explants in chemically defined medium for 9 to 12 days enables us to use this technique for investigating in vitro transformation of mammary cells by chemical carcinogenesis. In our earlier studies (16), we reported pathologic changes occurring in the mammary explants cultured in media containing carcinogen DMBA, and hormone combinations of insulin, progesterone, estrogen, and prolactin. These observed changes include squamous metaplasia occurring in mammary explants as early as six days in culture and anaplastic changes in the mammary epithelial cells on day 9 or 12 of culture. Subsequent experiments were carried out in 50- to 60-day-old Wistar/Furth (inbred) female rats. The mammary explants measuring at 1.0 X 1.0 cm in size were cultivated for nine days in a chemically defined medium containing hormone combination as described above. Four groups of experiments were carried out with different doses of DMBA. In Experiment 1, the mammary explants were cultured in the presence of pulse doses of DMBA 1 µg/ml medium every third day at the time the medium containing the hormone combination and DMBA was changed. In Experiment 2, the explants were treated

TABLE 2
Induction of Mammary Tumors in Organ Culture[a]

Dose of DMBA[b]	No. of rats with surviving transplants / Total no. of rats	No. of rats with tumors in surviving transplants
1 µg/ml × 3	3/5	2
1 µg/ml × 2	4/5	3[c]
1 µg/ml × 1	5/5	2
4 µg/ml × 1	4/5	3[c]

[a]Reproduced from J. Nat. Cancer Inst., 49, 591-593 (1972), by permission of the publishers.

[b]Amount of DMBA per milliliter of medium, which also contains combinations of insulin 5 µg/ml, prolactin 1 µg/ml, 17β-estradiol 0.001 µg/ml, and progesterone 1 µg/ml. Total volume of medium per culture dish is 4 ml.

[c]One in every group is a fibroma.

with two doses of DMBA 1 µg/ml of medium, i.e., DMBA was added on day 1 of the culture and also on day 4 of the culture when the medium was changed. In Experiments 3 and 4, the mammary explants were treated with only one dose of 1 µg/ml medium and one dose of 4 µg/ml medium, respectively. As controls, explants of mammary gland were cultured in medium containing only the hormone combination without DMBA. At the end of day 9 of the culture, four pieces of mammary explants were transplanted into the interscapular region of the isologous hosts. The hosts bearing mammary transplants were killed 90 days after the transplant and all mammary explants, whether they contained tumor or not, were removed for either wholemount preparation or histologic sections. We found that 80% of mammary explants survived in the recipient hosts. We could not be certain whether the nonsurviving graft was the result of rejection or the death of the explants at the time of transplantation. In 16 surviving mammary explants, 10 tumors developed, including eight papillary adenocarcinomas and two fibromas (17) (Fig. 4). All these tumors were grossly discernible at autopsy.

There has been no previous report of successful induction of mammary adenocarcinoma in organ culture by a chemical carcinogen. We believe that neoplastic transformation apparently occurs in mammary cells in vitro before transplantation into host since anaplastic changes are observed in these explants after nine days of culture. We are now studying the metabolism of DMBA in vitro.

ARE CARCINOGENIC HYDROCARBONS HORMONE MIMETIC?

Alteration of endocrine function as a result of treatment with a chemical carcinogen was observed in experiments designed to induce mammary cancer in male rats. We reported earlier the induction of mammary cancer by 3-MC in castrated male rats bearing functional ovarian grafts (18). In these experiments, we also observed induction of "lactation" (formation of large milk cysts) in the mammary gland irrespective of the presence or absence of mammary tumors. The formation of milk cysts appears to occur only in the castrated rats bearing ovarian grafts, and these rats were also given 3-MC. Later Dao reported the occurrence of lactation following DMBA treatment in female rats treated neonatally with testosterone (19). Such augmentation of lactogenesis by carcinogenic hydrocarbon was later confirmed by other investigators (20). Recent work in our laboratory (21) further substantiated these earlier observations. These data clearly indicate that carcinogenic hydrocarbons such as 3-MC and DMBA can exert effects on the mammary gland by indirectly causing the pituitary to release prolactin. This action of 3-MC or DMBA closely resembles the estrogenic effect, i. e., the inhibition of PIF (prolactin inhibitory factor) of the hypothalamus and increased secretion of prolactin from the pituitary. Preliminary data from our laboratory show that a single dose of DMBA can induce a sharp rise of plasma prolactin within 6 hr, suggesting the possible estrogen mimetic effect of mammary carcinogens. The association between the capacity of DMBA to enhance lactogenesis and its effect on the induction of mammary cancer should be ascertained.

CONCLUSION

The development of techniques for in vitro cultivation of mammary gland and the demonstration of induction of mammary cancer in explants cultured in vitro are important steps for further elucidation of the mechanism of mammary carcinogenesis, particularly in investigating the exact role of the hormones. Our in vivo studies have begun to unveil the intricate relationship between prolactin and estrogen in mammary tumor growth, and this may lead to better methods for treatment of breast cancer in humans.

REFERENCES

1. C. F. Geschickter and E. W. Byrnes, Factors influencing the development and time of appearance of mammary cancer in the rat in response to estrogens, Arch. Pathol., 33, 334 (1942).

2. R. L. Noble and J. B. Collip, Regression of estrogen-induced mammary tumors in female rats following removal of the stimulus, Can. Med. Assoc. J., 44, 1 (1941).

3. H. Shay, E. A. Aegerter, M. Gruenstein, and S. A. Komarov, Development of adenocarcinoma of the breast in the Wistar rat following the gastric instillation of methylcholanthrene, J. Nat. Cancer Inst., 10, 255 (1949).

4. C. Huggins, L. C. Grand, and F. P. Brillantes, Mammary cancer induced by a single feeding of polynuclear hydrocarbons and its suppression, Nature, 189, 204 (1961).

5. S. Nandi, Interactions among hormonal, viral and genetic factors in mouse mammary tumorigenesis, Can. Cancer Conf., 6, 69 (1966).

6. S. Nandi, H. A. Bern, and K. B. DeOme, Effect of hormones on growth and neoplastic development of transplanted hyperplastic alveolar nodules of the mammary gland of C3H/Crgl mice, J. Nat. Cancer Inst., 24, 883 (1960).

7. T. L. Dao, The role of ovarian hormones in initiating the induction of mammary cancer in rats by polynuclear hydrocarbons, Cancer Res., 22, 973 (1962).

8. J. Meites, "The Relation of Estrogen and Prolactin to Mammary Tumorigenesis in the Rat," in Estrogen Target Tissues and Neoplasia (T. L. Dao, ed.), Univ. of Chicago Press, Chicago, 1972, p. 275.

9. H. Nagasawa and R. Yanai, Effects of prolactin or growth hormone on growth of carcinogen-induced mammary tumors of adrenoovariectomized rats, Intern. J. Cancer, 6, 488 (1970).

10. C. W. Welsch, "Effects of Brain Lesions on Mammary Tumorigenesis," in Estrogen Target Tissues and Neoplasia (T. L. Dao, ed.), Univ. of Chicago Press, Chicago, 1972, p. 317.

11. L. M. Boot, O. Muhlbock, and G. Ropke, Prolactin and the induction of mammary tumors in mice, Gen. Comp. Endocrinol., 2, 601 (1962).

12. D. Sinha and T. L. Dao, "Estrogen and Induction of Mammary Cancer," in Estrogen Target Tissues and Neoplasia (T. L. Dao, ed.), Univ. of Chicago Press, Chicago, 1972, p. 307.

13. D. Sinha, D. Cooper, and T. L. Dao, The nature of estrogen and prolactin effect on mammary tumorigenesis, Cancer Res., 33, 411 (1973).

14. J.A. Clemens, C.W. Welsch, and J. Meites, Effects of hypo-
    thalamic lesions on incidence and growth of mammary tumors in
    carcinogen treated rats, Proc. Soc. Exptl. Biol. Med., 127,
    969 (1968).
15. T. Oka and Y. Topper, Is prolactin mitogenic for mammary epi-
    thelium?, Proc. Nat. Acad. Sci., 69, 1693 (1972).
16. H. Koyama, D. Sinha, and T.L. Dao, Effects of hormones and
    7,12-dimethylbenz(a)anthracene on rat mammary tissue grown in
    organ culture, J. Nat. Cancer Inst., 48, 1671 (1972).
17. T.L. Dao and D. Sinha, Mammary adenocarcinoma induced in
    organ culture by 7,12-dimethylbenz(a)anthracene, J. Nat. Cancer
    Inst., 49, 591 (1972).
18. T.L. Dao and J. Greiner, Mammary carcinogenesis by 3-methyl-
    cholanthrene. III. Induction of mammary carcinoma and milk-
    secretion in male rats bearing ovarian grafts, J. Nat. Cancer
    Inst., 27, 333 (1961).
19. T.L. Dao, Mammary tumorigenesis in female rats receiving andro-
    gen neonatally, Proc. Amer. Assoc. Cancer Res. Abstr. #62,
    1966, p. 16.
20. E. Stern, M.R. Mickey, and L. Osvaldo, Lactogenesis in the
    androgen-sterile rat: Augmentation following 7,12-dimethylbenz(a)-
    anthracene, Nature, 206, 369 (1965).
21. S. Christakos, D. Sinha, and T.L. Dao, Mammary carcinogenesis
    in neonatally androgenized and ovariectomized rats, Proc. Amer.
    Assoc. Cancer Res., 14:67, Abstr. #266.

Chapter 26

EXPERIMENTAL APPROACHES TO PROBLEMS IN CARCINOGENESIS

A. Bendich, E. Borenfreund, P. J. Higgins,
S. S. Sternberg, and E. H. Stonehill

Memorial Sloan-Kettering Cancer Center
New York, New York

The change of a normal cell into a malignant one appears to have a genetic basis since the ensuing heritable properties of unrestrained growth are passed on to offspring cells indefinitely (1). At the molecular level, this kind of change could arise in a number of ways.

1. Mutational change. Support for this possibility comes from the demonstration of the mutagenic action of many carcinogens. This aspect is treated more fully by others in these volumes. The apparent reversibility (2-4) of the malignant state raises new questions about mutagenesis and the nature of mammalian genetics, and this point is discussed in another context below.

2. Derepression of dormant, presumably embryonal, genes. This may involve the turning-on of silent genes and is manifested by new proliferative activity. Evidence for this possibility is seen in the frequent appearance of embryonal gene products (identified as enzymes or as antigens) in tumors of various sorts and in many species (5-10). The phenomenon is of special importance since certain embryonal components may confer adult animals with immunoprotection against transplantation challenge with tumor cells (11, 12).

3. Acquisition of new or additional genetic determinants. This is observed following the infection and malignant transformation of cells by oncogenic viruses of both the DNA and RNA type (13, 14). In the former case, the viral DNA may become integrated into the host genome, and in the latter case, the RNA viral information may be transcribed into cellular DNA (15), and back again to form the original RNA virus (16).

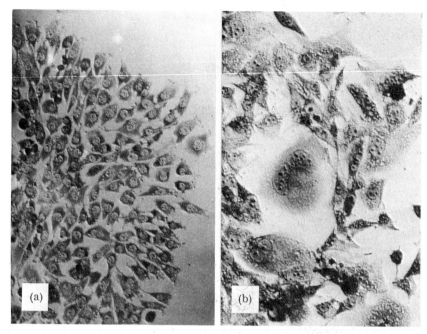

FIG. 1. Edge of a colony of an established line of Chinese hamster (CH) cells, originally derived from bone marrow by Dr. J. Biedler
of this Institute; cultural and morphologic characteristics have been
described (18, 19); (a) before, and (b) after treatment with methylazoxymethanol acetate, 2 μg/ml (Giemsa; Nomarski optics; X 210).

The malignant change may thus be viewed as involving the cellular DNA as the common denominator in all instances, regardless of
the carcinogenic agent that induced the change. To obtain further
information pertinent to this view, experiments were carried out to
learn whether malignant potential could be expressed by nontumor
cells after acquisition of DNA from cancer cells, or even from normal
sources.

We have been studying the in vitro malignant transformation of
Chinese hamster (CH) cells, employing the oncogenic DNA-containing
viruses, polyoma and SV40, a number of polycyclic hydrocarbon carcinogens, and DNA from tumor cells (17-19). Using the viruses as
standards for comparison— since there was little ambiguity about their
ultimate effect on the cells— it was apparent that the chemical carcinogens were having much the same effect. After cells were exposed to
SV40, polyoma, benzpyrene, methylcholanthrene, or dimethylbenz-
anthracene, and cloned for transformants, the spread of chromosome

numbers widened considerably, broadening even more after growth as tumors in animals (17).

It may well be that no two tumor cells are truly identical. This can be seen from many studies that have revealed the great variability in properties of cells of the same tumor, even in multiply recloned tumor cell lines. The exceptions are rare indeed (20). Not only is there great diversity and instability in chromosome number, but there is also diversity in antigenic composition, tumorigenicity, inducibility of enzyme activity, and other characteristics (21-25). Perhaps the state or level of differentiation may also be affected. A possible source of such diversity may be the lack of constancy of DNA content per cell (26), passage of some DNA between tumor cells, or unequal partition of DNA between daughter cells at mitosis (27). We have not yet seen this with nontumor cells.

Figure 1(a) is a photograph of the edge of a colony of about 500 cells that arose several days after single cells were seeded on microscope cover slips in a culture dish. If permitted to grow further, the colony would have covered the entire surface as a monolayer of typically contact-inhibited cells with a regular, parallel orientation (18). The pattern changes drastically [Fig. 1(b)] when cells, briefly treated with low dosages of the potent carcinogen methylazoxymethanol acetate (28), are similarly plated and contemporaneously observed with the control. Although it is not yet experimentally feasible to know which of the cells shown in Fig. 1(b) had been transformed to the malignant state, it is nonetheless clear that the brief exposure to the carcinogen has led to nuclear and morphologic changes that are seen after division.

The various changes that attend continuous propagation of tumor cells make it unlikely that the initial primary carcinogenic event will be uncovered merely by comparing clones or large populations of tumor cells with the nontumor cells from which they arose. Nonetheless, this is an experimental approach widely used to study hoped-for pertinent differences between normal and tumor cells.

When we examined live cultures of cells after malignant conversion with various viral or chemical carcinogens, connections, interactions, and bridges between some of the cells were seen. When this phenomenon was studied with cells in which the DNA had been labeled with [³H]thymidine, autoradiograms revealed some of the bridges to contain DNA (18, 27, 29). Control cultures of nontumor cells did not show such evidence of information transfer between cells. This intercellular reshuffling of chromosomal material may serve to explain some of the variability among tumor cells mentioned above, and why their recloning may be misleading. Could it be that carcinogenic agents initiate

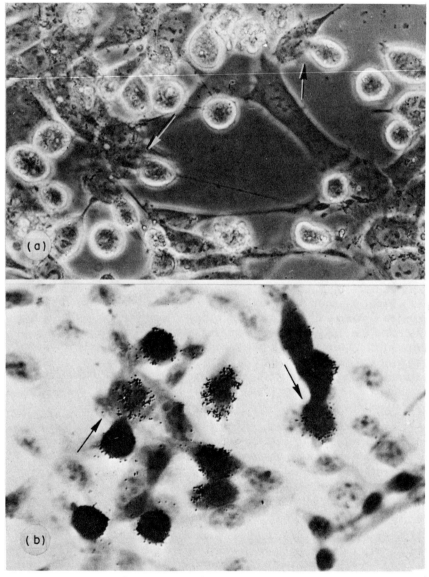

FIG. 2. Interaction of CH and Ehrlich ascites cells. (a) Living co-cultures, 5 hr after admixture; phase contrast optics; arrows indicate intimate cell-cell interactions (X 510). (b) Autoradiograph of 48-hr co-culture of CH and [^{3}H]thymidine-labeled EA cells (Giemsa; Nomarski optics); arrows indicate transfer of labeled DNA from EA to CH cells (X 700).

changes in chromosomal components that can then be shifted from one cell to another?

Since DNA-containing bridges were seen between tumor cells but not between nontumor cells, it was of interest to learn whether one type of cell would affect the other. Of the various pairs of cells studied, the mixture that yielded the most information consisted of CH and of (mouse) Ehrlich ascites (EA) cells. The two are readily distinguished. The EA cells are spherical, they do not adhere to plastic or glass surfaces, they do not multiply in culture, they appear yellowish under the visible light microscope, they stain a deep blue with Giemsa, and their chromosomes are nearly all telocentric, varying in number from about 67 to 75. They will grow in the cheek pouch of the cortisone-conditioned Syrian hamster, whereas the CH cells do not. None of the chromosomes of the CH cells (n = 22) is telocentric. The fibroplastic CH cells grow as monolayers in culture, appear gray in the living state, stain differently from EA with Giemsa. The cells, and several of their macromolecular components, can also be readily distinguished immunochemically. Within a few hours after admixture, connections and bridges formed between the two types of cells [Fig. 2(a)]. Using specific antisera and immunofluoroscopy, it was clear that the bridges had emanated from the EA but not from the CH cells (18, 19). An occasional intercellular passage of DNA from EA to CH cells was observed [Fig. 2(b)] by autoradiography two to three days after co-culture of labeled cells; DNA transfer in the reverse direction was not seen (18, 19).

A likely consequence of this type of cell-cell interaction was the emergence, after at least 10 weeks of co-culture, of a new type of cell with growth and morphologic characteristics of CH cells that appeared to have synthesized mouse-reactive antigens as revealed by specific immunofluorescence reactions. Though very laborious, it was possible to select colonies in which all the cells showed the immunofluorescence, Ouchterlony immunodiffusion, and mixed-cell hemagglutination reactions expected therein of mouse antigens, yet the karyotype was typically CH. Some of the colonies gave rise to transplantable spindle-cell sarcomas in the cheek pouch of the conditioned Syrian hamster. Cells cultured from the tumors showed a variable chromosome number, and this property as well as the mouse-specific antigenicity persisted for about a year in which subcultures were studied. Although the typical CH character of the karyotype made it unlikely that the new cells had resulted from fusion of CH and EA cells, this possibility was eliminated when the same kinds of results and the same persistence of properties were obtained following the exposure of CH cells to the DNA isolated from EA cells (19).

Thus, heritable acquisition of oncogenic potential could result from exposure of nontumor cells to tumor cells or to the DNA derived from them. It may be argued that this resulted from the functional acquisition of tumorigenic genetic determinants. Rigorous proof for this conclusion requires demonstration that the altered cells were progeny of a cell that had actually acquired DNA originating from the tumor cell. A great difficulty in establishing this point arises from the current inability to determine whether a given living cell, under observation, has undergone oncogenic transformation, or even whether a particular cell is malignant. The achievement of such an identification should make it easier to study and follow the molecular events in carcinogenesis. It is quite probable that several steps are required before the pertinent expression of the carcinogenic change is manifested, and this in turn may require several cell divisions in addition to those necessary for the establishment of a tumor. A serious problem in the study of interactions between cells is to identify which components pass between them and which are responsible for any new cells or new biologic effect that may result thereby [cf. Ref. 30]. In the above experiments, only those cell components labeled with [^{3}H] thymidine were followed. In the experiments in which isolated DNA was used, the usual controls (treatment with DNase, RNase, pronase, use of DNA from sources other than EA cells, etc.) increased the probability that the agent responsible for the ultimate oncogenic and genetic alterations was a specific deoxyribonucleic acid (19, 31, 32). To learn more about cell-cell interactions and the effects of DNA on mammalian cells, several studies are under way in our laboratory, some of which are described below.

The characteristic appearance of embryonal antigens in many tumors, mentioned above, prompted a study of the interaction of sperm with nonmalignant diploid cells to learn, for example, whether synthesis of such antigens could be turned on thereby (as occurs after fertilization) and whether the cells would then become malignant. For initial orienting experiments, living sperm, collected aseptically from mouse epididymus and vas deferens, were added to cultures of various nontumor and tumor cell lines maintained in our laboratory. Apparent penetration occurred with cells of all the lines as judged by light microscopy. When sperm were mixed in equal numbers with suspended CH cells, penetration of many of the cells could be seen within the first few hours by light microscopy [Fig. 3(a)], and by scanning [Fig. 3(b)], and transmission electron microscopy. When sperm that had been labeled in vivo with [^{3}H] thymidine were used, autoradiography revealed DNA uptake in nuclei of CH cells after three days of co-culture (Fig. 4), suggesting release of DNA after penetration (33). Descendent cells are under study to learn whether functional informa-

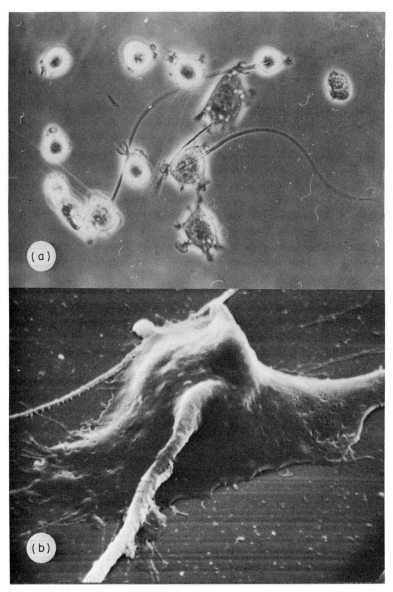

FIG. 3. Penetration of CH cells by mouse sperm 3 hr after admixture in culture. (a) Photographed in the living state with phase contrast optics (X 510). (b) Fixed specimen; scanning electron photomicrograph (X 5000).

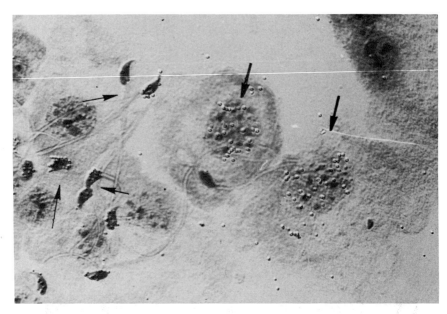

FIG. 4. Autoradiograph of 3-day co-culture of CH and [^{3}H] thymi-
dine-labeled mouse sperm cells (Giemsa; partial Nomarski optics;
X 1300). The number of silver grains above the labeled CH cells (heavy
arrows) is about the same as the average number over the pre-labeled
sperm (light arrows), suggesting a direct transfer of DNA from sperm
to CH cells after penetration.

tion transfer had resulted. Clones of cells are being collected to see
if murine gene products, especially embryonal antigens, can be detected (6, 7) and if malignant potential had been acquired. In a parallel
set of experiments, we are employing isolated sperm DNA (34) as
another experimental approach to this problem.

We have been studying ways to increase the efficiency of DNA
uptake by mammalian cells [cf. Refs. 35, 36], and to improve the
means of visualizing and defining its consequence on cells. Poly-
amines such as diethylaminoethyl dextran (DEAE-D) not only enhance
DNA uptake (35) but also form fibers with DNA that can be visualized
in their reactions with cells (19, 31). An example (Fig. 5) shows an
apparent nuclear uptake of labeled DNA from EA cells by cultured fibroblasts originating from a skin biopsy taken from a child with Lesch-
Nyhan syndrome (37); labeling is insignificant in absence of DEAE-D.
(We are grateful to Dr. R. Cox, New York University, for a culture of
these cells.) Cells of individuals with this genetic disease (L-N) are
unable to utilize exogenously supplied hypoxanthine or guanine for

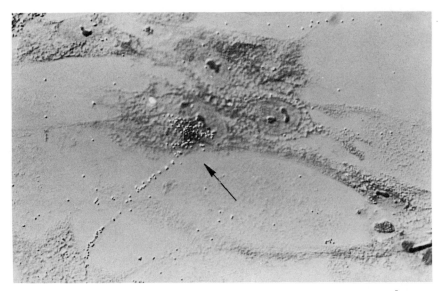

FIG. 5. Autoradiograph showing interaction of fibroblasts [taken from a skin biopsy of a child with Lesch-Nyhan (L-N) syndrome] with fibers prepared from diethylaminoethyl-dextran and [³H]-labeled DNA isolated from Ehrlich ascites tumor cells [cf. (19]; 48 hr after admixture in culture (Giemsa; Nomarski optics; X 640). Photograph shows a nuclear uptake of labeled DNA (arrow).

nucleic acid biosynthesis because of a deficiency of the enzyme hypoxanthine-guanine phosphoribosyltransferase, presumably because of the absence of the pertinent genetic determinants that specify the enzyme. EA cells have this enzyme; presumably their DNA contains the appropriate genetic information. Tests for the presence of the enzyme in cultured cells are straightforward. When exposed to [³H] hypoxanthine and examined by autoradiography under standardized conditions, cells such as EA or normal human cells show heavy labeling of their nucleic acids; L-N cells do not (37, 38). After exposure to unlabeled DNA-DEAE-D complexes and subsequent growth, cultures of L-N cells assayed for their ability to utilize [³H] hypoxanthine for nucleic acid biosynthesis were found (Fig. 6) to contain cells (frequency, about 1:10,000) that had apparently regained this activity, and retained it for at least three months (39). Control cultures were routinely negative (Fig. 6). Culture procedures using various selective media have to date consistently failed to enrich the population with those cells that appear to have regained the enzyme; the cloning methods have not been fruitful in this regard since the skin cells employed are quite motile. This has thus far prevented our

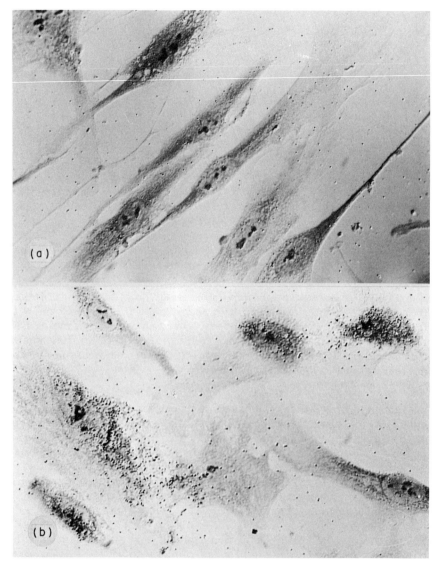

FIG. 6. Autoradiographs of L-N skin fibroblasts. The cells were grown for 12 days and the culture media was then supplemented over-night with [³H]hypoxanthine; the cells were fixed, autoradiographs prepared, and cells then stained with Giemsa (Nomarski optics; X 510). (a) Represents a control culture and (b) a parallel culture exposed for 48 hr to fibers of unlabeled EA-DNA and DEAE-D (see Fig. 5). Part (a) is typical of L-N cells, which do not utilize hypoxanthine for nucleic acid biosynthesis. Part (b) is a selected field showing four cells that have utilized [³H]hypoxanthine for nucleic acid biosynthesis. The frequency of such positive cells was about 1:10,000.

isolation of changed cells for the mass cultures necessary for biochemical identification of enzyme changes and for studies of whether
and at what time oncogenic changes result from the uptake of EA DNA.

We can regard the gain of new genetic determinants and the subsequent acquisition of oncogenic potential as examples of mutagenic
change. The findings of apparent reversal of malignancy (2-4) and even
loss of malignancy that attends completion of differentiation (40) raise
questions concerning the adequacy of mutagenesis as an explanation
of oncogenesis. Persuasive arguments have been raised in support of
the concept that cancer is a disease of differentiation (41, 42).

The reported decrease in the malignancy of Friend erythroleukemic
cells and the marked enhancement of their differentiation along the
erythroid pathway by treatment with so simple a chemical as dimethylsulfoxide (DMSO) (43) stimulated a study of the effect of this agent,
and the related solvent dimethylformamide (DMF), on the various malignant cell lines used in our laboratory. The addition of DMSO or DMF
to cultures of tumor cells induced them to grow in patterns that were
much more characteristic of normal than of tumor cells. Examples of
this phenomenon are shown in Fig. 7, which compares the morphology
of the growth of highly malignant methylcholanthrene-induced tumor
cells in the absence and presence of DMSO. The effect of DMF is
very similar. In the absence of the agents, the cells grow in disarray,
move over one another, and pile up forming colonies several cells
thick. When the medium is supplemented for at least three days with
1 to 2% DMSO, or 0.5 to 1% DMF, the cells grow in a regular parallel
pattern, showing "contact inhibition." This social behavior is maintained so long as the agents are kept in the culture. When the agents
are removed from the media, the growth pattern reverts to the old one
after three days. The process can be repeatedly turned on or off by
simply adding or withholding DMSO or DMF. Since there is no death
when the cells are grown in the presence of the agents, selective
mechanisms are not operative in this easily reversible system. We
were disappointed at first when DMSO-treated cells still grew as
tumors upon inoculation into mice. However, the time needed (about
8 to 10 days) for the appearance of tumors after injection into mice
would have been quite sufficient to restore the malignant growth pattern
if the cells had been kept in culture in the absence of DMSO for this
period. Accordingly, recipient mice were pretreated for three days with
DMSO and maintained on this agent after DMSO-treated tumor cells
were injected. Tumors failed to appear in 40% of the animals so treated,
and tumor growth in the remaining animals was considerably retarded
(44). We are seeking an explanation of these effects, which appear to
involve the cell surface. What seems clear is that chemicals as simple
as DMSO can inhibit tumorigenic expression reversibly. This finding
has bearing on arguments dealing with the origin and nature of carcinogenesis.

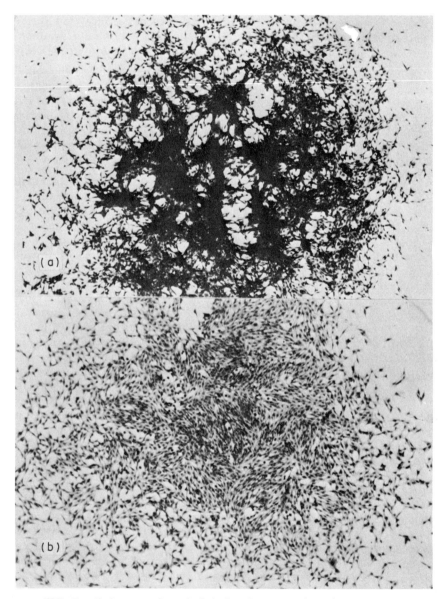

FIG. 7. Cultures of methylcholanthrene-induced mouse tumor cells grown for eight days in (a) the absence and (b) the presence of 2% dimethylsulfoxide (Giemsa; X 32).

CONCLUDING REMARKS

It is tempting to speculate that cancer cells contain tumorigenic DNA that is responsible for their malignancy, and that this trait can be passed on or spread to others by appropriate cell-cell contact, or by DNA-cell interactions. It is possible that an unequal division, or an acquisition of new DNA may initiate an imbalance that ultimately gives rise to cells that have lost the autoregulatory mechanisms that control normal growth and development. Perhaps cells exposed to carcinogenic agents develop a tendency to divide unequally; this may be an expression of an affected cell to rid itself of altered genetic determinants. A carcinogen might also induce a cell to undergo some form of dedifferentiation. The conversion of a normal to a tumor cell and the persistence of this change through many cell generations would appear to require some qualitative or quantitative alteration in the genetic information of the cell. All these statements, which receive support from many experimental findings, presented here and elsewhere, may require serious revision in the light of the facile experimental reversibility of malignant expression. It is hoped that the studies reported here will provide further suggestions for experimental exploration.

ACKNOWLEDGMENT

The work was supported by the National Cancer Institute grant CA08748, the Atomic Energy Commission contract AT[11-1]-3521, and the American Cancer Society, grant IC-20M.

REFERENCES

1. F.L. Horsfall, Jr., Some new concepts in biology, Arch. Biochem., Suppl. 1, 63, 1962.
2. I. Macpherson, Reversion in hamster cells transformed by Rous sarcoma virus, Science, 148, 1731 (1965).
3. R. Pollach, S. Wolman, and A. Vogel, Reversion of virus-transformed cell lines: hyperploidy accompanies retention of viral genes, Nature, 228, 938 (1970).
4. S. Hitotsumachi, Z. Rabinowitz, and L. Sachs, Chromosomal control of reversion in hamster cells, Nature, 231, 511 (1971).

5. P. Gold and S. O. Freedman, Specific carcinoembryonic antigens of the human digestive system, J. Exptl. Med., 122, 467 (1965).

6. E. H. Stonehill and A. Bendich, Retrogenetic expression: the reappearance of embryonal antigens in cancer cells, Nature, 228, 370 (1970).

7. E. H. Stonehill, E. Borenfreund, and A. Bendich, "Anachronistic Genetic Expression Recognized by the Production of Fetal Antigens in Cancer Cells," in Proceedings of the First Conference and Workshop on Embryonic and Fetal Antigens in Cancer (N. G. Anderson and J. H. Coggin, eds.), Oak Ridge Natl. Lab., Tennessee, May 24-26, 1971, pp. 85-104.

8. S. Weinhouse, Isozymes in cancer, Cancer Res., 31, 1166 (1971).

9. E. M. Edynak, L. J. Old, M. Vrana, and B. S. Lardis, A fetal antigen associated with human neoplasia, New Engl. J. Med., 286, 1178 (1972).

10. P. Alexander, Foetal "antigens" in cancer, Nature, 235, 137 (1972).

11. J. H. Coggin, K. R. Ambrose, and N. G. Anderson, Fetal antigen capable of inducing transplantation immunity against SV40 hamster tumor cells, J. Immunol., 105, 524 (1970).

12. A. Bendich, E. Borenfreund, and E. H. Stonehill, Protection of adult mice against tumor challenge by immunization with irradiated adult skin or embryo cells, J. Immunol., 111, 284 (1973).

13. K. Habel, The biology of viral carcinogenesis, Cancer Res., 28, 1825 (1968).

14. R. Dulbecco, Cell transformation by viruses, Science, 166, 962 (1969).

15. H. M. Temin, RNA-directed DNA synthesis, Sci. Amer., 226, No. 1, 24 (1972).

16. M. Hill and J. Hillova, Virus recovery in chicken cells tested with Rous sarcoma cell DNA, Nature New Biol., 237, 35 (1972).

17. E. Borenfreund, M. Krim, F. K. Sanders, S. Sternberg, and A. Bendich, Malignant conversion of cells in vitro by carcinogens and viruses, Proc. Nat. Acad. Sci., 56, 672 (1966).

18. A. Bendich, E. Borenfreund, Y. Honda, and M. Steinglass, Cell transformation and the genesis of cancer, Arch. Environ. Health, 19, 157 (1969).

19. E. Borenfreund, Y. Honda, M. Steinglass, and A. Bendich, Studies on DNA-induced heritable alteration of mammalian cells, J. Exptl. Med., 132, 1071 (1970).

20. G. E. Moore and A. A. Sandberg, Studies of a human tumor cell line with a diploid karyotype, Cancer, 17, 170 (1964).

21. V. Defendi and J. M. Lehman, Transformation of hamster embryo cells in vitro by polyoma virus: morphological, karyological, immunological and transplantation characteristics, J. Cell Comp. Physiol., 66, 351 (1965).

22. A. A. Sandberg, I. D. J. Bross, N. Takagi, and M. L. Schmidt,
    Chromosomes and causation of human cancer and leukemia,
    Cancer, 21, 77 (1968).
23. F. Weiner, G. Klein, and H. Harris, The analysis of malignancy
    by cell fusion. III. Hybrids between diploid fibroblasts and other
    tumor cells, J. Cell. Sci., 8, 681 (1971).
24. M. A. Basombrio and R. T. Prehn, Antigenic diversity of tumors
    chemically induced within the progeny of a single cell, Intern. J.
    Cancer, 10, 1 (1972).
25. D. Aviv and E. B. Thompson, Variation in tyrosine amino-transfer-
    ase induction in HTC cell clones, Science, 117, 1201 (1972).
26. H. F. Stich, The DNA content of tumor cells. II. Alterations during
    the formation of hepatomas in rats, J. Nat. Cancer Inst., 24,
    1283 (1960).
27. A. Bendich, A. D. Vizoso, and R. G. Harris, Intercellular bridges
    between mammalian cells in culture, Proc. Nat. Acad. Sci., 57,
    1029 (1967).
28. M. S. Zedeck, S. S. Sternberg, J. McGowan, and R. W. Poynter,
    Methylazoxymethanol acetate: induction of tumors and early effects
    on RNA synthesis, Proc. Fed. Amer. Soc. Exptl. Biol., 31, 1485
    (1972).
29. A. Bendich, E. Borenfreund, A. D. Vizoso, and R. G. Harris,
    "Malignant Transformation and Intercell Communication Involving
    DNA," in Subviral Carcinogenesis (Y. Ito, ed.), Monograph of 1st
    Intern. Symp. on Tumor Viruses, Nissha Printing Co., Nagoya,
    Japan, July, 1966, pp. 99–115.
30. M. Chorazy, A. Bendich, E. Borenfreund, O. L. Ittensohn, and
    D. J. Hutchison, Uptake of mammalian chromosomes by mammalian
    cells, J. Cell. Biol., 19, 71 (1963).
31. A. Bendich, E. Borenfreund, and Y. Honda, "DNA-Induced Herit-
    able Alteration of Mammalian Cells," in Informative Molecules in
    Biological Systems (L. G. H. Ledoux, ed.), North-Holland, Amster-
    dam, 1971, p. 80.
32. A. Bendich, T. Wilczok, and E. Borenfreund, Circulating DNA as
    a possible factor in oncogenesis, Science, 148, 374 (1965).
33. A. Bendich, E. Borenfreund, and S. S. Sternberg, Penetration of
    somatic mammalian cells by sperm, Science, in press (1974).
34. E. Borenfreund, E. Fitt, and A. Bendich, Isolation and properties
    of DNA from mammalian sperm, Nature, 191, 1375 (1961).
35. J. S. Pagano, Biologic activity of isolated viral nucleic acids,
    Progr. Med. Virol., 12, 1 (1970).
36. L. G. H. Ledoux, ed., Informative Molecules in Biological Sys-
    tems, North-Holland, Amsterdam, 1971.
37. W. N. Kelley and J. B. Wyngaarden, "The Lesch-Nyhan Syndrome,"
    in The Metabolic Basis of Inherited Disease, 3rd Ed. (J. B. Stan-
    bury, J. B. Wyngaarden, and D. S. Fredrickson, eds.), McGraw-
    Hill, New York, 1972, p. 969.

38. W.Y. Fujimoto and J.E. Seegmiller, Hypoxanthine-guanine phosphoribosyltransferase deficiency: activity in normal, mutant, and heterozygote-cultured human skin fibroblasts, Proc. Nat. Acad. Sci., 65, 577 (1970).

39. E. Borenfreund and A. Bendich, Studies of the repair of genetic defects, in preparation.

40. G.B. Pierce and C. Wallace, Differentiation of malignant to benign cells, Cancer Res., 31, 127 (1971).

41. C.L. Markert, Neoplasia: a disease of cell differentiation, Cancer Res., 28, 1908 (1968).

42. G.B. Pierce, Differentiation of normal and malignant cells, Proc. Fed. Amer. Soc. Exptl. Biol., 29, 1248 (1970).

43. C. Friend, W. Scher, J.G. Holland, and T. Sato, Hemoglobin synthesis in murine virus-induced cells in vitro: stimulation of erythroid differentiation by dimethylsulfoxide, Proc. Nat. Acad. Sci., 68, 372 (1971).

44. E. Borenfreund and A. Bendich, The effect of dimethylsulfoxide and dimethylformamide on tumor cells in vitro, in "Symposium on the biological actions of DMSO, " N.Y. Academy of Sciences, January, 1974.

Chapter 27

MOLECULAR EVENTS IN DIFFERENTIATION AND DE-DIFFERENTIATION

James Bonner

Division of Biology
California Institute of Technology
Pasadena, California

Chemical carcinogenesis, however it is initiated, results in the turning on of genes previously turned off. To put it as a bacterial geneticist would put it, "Carcinogenesis turns on the mitosis operon"; therefore, once we know which nuclear component the carcinogenic chemical binds to, the next thing we want to know is how this first carcinogenetic act results in derepression of genes previously repressed. It is my charge to tell what is known about the derepression of repressed eukaryote genes. The examples will be drawn from normal adult rat liver and from rat liver regenerating after partial hepatectomy. In normal rat liver about 20% of the DNA of the genome is available for transcription by RNA polymerase. In regenerating rat liver, a few hours after the operation, the proportion of DNA available for transcription by RNA polymerase has increased by about 60%. In this time therefore a massive derepression has occurred. Let me remind all of us that these events precede and set the stage for DNA replication, which begins about 15 hr after partial hepatectomy, as well as cell division, which occurs after about 24 hr.

I first summarize what we already know about the genome and the interphase chromosomes (chromatin) of rat liver. About 80 to 85% of the DNA of such chromatin is complexed with the characteristic chromosomal proteins, the histones. About 15 to 20% of the DNA is complexed with nonhistone chromosomal protein. It is only the DNA of the latter category that is available for transcription. This is most clearly shown by experiments of Marushige and Bonner (1) and of Billing and Bonner (2), who sheared chromatin to small size (about 200 to 400 base pairs) using endonuclease II and then physically separated the two classes (histone-complexed DNA is insoluble in 0.15 M NaCl; DNA complexed with nonhistone chromosomal proteins

is soluble in this material). Essentially all histone is recovered in
the histone-complexed fragments. Essentially all nonhistone chromosomal proteins are recovered in the nonhistone chromosomal protein-
complexed fragments. Suppose now we pulse label the growing RNA
chains on the chromosomes in vivo, with labeled uridine or other
labeled nucleotides. Suppose we then isolate chromatin, shear,
separate as outlined above — over 90 % of the nascent RNA chains are
borne by the nonhistone chromosomal protein-complexed fragments.

Thus, our chromosomal system is clear enough. It seems that
DNA is made untranscribable by being complexed with histones and
that for the DNA to become transcribable, the histones must be
removed. We consider this below.

First, one further feature of histone chemistry and one further
feature of eukaryote DNA. Histones cannot read base sequence.
They bind to any available DNA. For histones to be deposited or
removed from specific DNA sequences would appear to require the
intervention of accessory molecules that can read base sequence.
We look into this question below.

Eukaryote DNA, unlike that of bacteria or of viruses, is characterized by the presence not only of sequences each represented only
one time per genome (single-copy or unique DNA — the structural
genes) but also by the presence of sequences represented several or
many times per genome — the redundant or repetitive sequences. In
the rat, for example, one sequence of about 200 base pairs in length
is repeated one million times. This is the centromeric or satellite
DNA, and it is apparently never expressed by transcription into RNA.
About 20% of rat DNA is, however, made up of sequences represented
on the average of a few hundred times each. These are the middle
repetitive DNA sequences. Wu, in work already published, has
described methods for the determination of the length and distribution
of these middle repetitive segments of DNA (3). They are short, about
100 to 150 base pairs in length, and they are interspersed between
the single-copy sequences, which average about 800 base pairs in
length. Many chromosomologists feel, although it is not yet proven,
that these short repetitive segments are some sort of control sequences,
each controlling (by binding a derepressor to itself) the expression of
the adjacent structural gene (4).

Now let us return to changes in liver chromatin that result from
partial hepatectomy. As noted above, the template activity of the
chromatin in support of RNA synthesis by RNA polymerase increases
after partial hepatectomy, as shown in Fig. 1. This is paralleled by
a decrease in the histone:DNA ratio of the chromatin, as shown by
Garrard and Bonner (5), and also shown in Fig. 1. During this period

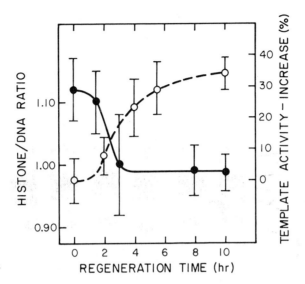

FIG. 1. Template activity for RNA synthesis and histone:DNA ratio of the chromatin of regenerating rat liver as a function of time after partial hepatectomy. The solid circles and solid line indicate histone:DNA ratio, which drops from an initial value of 1.11 to a value after about 4 hr of about 0.97. The open circles and dotted line indicate template activity which increases by 35% over the same period. From Garrard and Bonner (5).

there is no DNA synthesis; therefore, histones must be destroyed. They are not destroyed selectively. All five major species are destroyed equally, as shown in Fig. 2 and Table 1.

Among the chromosomal nonhistone proteins is a neutral protease whose specificity is that it attacks histones almost exclusively (6). Although this protease does not appear to attack histones in normal, stable cells [it has been shown by Hancock (7) that histones do not turn over in normal, stable cells], it does attack histones of the chromatin of which it is a component in regenerating liver. Thus when chromatin of 3-hr regenerating liver is isolated and incubated for a few minutes, and then its acid-soluble proteins are prepared and chromatographed, large peptides, which are degradation products of the histones, are recovered (5). Similar findings have been made by Marushige and Dixon (8), in connection with histone replacement by protamine in maturing trout sperm.

Thus, the chromosomal histone protease attacks a portion of the histones of regenerating liver chromatin. But it attacks only some of them, not all. What is the signal that labels the histones of a

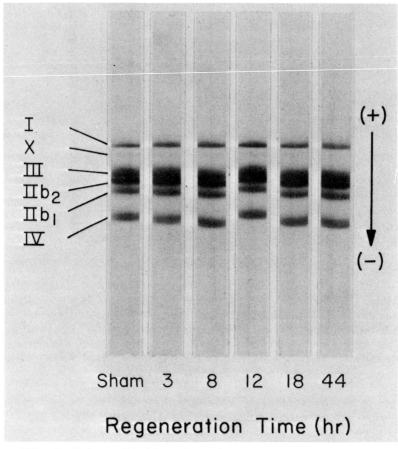

FIG. 2. Polyacrylamide gel electrophoresis of histones of regenerating rat liver chromatin prepared at various times after partial hepatectomy. The acrylamide gels are run according to the method described in Bonner et al. [from Garrard and Bonner (5)].

particular gene for destruction? Phosphorylation of the relevant histone molecules has been suggested, but we have found that this is not the case in regenerating rat liver. Acetylation, also known to be a naturally occurring modification of histone molecules (9), may perhaps mark histone molecules for destruction by histone protease, but we do not as yet know. In any case, the answer to this question would merely shift the problem of who or what determines which particular histone molecule is marked for destruction in this activation of the DNA to which it is complexed. And in this way we return to the question, what element introduces the principle of sequence specificity into histone–DNA interaction? There are two classes of

TABLE 1

Changes in the Relative Amounts of the Several Histone Species of
Rat Liver Chromatin during Liver Regeneration[a]

Time, hr	Histone, percent of total				
	I	IIb_1	IIb_2	III	IV
0, sham	10.5 ± 0.5	14.9 ± 0.7	25.7 ± 4.2	29.7 ± 2.6	19.2 ± 1.1
3	10.2 ± 0.8	15.6 ± 0.8	24.7 ± 2.6	31.1 ± 4.0	18.4 ± 1.1
8	10.1 ± 0.7	15.8 ± 0.3	24.4 ± 3.1	31.3 ± 2.8	18.4 ± 1.5
12	10.8	15.4	25.6	30.5	17.7
18	9.9	14.7	22.0	34.5	18.9
44	10.5	15.0	22.4	33.7	18.4

[a] The histone nomenclature is that of Fambrough and Bonner (Ref. 5).

candidates for this role. One might imagine that among the nonhistone chromosomal proteins are species that can recognize specific
DNA sequences and that by their binding to these sequences can
either cause histones to be destroyed or not to be deposited there.
We have therefore looked for the appearance of new species of nonhistone chromosomal proteins in regenerating rat liver and have found
that one of the 30 or so principal components does increase under
these conditions, as shown in Figs. 3 and 4. We and others are
hard at work on studies of the role of nonhistone chromosomal proteins in the sequence-specific recognition of DNA by histones. We
have found, however, that only about 2% of the total nonhistone
chromosomal protein of rat liver chromatin interacts sequence-
specifically with homologous DNA (10). A similar finding has been
made by Georgiev (11) in Moscow, except that his number was lower,
namely 0%. No-one has yet devised a clear-cut experiment to test
the role of nonhistone chromosomal proteins in histone-DNA interaction.

The second candidate is to be found among the RNA components
of chromatin. These include a species of RNA molecule unique to
chromosomes — short (about 40 to 80 nucleotides in length depending
on species), rich in dihydropyrimidine, and able to hybridize only to
the short, middle-repetitive segments of the genome (12). This class
of RNA also has the characteristic that the more active the genome
(that is, the more it is transcribable by RNA polymerase), the more
of its middle repetitive sequences contain, and/or can hybridize to,
this particular class of RNA, which we term chromosomal RNA.

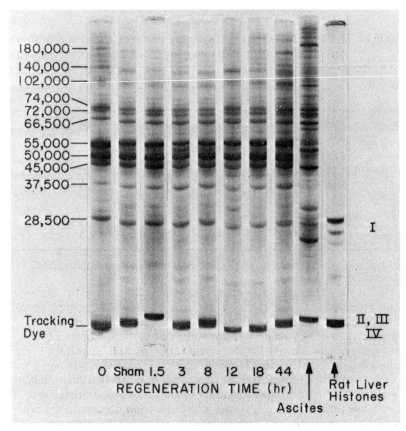

FIG. 3. Sodium dodecyl sulfate-polyacrylamide gel electrophoresis of the nonhistone chromosomal proteins of normal rat liver.
Scans of such gels for three different preparations are reproduced
here to demonstrate the reproducibility in the identification of the
major nonhistone chromosomal protein components [from Garrard and
Bonner (5)].

We will not cover the experiments that have been done to test
the idea that chromosomal RNA is responsible for introducing sequence
specificity into histone DNA interaction (13, 14). Although this role
is suggested for chromosomal RNA, it does not exclude a role also for
the nonhistone chromosomal proteins.

One last fact about chromosomal RNA, however. Holmes (15)
has shown that all of the sequences contained in chromosonal RNA of
any given cell are contained in the giant nuclear RNA (HnRNA) of that
cell. We know from Church and McCarthy (16) that within 15 min of

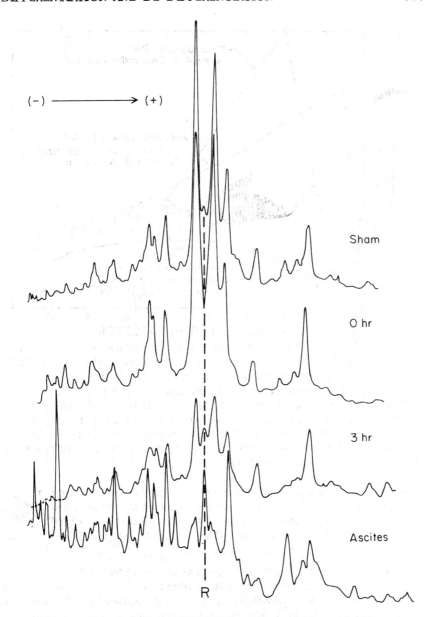

FIG. 4. Scans of sodium dodecyl sulfate-polyacrylamide gel electrophoresis preparations of the nonhistone chromosomal proteins of regenerating rat liver taken at various times during rat liver regeneration. The component labeled R clearly increases after partial hepatectomy and is also present in the rapidly growing liver-derived rat ascites tumor chromatin [from Garrard and Bonner (5)].

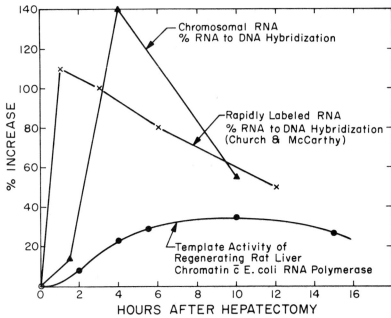

FIG. 5. A partial summary of early nuclear events during and immediately after partial hepatectomy. The first major biochemical event to be detected thus far is the increase in sequences found in rapidly labeled, rapidly turning over, nuclear RNA (HnRNA). The second event temporally is the appearance of new sequences of chromosomal RNA, sequences that are also contained in HnRNA and that may be derived from it. The third feature is an increase in template activity of chromatin for RNA synthesis by RNA polymerase [from Mayfield and Bonner (17)].

partial hepatectomy, new sequences of HnRNA begin to appear, as shown in Fig. 5. With the lag of about an hour, these same sequences begin to appear as chromosomal RNA molecules (17). With another brief lag, previously repressed DNA begins to become derepressed. These ideas are summarized in Fig. 6.

In this most general form, the model presented in Fig. 6 suggests that the genome contains particular sensor genes, genes sensitive to the presence of one or another kind of small molecule. These might, for example, be those kinds of small molecules that we know as hormones, for which we know to increase the number of genes available for transcription in various kinds of chromatin. They might be the particular kinds of small molecules by means of which a partially hepatectomized rat liver knows that it is not complete and must

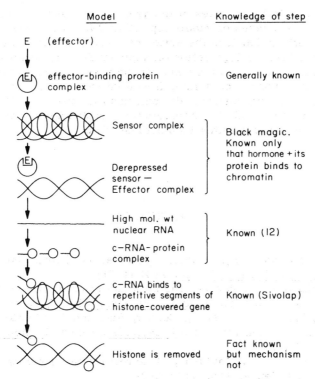

FIG. 6. A summary model of this author's interpretation of what we know today and can reasonably interpret from what we know about how small, biologically active, effector molecules cause previously repressed genes to become turned on.

regenerate itself, or they might include the carcinogenic hydrocarbons. In the case of the hormones in particular, we know that the hormone, as for example estrogen, first binds to a specific hormone-binding protein; the complex of hormone and hormone-binding protein subsequently binds to particular sites on the chromatin of the target cell. We know also that there are only a few binding sites in chromatin for hormone bound to its hormone-binding protein. This is known with particular clarity in the case of estrogen, in which instance there are about 1000 binding sites per genome (18). In any case, the model of Fig. 6 goes on to suggest that the binding of the effector molecule to its effector-molecule-binding protein results in the subsequent binding of the complex to sensor genes that are then derepressed and that produce RNA molecules that are either processed into chromosomal RNA or perhaps in some cases translated into particular species of nonhistone chromosomal protein, which then bind sequence-specifically to particular DNA sequences of the genome, perhaps to classes of sequences as classes of middle repetitive RNA. The model of Fig. 6 suggests further that it is the action of these activator molecules that causes histone degradation on adjacent DNA sequences, and thus derepression. It is also the sense of the model of Fig. 6 that carcinogenic hydrocarbons should also, from what we know of chromosomal biochemistry today, interact with chromosomal proteins. It is my advice that we now study the interaction of carcinogenic hydrocarbons with nuclear proteins rather than nuclear DNA.

REFERENCES

1. K. Marushige and J. Bonner, Fractionation of liver chromatin, Proc. Nat. Acad. Sci., 68, 2941 (1971).
2. R. Billing and J. Bonner, The structure of chromatin as revealed by DNase digestion, Biochim. Biophys. Acta, 281, 453 (1972).
3. J. -R. Wu, J. Hurn, and J. Bonner, Size and distribution of the repetitive segments of the Drosophila genome, J. Mol. Biol., 64, 211 (1972).
4. R. Britten and E. Davidson, Gene regulation for higher cells: A theory, Science, 165, 349 (1969).
5. W. Garrard and J. Bonner, Molecular events in the derepression of regenerating liver chromatin, in preparation.
6. J. Garrels, S. C. R. Elgin, and J. Bonner, A histone protease of rat liver chromatin, Biochem. Biophys. Res. Commun., 46, 545 (1972).
7. R. Hancock, Conservation of histones during growth and mitosis in vitro, J. Mol. Biol., 40, 457 (1969).
8. K. Marushige, U. Ling, and G. Dixon, Phosphorylation of chromosomal basic proteins in maturing trout testes, J. Biol. Chem., 244, 5953 (1969).
9. R. DeLange, D. Fambrough, E. Smith, and J. Bonner, Calf and pea histone. IV. Complete amino acid sequence of pea seedling histone IV; comparison with the homologous calf thymus histone, J. Biol. Chem., 244, 5669 (1969).
10. J. van den Broek, L. Noodén, and J. S. Sevall, Isolation and characterization of native nonhistone chromosomal proteins, Biochemistry, in press.
11. G. Georgiev, personal communication, 1972.
12. D. Holmes, J. Mayfield, G. Sander, and J. Bonner, Chromosomal RNA: Its properties, Science, 177, 72 (1972).

13. I. Bekhor, G. Kung, and J. Bonner, Sequence-specific interaction of DNA and chromosomal protein, J. Mol. Biol., 39, 351 (1969).
14. R. C. Huang and P. C. Huang, Effect of protein bound RNA associated with chick embryo chromatin on template specificity of the chromatin, J. Mol. Biol., 39, 365 (1969).
15. D. Holmes, personal communication, 1972.
16. R. Church and B. McCarthy, RNA synthesis in regenerating and embryonic liver, J. Mol. Biol., 23, 477 (1967).
17. J. Mayfield and J. Bonner, A partial sequence of nuclear events in regenerating rat liver, Proc. Nat. Acad. Sci., 69, 7 (1972).
18. H. R. Maurer and G. R. Chalkley, Some properties of a nuclear binding site of estradiol., J. Mol. Biol., 27, 431 (1967).

V

MAMMALIAN CELL MUTAGENESIS AS RELATED TO CARCINOGENESIS

Chapter 28

DEVELOPMENT OF MUTATIONAL MODEL SYSTEMS FOR STUDY OF CARCINOGENESIS

H. V. Malling

National Institute of Environmental Health Sciences
Research Triangle Park, North Carolina

E. H. Y. Chu

Department of Human Genetics
University of Michigan Medical School
Ann Arbor, Michigan

INTRODUCTION

A mutational model system for the study of carcinogenesis is based on the assumption that certain types of mutations in a somatic cell increase the probability that this cell will transform into a neoplastic cell. This increase in susceptibility can be Mendelianly inherited (9) or induced by direct reaction of the carcinogen with biologic target molecules, probably DNA. Many types of damage can be induced by chemical and physical agents in this target molecule, and attempts have been made to correlate certain types of damage with carcinogenicity. The formation of oxygen-6 substituted guanine in DNA (17) and the production of inactivating DNA alterations (10) are examples of such correlations.

Many types of DNA damage result in the production of a mutation. The carcinogenicity of chemicals has been correlated with different types of mutations including: (a) production of chromosome aberrations (13), (b) production of frameshift mutations (1), (c) production of missense mutations (23), and (d) selective production of mutations in the rRNA genes (7). Since such studies are just beginning to be made, it is not as yet possible to reach any clearcut conclusion as to which type of genetic damage is the most likely to increase the susceptibility of the cells toward neoplastic transformation. Therefore, any mutational model system must contain a battery of tests by which these different mutational events can be measured.

Ideally, studies on the mutagenicity and mutagen specificity of carcinogens in mammals should be made in somatic cells in vivo, preferably in the organ in which tumors occur. Unfortunately, such systems have not yet been developed. As an alternative, various test systems ranging from viruses to mammalian cells in culture have been used to study mutagenicity of carcinogens. A mutational model system for study of carcinogenesis can be used for two distinct purposes: (a) identification of the genetic events that are most likely to result in tumors, or (b) prescreening of chemicals for their mutagenic activity to predict carcinogenic activity.

In man, many of the genes that increase the susceptibility of a cell toward neoplastic transformation are recessive (9); they do not express themselves in a diploid somatic cell heterozygous for such a gene. Two genetic mechanisms exist, however, that can result in homozygosity of heterozygous alleles in a diploid cell, namely mitotic recombination and gene conversion. Both of these mechanisms require subsequent mitoses leading to homozygosity of the recessive genes in some of the daughter cells. These two genetic mechanisms may occur in any number of cell divisions after the original insult, and they provide a genetic explanation for the long latent period for occurrence of tumors. The occurrence of gene conversion and mitotic recombination have not been firmly established in mammalian cells. Precise quantitative data on the induction of both mechanisms can be obtained in yeast (25, 34), and such an assay should be a part of any battery of tests for the prescreening of carcinogens.

The correlation between carcinogenicity and mutagenicity cannot be expected to be complete. The following factors clearly affect such a correlation: (a) carcinogenic hormones may not be mutagenic, (b) promotors may change the intracellular or extracellular conditions permitting preneoplastic cells to develop into tumors, but may not be mutagenic by themselves, (c) many carcinogens require metabolism in the mammals to become activated, and tests without the proper activation may not reveal their mutagenicity, and (d) a number of carcinogens or procarcinogens are almost water-insoluble and may not penetrate into the indicator cell or organism. In addition, many pitfalls may exist in mutagenicity tests of carcinogens because the tests have to be done in test systems both remote from the site and different from the type of cells in which the tumors occur.

In order to explore the possibilities, requirements, and pitfalls of mutational model systems as prescreening tests of carcinogens, three different mutation systems have been used, namely (a) Chinese hamster cells in tissue culture in which both forward mutations from azaguanine sensitivity to azaguanine resistance ($\underline{azg}^S \rightarrow \underline{azg}^r$) and reversion from resistance to sensitivity $\underline{azg}^r \rightarrow \underline{azg}^S$ have been

measured (4), (b) heterokaryotic conidia of Neurospora crassa in
which forward mutations are detected in the adenine-3 (ad-3) region
(5), and (c) cells of Salmonella typhimurium in which reversion of
histidine-requiring mutations are measured (1).

IN VITRO TESTS

A series of polycyclic hydrocarbons were tested in Chinese
hamster V79 cells in tissue culture for their ability to increase the
frequency of azaguanine-resistant cells among the sensitive cells
(Table 1). This series is composed of highly carcinogenic compounds
and noncarcinogenic analogs closely related in structure to the carcinogens. None of the tested polycyclic hydrocarbons were strong
mutagens. The potent carcinogen 3, 4-benzpyrene was negative,
whereas one of its metabolites, 3-hydroxy-3:4-benzpyrene gave a
slight but significant increase in the mutation frequency over the
control. The highest frequency of azaguanine-resistant colonies was
found after treatment with 9, 10-dimethyl-1, 2-benzanthracene. Of
this series of polycyclic hydrocarbons, 9, 10-dimethyl-1, 2-benz-
anthracene has the highest carcinogenic index, 151 (14).

The metabolism of 2-acetylaminofluorene has been carefully
worked out by the Millers, Weisburger, and others (27). This compound and its metabolites and derivatives form an almost classic
series of compounds for demonstrating that a procarcinogen is nonmutagenic (in vitro tests without activation) but that some of its
active metabolites exert mutagenic activity. In Chinese hamster
cells in tissue culture, N-acetoxy-2-acetylaminofluorene induced a
high frequency of azaguanine-resistant cells among the azaguanine-
sensitive cells (Table 2). This compound is not a metabolite of
2-acetylaminofluorene but is closely related to the sulfate ester of
N-hydroxy-2-acetylaminofluorene, which is believed to be one of the
ultimate carcinogenic metabolites.

Treatment of Chinese hamster cells (strain V79) with 2-nitroso-
fluorene gave only a doubling of the frequency of azaguanine-resistant
cells over the control (Table 2). By contrast, this compound gave a
dramatic increase in the frequency of reversion in two of three
histidine-requiring frameshift mutants of Salmonella typhimurium (2).

In Neurospora crassa, both N-hydroxy-2-acetylaminofluorene and
N-acetoxy-2-acetylaminofluorene were mutagenic (Table 3). The latter
compound exerted a mutagenic activity similar to such strong mutagens
as ethyl methanesulfonate and methyl methanesulfonate (24). The glucuronide of N-hydroxy-2-acetylaminofluorene was not mutagenic in
Neurospora crassa. This compound is a major metabolite of

TABLE 1

Frequency of Azaguanine-Resistant Cells (AZG^r) among Azaguanine
Sensitive Chinese Hamster Cells (V79) after 24 hr Treatment
with Various Polycyclic Hydrocarbons

Expt. No.	Chemical	Concentration	Percent Survival	AZG^r colonies per 10^5 survivors
1	Control	0	100	2.0
	DMF	100 mg/ml	62	2.4
	1.2-BP	10 μg/ml	49	2.5
	3.4-BP	10 μg/ml	43	2.9
2	Control	0	100	0.9
	3-O H- 3,4-BP	8 μg/ml	34	3.3[a]
3	Control	0	100	0.35
	1,2,3,4,-DBA	5.0 μg/ml	62	2.6[a]
	1,2,5,6-DBA	5.0 μg/ml	47	3.4[a]
	9.10 DMBA	5.0 μg/ml	25	8.8[a]

[a] Significantly greater than the control (P > 0.99). Abbreviations:
BP, benzpyrene; DBA, dibenzanthracene; DMBA, dimethylbenz-
antracene; DMF, dimethylformamide.

2-acetylaminofluorene in species susceptible to the carcinogenic action of 2-acetylaminofluorene (26) and can react with RNA and DNA in
vitro (33). The glucuronide of N-hydroxy-2-acetylaminofluorene induced cancers at the injection site, but the relative degree of carcinogenicity of this compound is much less than N-hydroxy-2-acetylamino-
fluorene (15). It has been suggested that a part of its carcinogenicity
is due to hydrolysis of glucuronide of N-hydroxy-2-acetylaminofluorene
to N-hydroxy-2-acetylaminofluorene and a subsequent reduction to
2-acetylaminofluorene by bacterial enzymes in the gut and to the re-
entering of 2-acetylaminofluorene into the mammalian body (32). In
summary, the mutation data obtained in Neurospora with 2-acetyl-
aminofluorene, its derivatives, and metabolites correlated well with
the metabolic and carcinogenic studies of these compounds.

We have concluded from these data that only the reactive metabolites of carcinogens are mutagenic in Chinese hamster cells in tissue
culture and in Neurospora crassa. This requirement for mutagenic

TABLE 2

Frequency of Azaguanine-Resistant Cells (AZG^r) among
Azaguanine-Sensitive Chinese Hamster Cells (V79) after
Treatment with AAF and Various Derivatives[a]

Expt. No.	Chemical	Concentration, M	Survival	AZG^r colonies per 10^5 survivors
1	Control	0	100	0. 1
	2-AAF	5×10^{-6}	68	0. 8
2	Control	0	100	11. 2
	N-HO-AAF	5×10^{-5}	28	20. 2
3	Control	0	100	5. 3
	N-AcO-AAF	2×10^{-6}	41. 6	58. 7
4	Control	0	100	13. 6
	2-nitroso-AF	4×10^{-6}	4. 6	28. 3

[a] Abbreviations: 2-AAF, 2-acetylaminofluorene; N-HO-AAF, N-hydroxy-2-acetylaminofluorene; N-AcO-AAF, N-acetoxy-2-acetylaminofluorene, 2-nitroso-AF, 2-nitroso-aminofluorene.

activity does not seem necessary for bacteria in which 2-amino-fluorene can induce reverse mutations (3). This may indicate unique features of the bacteria genome compared with that of eukaryotes, but may also point out that mutagenic activity can be detected in bacteria after treatment with compounds that are not activated carcinogens, and it may indicate a certain degree of unspecificity of the bacterial system.

ACTIVATION SYSTEMS

Many carcinogens cannot react directly with their biologic target molecule but need catalytic action by biochemical compounds or conversion to reactive metabolites. The reactivity of N-methyl-N'-nitro-N-nitrosoguanidine is strongly catalyzed by SH groups present in most living organisms (29). The mutagenic activity of cycasin depends upon the intestinal flora (11), and highly mutagenic break-down products are formed during the microsomal metabolism of

TABLE 3

Forward Mutation Frequencies in the AD-3 Region of Neurospora crassa after Treatment with AAF and Some of its Derivatives[a]

Chemical	Treatment			Survival of the heterokaryotic fractions, %	Forward mutation frequency per 10^6 survivors
	Temperature, °C	Concentration	Time, hr		
Control	4	0	18	100	0.4
DMSO	37	10%	18	83.5	0.3
AAF	37	0.005 M	18	73.9	0.9
N-OH-AAF	37	0.005 M	18	52.9	6.5
N-AcO-AAF	37	0.005 M	18	41.3	320.0
N-GlO-AAF	37	10 mg/ml	24	75.0	1.0

[a] Abbreviations: DMSO, dimethylsulfoxide; N-GlO-AAF, the glucuronide of N-hydroxy-2-acetylamino-fluorene.

TABLE 4

Induction of Histidine Reversions in S. typhimurium Strain G46
by DMN and DEN in the Microsomal System (from liver)[a]

Animal	Treatment	mM	Number of revertants	Reversions per 10^6 survivors
Rat	Control	0	11	0.06
Rat	DEN	45	8	0.05
Rat	DMN	45	20	0.11
Mouse	Control	0	9	0.06
Mouse	DEN	45	51	0.31
Mouse	DMN	45	1042	6.2

[a] Abbreviations: DEN, diethylnitrosamine; DMN, dimethylnitrosamine.

dimethylnitrosamine (19). Clearly for carcinogens, where the active
metabolite cannot be obtained in pure form, activation systems must
be employed for study of their mutagenesis. Formation of mutagens
during activation of carcinogens has been successfully demonstrated
to occur (a) chemically by Udenfriend's system (18, 31), (b) cata-
lytically by biochemical compounds (29), (c) probably enzymatically
by microbial enzymes (11, 28), (d) metabolically by liver microsomes
(19), or (e) in the host-mediated assay (12). The following discussion
briefly covers the results obtained in some of these systems.

Chemical System

Various chemical systems have been composed that, to a certain
degree, mimic the metabolism of drugs in the liver. In Udenfriend's
system (31), in the presence of oxygen both dimethylnitrosamine and
diethylnitrosamine induce reversion of adenine-requiring mutations in
Neurospora crassa (18). In ad-3, the forward-mutation system in
Neurospora crassa, diethylnitrosamine was a much more powerful
mutagen than dimethylnitrosamine (35).

Microsomal System

Liver microsomes from mice can convert dimethylnitrosamine to
a powerful mutagen that can induce revertants of the histidine-
requiring mutant (G46) of Salmonella typhimurium (19), and in Chinese
hamster cells. In comparative experiments with liver microsomes

TABLE 5

Effect of BHT-Containing Diet Fed to Mice on the Histidine Reversion
Frequency Induced in S. typh. G-46 by DMN Activated in the
Liver-Microsome System[a]

Expt. No.	Livers from mice on	Nitrosamine	% survival	No. of revertants	Revertants per 10^6 survivors
1	Normal food	0	100	0	0
	Normal food	DMN	85.9	1596	26.8
	Normal food + BHT	0	77.6	1	0.01
	Normal food + BHT	DMN	87.7	3786	62.3
2	Normal food	0	100	5	0.03
	Normal food	DMN	85.3	866	11.94
	Normal food + BHT	0	42.1[b]	5	0.07
	Normal food + BHT	DMN	69.1	2921	49.72

[a] Abbreviation: BHT, butylated hydroxytoluene.
[b] The low survival must be due to technical error.

from rats, dimethylnitrosamine induced little increase in the reverse-mutation frequency (Table 4). In the microsomal system from mice, diethylnitrosamine gave a much lower frequency than dimethylnitrosamine. Since the induction of the mutations are scored as revertants, relative differences in reversion frequencies do not necessarily indicate differences in the general mutagenic potency between dimethylnitrosamine and diethylnitrosamine.

Liver microsome fractions from male mice C3101F1(C3H × 101) prefed with butylated hydroxytoluene (7.5 g/kg food) increased the frequency of revertants induced by dimethylnitrosamine in the microsomal system by a factor of two above the control on normal food (Table 5) (36).

Host-Mediated Assay

In the host-mediated assay, the indicator organism for scoring mutations is injected into the animal, which is then treated with the compound under investigation. Several factors have to be considered in the use of this assay for study of mutagenicity. They are: (a) in heterologous host-mediated assays there may be an interaction between the host and the indicator organism, (b) the limited time the indicator organism can be kept in the animal, (c) tissue-specific mutagenic activation of the injected compound, (d) detoxification processes, and (e) difference between the repair mechanism of the host and the indicator organism.

Prolonged incubation of Neurospora conidia in mice and rats gave a dramatic increase in the mutation frequency per survivor in the adenine-3 region (20). Placing of barriers between the conidia and the animal dramatically decreased the mutation frequency per survivor even though it was still higher than the in vitro control. A similar increase in the frequency of azaguanine-resistant colonies among azaguanine-sensitive Chinese hamster cells in tissue culture was observed after incubation of the cells in dialysis bags implanted in rats (Table 6). Most of the mutations induced in Neurospora during the incubation in the animal are chromosome deletions (35). This mechanism may be a part of the defense mechanism of animals toward infections (20). Agents that can influence this mechanism may therefore give false positive results when tested for mutagenicity in a heterologous host-mediated assay. The ideal host-mediated assay should be performed with indicator organisms that the host cannot distinguish from its own cells. The mouse lymphoma cells 5178Y from DBA/2 mice, using DBA/2 mice as hosts, may come close to fulfilling this L5179Y requirement (8).

TABLE 6

Induction of Forward Mutations to 8-Azaguanine Resistance in
Chinese Hamster Cells Contained in Dialysis Bags and
Implanted for Various Times in Rats

Expt. No.	Number of rats tested	Time in rat, hr	% cell survival	Mutation frequency per 10^5 survivors (in the rat)	Mutation frequency in vitro, $\times 10^{-5}$
3	2	12	38	13.7	3.8
4	14	23	45	284.4	0.3
5	14	27	11	6.5	0.7
6	3	6	67	2.3	1.9
	3	12	41	3.5	1.9
	3	18	43	2.8	1.9
	3	24	16	4.5	1.9

In most types of host-mediated assays, the indicator organism is
exposed to the metabolites of the compound for a short time interval;
in the Salmonella system, 3 hr; in the Neurospora system, 18 hr (16);
and in the mouse lymphoma cell system, up to three days (37). The
host-mediated assay cannot be used to obtain an indication of the
effect of chronic administration of a carcinogen to an animal. Only
further experimentation can determine whether the host-mediated
assay is sufficiently sensitive to detect mutations induced by compounds requiring repeated or chronic administration before they exert
their carcinogenic activity. An accumulation of mutations during
chronic treatment may be detected if a system could be developed in
which the mutations are scored directly in the host's own cells.
Sutton (30) has suggested such a system based on histochemical
methods.

Many carcinogens are organ specific. This specificity depends
somewhat upon dose and route of administration of the carcinogen.
In the host-mediated assay, the preferred place to incubate the indicator organism is in the peritoneal cavity. Since some carcinogens
are metabolized to highly labile compounds by the liver the concentration of such active metabolites may not be high enough to give a
detectible increase in the mutation frequency of the indicator organism
placed in the peritoneal cavity. To study this possibility, Neurospora

TABLE 7

Effect of Route of Administration of Conidia and DMN or DEN on
Mutation Induction in _Neurospora conidia_ in the Host-Mediated Assay

Experiment No.	Treatment	Dose, mg/kg	Route of Administration		No. of ad-3 mutations	Mutations per 10^6 survivors
			Conidia	Chemical		
12-187	In vitro, control	0	–	–	0	0
	DEN, in mice	200	IP	IM	1	0.31
12-195	In mice, liver	0	IV	IP	5	0.65
	DEN, in mice, liver	150	IV	IP	14	1.74
12-187	In vitro, control, 37°C	0	–	–	0	0
	Control, in mice	0	IP	IM	0	0
	DMN, in mice	100	IP	IM	1	0.40
12-201	In vitro, control, 37°C	0	–	–	0	0
	Control, in mice, liver	0	IV	IM	0	0
	DMN, in mice, liver	75	IV	IM	528	286

TABLE 8

Comparison of Mutation Frequencies Induced by Various Mutagens
in the Adenine-3 Region of N. crassa in
vitro and in the Host-Mediated Assay

Compound	Concentration of compound, mg/kg	System	Ad-3 mutations per 10^6 survivors
MMS	330	In vitro	23
	250	In the host-mediated assay	23
EMS	3100	In vitro	5
	300	In the host-mediated assay	10
MNNG	3.5	In vitro	1040
	50	In the host-mediated assay	0
ICR-170	4.8	In vitro	1036
	8	In the host-mediated assay	0

[a] Abbreviations: MMS, methyl methanesulfonate; EMS, ethyl
methanesulfonate; MNNG, N-methyl-N'-nitro-N-nitrosoguanidine;
ICR-170, monofunctional acridine mustard.

conidia were either injected into the peritoneal cavity of mice C3B6F1
(C3H × C57B/6) and recovered from the peritoneal cavity or injected
into the tail vein of mice and recovered from the liver (Table 7). After
the injection of the conidia, the animals were treated with dimethylnitrosamine. Approximately a 600 times higher frequency of mutations was found among the conidia recovered from the liver than
among those recovered from the peritoneal cavity. When Salmonella
typhimurium was injected into the peritoneal cavity, reversions were
induced after treatment of the animal with dimethylnitrosamine.
Clearly the Salmonella is more sensitive than the Neurospora for the
mutagenic metabolites of dimethylnitrosamine.

N-methyl-N'-nitro-N-nitrosoguanidine and a monofunctional
acridine mustard (ICR-170) are potent mutagens in Neurospora when
the conidia are treated in vitro (Table 8). In the host-mediated assay,
these two compounds are hardly mutagenic when Neurospora is used as

the indicator organism and injected into the peritoneal cavity. The animal had either bound or detoxified the injected compounds so effectively that the compounds reached the indicator organism in insufficient concentrations to give a detectible increase in the mutation frequency. Nevertheless, N-methyl-N'-nitro-N-nitrosoguanidine is a potent carcinogen (6). In the mutational model systems for the prescreening of carcinogens it is necessary to include the in vitro treatment of the indicator organism.

TYPES OF MUTATIONS

We have so far concluded that there is, in general, a good correlation between the carcinogenic and the mutagenic activity of chemicals when metabolic activation or ultimate carcinogens are used. The next question one could raise is: "What type of genetic alterations are most likely to increase the susceptibility of the cell toward neoplastic transformation?" An answer to this question is of extreme importance for a rational selection of mutational model systems for prescreening of carcinogens. Unfortunately, there is no direct evidence about the nature of those genes in which mutation leads to a higher susceptibility toward neoplastic transformation. However, an elucidation of the nature of the genetic alteration induced by carcinogens can be obtained by a phenotypic description of the mutants and the identification of the genetic alteration at the molecular level.

Azaguanine-resistant colonies in Chinese hamster cells in tissue culture can be divided into two classes, those that can grow on medium supplemented with thymine, hypoxanthine, guanine, and aminopterin and those that cannot. Table 9 gives the distribution of the survival of the isolated azaguanine-resistant colonies (30 mg azaguanine per liter medium). Clearly all isolated colonies had a high plating efficiency on azaguanine-containing medium. Clones with a high plating efficiency on medium supplemented with thymine, hypoxanthine, guanine, and aminopterin (THAG) probably have a functional hypoxanthine-guanine phosphoribosyl transferase (HG-PRT). Among the spontaneous azaguanine-resistant clones, 78% (14/18) could grow on THAG-medium in contrast with the N-acetoxy-2-acetyl-aminofluorene induced clones, where only 34% could grow on this medium, which means that the spectrum of the pre-existing mutants is clearly different from the induced mutants.

Reverse mutations are detected on THAG medium, and only those clones that cannot grow on this medium can be tested for their revertibility with specific mutagens. Three mutagens were used: ethylmethanesulfonate, N-methyl-N-nitro-N'-nitrosoguanidine, and a monofunctional acridine mustard (ICR-170). Ethylmethanesulfonate and N-methyl-N-nitro-N'-nitrosoguanidine mainly induces base-pair

TABLE 9

Distribution of Plating Efficiencies among the Azaguanine-Resistant
Cones of Chinese Hamster Cells on Different Media

Origin of resistant colonies	Medium supplement	No. of clones with survival percentages within the ranges			
		< 1	1-19	20-49	50-100
Spontaneous	Azaguanine	0	0	3	15
	THAG	4	0	1	13
H-AcO-AAF-induced	Azaguanine	0	1	1	36
	THAG	23	2	2	11

TABLE 10

Revertibility of Azaguanine-Resistant Clones of Chinese Hamster
Cells Induced by Acetoxy-2-acetylaminofluorene

Origin	Revertibility				No. of clones in each class
	Spontaneous	After treatment with			
		EMS	MNNG	ICR-170	
Spontaneous	0	0	0	0	1
	+	+	+	+	2
N-AcO-AAF	0	0	0	0	14
	+/-	+	+	+	3
	+/-	(+)	+	0	1
	+/-	0	0	+	3

substitutions, while ICR-170 mainly induces base-pair insertions and
deletions. Of the 21 azaguanine-resistant clones isolated after treatment with acetoxy-2-acetylaminofluorene, 14 did not revert spontaneously or after treatment with any of the mutagens. The genetic
alteration in those clones may be deletions. Three clones reverted
after treatment with all mutagens and one clone after treatment with
N-methyl-N'-nitro-N-nitrosoguanidine only; the genetic alteration in
these two classes is probably a base-pair substitution. Three clones
reverted after treatment with ICR-170 only, probably the result of a
base-pair insertion or deletion (Table 10). In summary, most of the
common classes of mutations can be induced by N-acetoxy-2-
acetylaminofluorene.

TABLE 11

Genetic Alterations among Mutants in the ad-3 Region of
Neurospora crassa Induced by N-HO-AAF and N-AcO-AAF (37)[a]

	Point mutations				Total of point mutation	Chromosome deletions
		ad-3B^R				
	ad-3A^R	NP	P	NC		
N-HO-AAF	29	13	5	23	70	0
N-AcO-AAF	135	51	23	134	343	13
Total	164	64	28	157	413	13

[a] Abbreviations: NP, mutants with nonpolarized complementation pattern; P, mutants with polarized complementation pattern; NC, noncomplementing mutants; ad-3A^R, point mutations in the adenine-BA locus; ad-3B^R, point mutations in the adenine-3B locus.

From the study of reverse mutations of a series of histidine-requiring mutants of Salmonella typhimurium, it has been proposed that most carcinogens with fused ring structures induced frameshift mutations (2). On the other hand, dimethylnitrosamine in the liver microsome only induced revertants in histidine-requiring strains of Salmonella typhimurium, which reverted by base-pair substitution.

Table 11 gives the range of genetic alterations among mutants induced in the ad-3 region of Neurospora crassa by N-hydroxy-2-acetylaminofluorene and N-acetoxy-2-acetylaminofluorene. Since these data are not significantly different from each other, they can be pooled. Among the induced mutants, only 3% were due to chromosome deletions. The point mutations in the ad-3B locus can be divided into three classes according to their complementation response: complementing mutants that have either a nonpolarized or a polarized complementation pattern and noncomplementing mutants. Mutants with nonpolarized complementation patterns arise from base-pair substitutions (21, 22). Among the ad-3B mutants induced by the 2-acetylaminofluorene derivatives, 26% had a nonpolarized complementation pattern indicating that they arose by base-pair substitution.

The identification of the genetic alteration in mutants induced by various carcinogens showed that the mutants arose from a wide spectrum of molecular events. This lack of uniformity in the type of genetic alterations induced by carcinogens could be a reflection of the specificity of the test organisms. This seems unlikely, however, since mutagens, in general, possess common specificity through the phylogenetic system. An alternate hypothesis is that malfunction or lack of function of the product coded by different types of genes may increase the susceptibility of the cell toward neoplastic transformation. Thus, a frameshift mutation in a tRNA gene results in a totally different phenotype than a frameshift mutation in a structural gene. The first type of genetic alteration may lead to infidelity in the translation of the code for many different polypeptide chains; the second type may result in complete lack of function of only the particular protein coded by the mutated gene.

CONCLUSIONS

It is likely that most carcinogens will also be mutagenic. Test for mutagenicity of toxic agents probably requires less resources than test for carcinogenicity of the same agents. It is certain that the mutagenicity test can be done in a much shorter time than the test for carcinogenicity. Identification of carcinogens in the environment by a mutational prescreen would save both time and effort. Carcinogens can induce many types of genetic alterations. Within certain chemical groups of carcinogens, certain types of mutations may be prevalently induced. The polycyclic hydrocarbons and other carcinogens that contain fused ring structures may predominantly induce base-pair insertions or deletions. The alkyl carcinogens such as dimethylnitrosamine may induce predominantly base-pair substitutions. In view of these facts, test systems selected for study of the mutagenicity and the mutagenic specificity of carcinogens must be able to detect all types of genetic alterations and not just a particular type. Many carcinogens require metabolic activation in the mammal to exert their effects. The induction of mutations must be measured under such activation conditions. The activation can be obtained chemically, enzymatically, or by using the host-mediated assay. Since it has been shown that the untreated mammal possesses the mechanisms to induce mutations in some indicator organisms or cells, it is important that the interaction between the host and the indicator organism be minimized. Many Mendelian traits that increase the possibility for cells to undergo neoplastic transformation are recessive. In a mammal heterozygous for such a gene, the possibility exists that through gene conversion and/or mitotic recombination, cells can arise that are homozygous for such genes and thereby develop into tumors. Gene conversion and somatic recombination can best be measured in yeast. The battery of mutation systems to be used for prescreening of carcinogens must therefore contain a yeast system to measure these two genetic events.

REFERENCES

1. B. N. Ames, "The Detection of Chemical Mutagens with Enteric
   Bacteria, " from Chemical Mutagens: Principles and Methods
   for Their Detection (A. Hollaender, ed.) Plenum, New York, 1971.
2. B. N. Ames, P. Sims, and P. L. Grover, Epoxides of carcinogenic
   polycyclic hydrocarbons are frameshift mutagens, Science, 176,
   47 (1972).
3. B. N. Ames, E. G. Garney, J. A. Miller, and H. Bartsch, Carino-
   gens as frameshift mutagens: metabolites and derivatives of 2-
   acetylaminofluorene and other aromatic amine carcinogens, Proc.
   Nat. Acad. Sci., 69, 3128 (1972).
4. E. H. Y. Chu, "Induction and Analysis of Gene Mutations in
   Mammalian Cell Cultures, " in Environmental Chemical Mutagens:
   Principles and Methods for Their Detection (A. Hollaender, ed.),
   Plenum, New York, 1971, pp. 411-444.
5. F. J. de Serres and H. V. Malling, "Measurement of Recessive
   Lethal Damage over the Entire Genome and at Two Specific Loci
   in the ad-3 Region of Neurospora crassa with a Two Component
   Heterokaryon, " in Chemical Mutagens: Principles and Methods
   for Their Detection (A. Hollaender, ed.), Plenum, New York,
   1971.
6. H. Druckrey, R. Preussman, S. Ivankovic, B. T. So, C. H. Schmidt,
   and J. Bucheler, Zur Erzeugung subcutaner sarkome an ratten
   carcinogene wirkung von hydrazodicarbon - saure-bis-(methyl-
   mitrasamid), N-nitroso-N-n-butyl-harnstofj, N-methyl-N-nitro-
   nitrosoguandin and N-nitroso-imidazolidon, Z. Krebsforsch., 68,
   87 (1966).
7. O. G. Fahmy and M. J. Fahmy, Mutagenic selectivity for the RNA-
   forming genes in relation to the carcinogenicity of alkylating
   agents and polycyclic aromatics, Cancer Res., 32, 550 (1972).
8. G. A. Fischer, Predictive tests in culture of drug-resistant mutants
   selected in vivo, National Cancer Inst. Monograph 34, 131
   (1971).
9. F. J. Fraumeni, Jr., Genetic determinants of cancer, Conference
   on Host-Environment Interactions on the Etiology of Cancer in
   Man — Implementation in Research, Primosten, Yugoslavia,
   August 27-September 2, 1972.
10. E. Freese and E. B. Freese, Mutagenic and inactivating DNA
    alterations, Radiation Res. Suppl., 6, 97 (1966).
11. M. G. Gabridge, A. Denunzio, and M. S. Legator, Cycasin: de-
    tection of associated mutagenic activity in vivo, Science, 163,
    689 (1969).

12. M. G. Gabridge and M. S. Legator, A host-mediated assay for the detection of mutagenic compounds, Proc. Soc. Exptl. Biol. Med., 130, 831 (1969).

13. S. Hitotsumachi, Z. Rabinowitz, and L. Sachs, Chromosomal control of chemical carcinogenesis, Intern. J. Cancer, 9, 305 (1972).

14. J. Iball, The relative potency of carcinogenic compounds, Amer. J. Cancer, 35, 188 (1939).

15. C. C. Irving and R. Wiseman, Jr., Metabolism of the glucuronide of N-hydroxy-2-acetylaminofluorene, Cancer Res., 29, 812 (1969).

16. M. S. Legator and H. V. Malling, "The Host-Mediated Assay, a Practical Procedure for Evaluating Potential Mutagenic Agents in Mammals," in Chemical Mutagens: Principles and Methods for Their Detection (A. Hollaender, ed.), Plenum, New York, 1970, pp. 569-590.

17. A. Loveless, Possible relevance of 0-6 alleylation of dcotyguanosine to the mutagenicity and carcinogenicity of nitrosamines, Nature, 223, 206 (1969).

18. H. V. Malling, Mutagenicity of two potent carcinogens dimethylnitrosamine and diethylnitrosamine in Neurospora crassa, Mutation Res., 3, 537 (1966).

19. H. V. Malling, Dimethylnitrosamine: formation of mutagenic compounds by interaction with mouse liver microsomes, Mutation Res., 13, 425 (1971).

20. H. V. Malling, Mutation induction in Neurospora crassa incubated in mice and rats, Mol. Gen. Genet., 116, 211 (1972).

21. H. V. Malling and F. J. de Serres, Relation between complementation patterns and genetic alterations in nitrous acid-induced ad-3B mutants of Neurospora crassa, Mutation Res., 4, 425 (1967).

22. H. V. Malling and F. J. de Serres, Correlation between base-pair transition and complementation pattern in nitrous acid-induced ad-3B mutants of Neurospora crassa, Mutation Res., 5, 359 (1968).

23. H. V. Malling and F. J. de Serres, Mutagenicity of alleylating carcinogens, Ann. N. Y. Acad. Sci., 163, 788 (1969).

24. H. V. Malling and F. J. de Serres, Genetic analysis of purple adenine (ad-3) mutants induced by methylmethanesulfonate in Neurospora crassa, Mutation Res., 18, 1 (1973).

25. H. Marquardt, F. K. Zimmermann, H. Dannenberg, H. G. Neumann, A. Bodenberger, and M. Metzler, Die genetische wirkung von aromatischen aminen und ihren derivates: Induktion mitotischer conversionen beider hefe, Z. Krebsforsch., 74, 412 (1970).

26. J. A. Miller, J. W. Cramer, and E. L. Miller, The N-and ring hydroxylation of 2-acetylaminofluorene during carcinogenesis in the rat, Cancer Res., 20, 950 (1960).

27. J. A. Miller and E. C. Miller, The metabolic activation of carcinogenic aromatic amines and amides, Prog. Exptl. Tumor Res., 11, 273 (1969).

28. D. W. E. Smith, Mutagenicity of cycasin aglycone (methyl-azaxymethanol) a naturally occurring carcinogen, Science, 152, 1273 (1966).

29. R. Suessmuth and F. Lingens, IV. Beständigkeit den NNMG, beziehungen zwischen mutationsrate und autnahme des mutagens durch die zelle und förderung des methylierung durch sulfhydryl-gruppin in abhängigkeit vom pH-wert, Z. Naturforsch., 24b, 903 (1964).

30. H. E. Sutton, Workshop on monitoring of human mutagenesis, Teratology, 4, 103 (1971).

31. S. Udenfriend, C. T. Clark, J. Axelrod, and B. B. Brodie, Asorbic acid in aromatic hydroxylation, I. A model system for aromatic hydroxylation, J. Biol. Chem., 208, 731 (1954).

32. J. R. Williams, Jr., P. H. Grantham, J. H. Weisburger, and H. H. March III, Dehydroxylation of the carcinogen N-hydroxy-N-2-fluorenylacetamide by bacterial enzymes of rat cecal contents, Fed. Proc. Fed. Amer. Soc. Exptl. Biol., 27, 650 (1968).

33. R. Wiseman, Jr., R. A. Veazay, and C. C. Irving, Studies on the metabolism and reactivity of the glucuronide of N-hydroxy-2-acetylaminofluorene (N-GIO-AAF), Proc. Amer. Assoc. Cancer Res., 9, 78 (1968).

34. F. K. Zimmermann, R. Schwaier, and U. Von Laer, Mitotic recombination in Saccharomyces cerevisiae with nitrous acid, diethyl sulfate and carcinogenic alkylating nitrosamides, Z. Erbungslr., 98, 230 (1966).

35. H. V. Malling and F. J. de Serres, unpublished.

36. H. V. Malling and R. B. Cumming, unpublished.

37. G. A. Fisher, personal communication.

Chapter 29

CELL MUTAGENESIS STUDIES IN VITRO
USING AUXOTROPHIC MARKERS

Fa-Ten Kao

Department of Biophysics and Genetics
University of Colorado Medical School
Denver, Colorado

Quantitative studies of mammalian cells in vitro have become increasingly important in analysis and elucidation of a large variety of biologic phenomena (1). The development of various cell culture techniques has indeed contributed a great deal to the rapid progress of mammalian cell genetics. Some examples of important advances in these techniques include single cell plating, clone isolation, chemically defined culture media, and rigid control of growth environment.

In the past several years, our laboratory has been engaged in developing techniques for isolating nutritionally deficient mutants in mammalian cells (2, 3). We are particularly interested in auxotrophic mutants because this class of mutants has proved in microbial systems to be especially suitable for carrying out genetic experiments with high resolution (4), and because the genetic nature of such mutants can be demonstrated in most cases to be due to single gene mutations that result in deficiencies of specific enzymes involved in the metabolic pathways (5).

The studies on cell mutagenesis described here have been conducted in collaboration with Dr. T. T. Puck, Dr. L. A. Chasin, Dr. R. T. Johnson, and Dr. C. Waldren. The standard cell used in these studies is a subclone CHO-K1 derived from the Chinese hamster ovary cell. This cell multiplies maximally in F12 medium with a generation time of 12 hr. The short generation of this cell has facilitated genetic experiments enormously. Moreover, the CHO-K1 clone has a modal chromosome number of 20, which is two chromosomes less than that of the normal Chinese hamster cell. Thus it is likely that some

TABLE 1

Yield of Auxotrophic Mutants in the Chinese Hamster Cells Treated with
Various Agents and Isolated by BUdR + Visible Light Method

Agents	Concentration	Survival, %	No. cells surviving treatment which were tested, ×10^5	Number of mutants found					Mutant frequency, ×10^{-5}
				gly$^-$	ino$^-$	ade$^-$	thy$^-$	gly$^-$ + ade$^-$ + thy$^-$	
None	0	100	50.0	0	0	0	0	0	0
EMS	200 μg/ml	78	4.2	20	0	0	0	1	5.0
MNNG	0.5 μg/ml	26	4.9	4	1	0	0	10	3.5
ICR-191	1.5 μg/ml	21	8.8	4	0	4	0	0	1.0
Caffeine	6000 μg/ml	21	5.0	0	0	0	0	0	0
UV	180 ergs/mm^2	21	5.0	4	0	0	0	6	2.0
X ray	600 rad	12	4.6	2	0	0	0	0	0.4
NDMA	15,000 μg/ml	20	2.2	0	0	5	1	0	2.7
NMU	75 μg/ml	20	1.0	0	0	0	2	0	2.0
NMUT	0.1 μg/ml	20	4.5	7	0	3	0	2	2.7

chromatin material is lost from this hypodiploid clone and certain genes are possibly in hemizygous condition.

It has been well recognized that mammalian cells in culture can not synthesize a large number of nutrilites and require exogenous supplement. However, there are certain metabolites that mammalian cells can synthesize, and thus it would appear a reasonable expectation that auxotrophic mutants of this class could be isolated. For example, mammalian cells have all the necessary enzymes for the endogenous synthesis of purines, pyrimidines, and several amino acids including alanine, glycine, proline, aspartic acid, and glutamic acid (6).

When auxotrophic mutants are starved for specific nutrilites, they stop cell division and the rate of DNA synthesis in these cells is greatly reduced. If a thymidine analog 5-bromodeoxyuridine (BUdR) is added to the medium, unlike normal cells which undergo DNA synthesis and incorporate BUdR into their DNA, the mutants do not incorporate BUdR. When these cells are illuminated with near-visible light, only the BUdR-containing normal cells are killed while mutant cells remain unaffected (3). Subsequent change of medium to an enriched one enables the mutant cells to develop into colonies that can be isolated to initiate a clonal auxotrophic mutant culture.

Application of this technique to the CHO-K1 cell permitted us to isolate auxotrophic mutants with nutritional requirements for additional amino acids, carbohydrates, purines, and pyrimidines (7-9). The cells were treated with a variety of different mutagenic agents such as ethyl methanesulfonate (EMS), N-methyl-N'-nitro-N-nitrosoguanidine (MNNG), ICR-191 (an acridine mustard that appears to act as a frame-shift mutagen), caffeine, X rays, and ultraviolet light (UV). Various auxotrophic mutants have also been induced by several carcinogenic nitroso compounds such as N-nitrosodimethylamine (NDMA), N-nitrosomethylurea (NMU), and N-nitrosomethylurethane (NMUT).

Table 1 summarizes the kinds and frequencies of auxotrophic mutants isolated in CHO-K1 cells after treatment with various mutagens. A total of more than 5×10^6 cells were tested for spontaneous auxotrophic mutants using BUdR plus visible light procedure and none was found in these cells without mutagenic treatment, indicating a spontaneous mutant frequency of $\leq 2 \times 10^{-7}$ per cell for all of the loci tested. All of the agents tested, except caffeine, have produced auxotrophic mutants of various kinds. All the mutants listed in Table 1 are of the nonleaky type, exhibiting all-or-none response toward the critical metabolites responsible for each auxotrophy. They are stable with a spontaneous reversion frequency of less than 10^{-8} per cell. These mutants also maintain a near-diploid chromosome number similar to that of the parental cell.

Although caffeine failed to induce any auxotrophic mutants, it exhibited a unique feature in eliminating the shoulder region of the X ray survival curves in CHO-K1 and other mammalian cells (16). Experiments are now in progress to study the combined effect of caffeine and X ray on the production of auxotrophic mutations.

Analysis of the effectiveness of these various agents in producing chromatid breaks has also been carried out (8, 9). Based on the efficiency of producing auxotrophic mutations and chromatid breaks, these agents can be classified into three groups: (a) highly efficient in producing mutations but not breaks, e. g., ICR-191; (b) highly efficient in producing breaks but not mutations, e. g., caffeine; (c) highly efficient in producing both mutations and breaks, e. g., EMS, MNNG, UV, X ray, NDMA, NMU, NMUT.

Since the glycine-requiring (gly^-) mutants are the most abundant auxotrophy produced in CHO-K1 cells by these agents, it is of interest to determine whether mutations have occurred in the same gene or whether different genes exist, all of which are necessary for the biosynthesis of glycine and any of which can mutate to produce a glycine auxotrophy. Complementation tests were carried out by pairwise crosses in all combinations among 13 gly^- mutants. Cell fusion was completed either spontaneously (10) or with the aid of UV-inactivated Sendai virus (11). The yield of hybrids by these two techniques was about 10^{-5} and 10^{-2}, respectively.

The results from these crosses clearly showed that these 13 gly^- mutants can be grouped into four complementation classes, designated glyA, glyB, glyC, and glyD. Hybrids formed between mutants in the same class do not complement and thus fail to grow without glycine, while hybrids formed from mutants in different classes exhibit complementation and are capable of growing maximally in the absence of glycine (10). Therefore, it may be concluded from these genetic experiments that there are at least four different genes that can affect the synthesis of glycine in mammalian cells.

These four gly^- complementation classes can also be distinguished by their biochemical and nutritional characteristics as shown in Table 2. The serine hydroxymethylase, an enzyme that normally converts serine to glycine, is deficient in glyA class mutants, whereas no significant difference in the enzyme activity is found between the normal cell and the mutants of the other three classes. Since tetrahydrofolate (FH_4) is known to act as a coenzyme of serine hydroxymethylase, experiments were conducted by testing one of its stable precursors, folinic acid (N^5-formyl-FH_4), for its ability to support growth of these three classes of gly^- mutants. When folinic acid (10^{-4} M) was added to the glycine-free medium, glyB exhibited complete restoration of growth, although

TABLE 2

Biochemical and Nutritional Characteristics of the Four gly
Complementation Classes and Their Parental Cell CHO-Kl

Comple- mentation class	Serine hydroxy- methylase activity	Growth response in glycine-free medium		
		No addition	Add folinic acid	Add folinic acid plus 10^{-5} M glycine
glyA	-	-	-	-
glyB	+	-	+	+
glyC	+	-	-	+
glyD	+	-	-	-
CHO-Kl	+	+	+	+

glyC and glyD failed to respond. However, as suboptimal concentration of glycine (10^{-5} M) was added together with 10^{-4} M of folinic acid,
the growth of glyC was stimulated. Thus it is possible that the mutations in glyB and glyC may involve defects in the FH_4 metabolism.
The glyD class mutants did not respond to any of these treatments.

Similarly, 11 adenine-requiring mutants (ade$^-$) induced by various
agents have also been tested for complementation. The results revealed
that two mutually exclusive complementation classes, designated adeA
and adeB, exist in these mutants. The enzyme deficiencies of the two
mutant classes appear to lie in the early biosynthetic steps of purines,
possibly between 5-phosphoribosyl-1-pyrophosphate and 5-amino-
imidazole-4-carboxamide (AIC) ribonucleotide (12).

Two other auxotrophic mutants induced by UV and NMUT, respectively, have triple nutritional requirements for glycine, adenine, and
thymidine (GAT$^-$). This class of mutants appears to involve a single
gene mutation that results in a deficiency of a key precursor needed
for synthesis of all these three metabolites (12). One possible candidate for this key precursor might involve the availability of FH_4 since
it is known that aminopterin, which inhibits folate reductase and prevents formation of FH_4, can produce the same triple growth requirements for glycine, adenine, and thymidine in mammalian cells. The
two GAT$^-$ mutants were demonstrated by cell fusion not to complement
each other, indicating that the mutations that had occurred in these
mutants, although induced by different mutagens, involved the same
gene.

TABLE 3

List of Individual Genes in CHO-K1 Cells in Which Recessive
Mutations Have Been Induced by Various Agents and the
Identity of Each Gene Has Been Confirmed by
Complementation Analysis

Gene desig- nation	Growth requirements of the mutant form	Agents which are effective in producing mutants	Number of mutants analyzed
glyA	glycine	EMS, MNNG, X ray	4
glyB	glycine or folinic acid	EMS, MNNG, UV, NMUT	12
glyC	glycine	EMS, UV	2
glyD	glycine	EMS, UV	2
adeA	hypoxanthine, adenine, inosinic acid, their riboside or ribotide, or AIC	ICR-191	1
adeB	same as adeA	ICR-191, NDMA, NMUT	10
ino	inositol	MNNG	1
GAT	glycine, adenine, and thymidine	EMS, MNNG, UV, NMUT	2

Finally, four gly^- mutants, two ade^- mutants, one GAT^- mutant, and one inositol-requiring mutant (ino^-) were tested for complementation. It was found that they exhibited complementation in all possible combinations of crosses (12). Thus a total of eight individual genes have been identified in the CHO-K1 cells in which single, recessive mutations have been induced by various physical and chemical agents. Table 3 summarizes some of the characteristics of these eight genes and lists the various kinds of mutagenic agents that are responsible for producing mutations in each gene.

This multiply marked CHO-K1 cell appears to provide a highly sensitive system for testing mutagenic action of a large variety of physical, chemical, and biologic agents of great environmental concern. Forward mutations, if they occurred in any one of these eight genes, would be detectable. Thus mutagenic specificity inherent to a particular agent or a particular locus can be reduced to a minimum. It is equally desirable to use this well-marked genetic system to explore the possible correlation between mutagenesis and carcinogenesis.

In addition, the auxotrophic mutants here described are also useful for human linkage studies. When Chinese hamster cells are hybridized with human cells, the loss of human chromosomes from the hybrids is rapid and extensive. Within a week after fusion, only one or very few human chromosomes remain in the hybrids. Thus if a specific Chinese hamster auxotroph is used in the cross, it would be possible to establish hybrid cells retaining a single specific human chromosome whose presence is required in order to provide the needed human gene to compensate for the auxotrophy so that the hybrids can survive in the selective medium. After the hybrid cells of this kind are established, other human genes can be studied to determine linkage relationships with respect to the auxotrophic markers and to each other. Using these approaches, human gene linkage has been established between lactate dehydrogenase A gene and a gene responsible for a lethal antigen (13), and serine hydroxymethylase gene and lactate dehydrogenase B gene (14).

Recently, a human regulatory gene has been identified using such techniques (15). When an adeB mutant is hybridized with human cells and the hybrids are grown in the adenine-free medium, a single chromosome resembling the human B-group is always retained. Furthermore, after acrylamide gel electrophoresis, the hybrids have three additional esterase bands that are distinctly different from the esterases present in either parental cells in their electrophoretic mobility and substrate specificity. The extra esterase bands present in the hybrids are also found in the tissue cells from Chinese hamsters but not from humans. It was proposed that these extra esterase bands that appeared in the adeB-human hybrids are Chinese hamster enzymes but become inactivated after long-term growth in culture. Upon hybridization of adeB mutant and the human cell, the specific human chromosome that is retained in the hybrids carries, in addition to the adeB gene, an esterase activator gene that reactivates the previously inactivated Chinese hamster esterase genes.

Conceptually, the development of somatic mammalian cell genetics appears to be a logical followup of microbial genetics. However, the uniqueness of the eukaryotic cell, its chromosome structure and genome complexity, its growth control and differentiation, make it quite distinct from prokaryotic cells. A simple extrapolation of many genetic phenomena from bacterial to mammalian cells may not be so straightforward and requires great caution. It is quite conceivable that mammalian cells may have a set of unique genetic principles yet to be formulated. This is particularly important in designing experiments for studying regulatory mechanisms underlying carcinogenesis as well as differentiation. The techniques described above using Chinese hamster CHO-K1 cell and its various auxotrophic mutants may facilitate such studies.

ACKNOWLEDGMENTS

This investigation is a contribution from the Eleanor Roosevelt Institute for Cancer Research and the Department of Biophysics and Genetics (Number 512), and was aided by U.S. Public Health Service Grant No. 5 P01 HD02080 and by American Cancer Society Grant No. VC-81B.

REFERENCES

1. T. T. Puck, The Mammalian Cell as a Microorganism, Holden-Day, San Francisco, 1972.
2. F. T. Kao and T. T. Puck, Genetics of somatic mammalian cells. IV. Properties of Chinese hamster cell mutants with respect to the requirement for proline, Genetics, 55, 513 (1967).
3. T. T. Puck and F. T. Kao, Genetics of somatic mammalian cells. V. Treatment with 5-bromodeoxyuridine and visible light for isolation of nutritionally deficient mutants, Proc. Nat. Acad. Sci., 58, 1227 (1967).
4. W. Hayes, The Genetics of Bacteria and Their Viruses, 2nd ed., Wiley, New York, 1968.
5. R. P. Wagner and H. K. Mitchell, Genetics and Metabolism, 2nd ed., Wiley, New York, 1964.
6. L. Levintow and H. Eagle, Biochemistry of cultured mammalian cells, Ann. Rev. Biochem., 30, 605 (1961).
7. F. T. Kao and T. T. Puck, Genetics of somatic mammalian cells. VII. Induction and isolation of nutritional mutants in Chinese hamster cells, Proc. Nat. Acad. Sci., 60, 1275 (1968).
8. F. T. Kao and T. T. Puck, Genetics of somatic mammalian cells. IX. Quantitation of mutagenesis by physical and chemical agents, J. Cell Physiol., 74, 245 (1969).

9. F. T. Kao and T. T. Puck, Genetics of somatic mammalian cells. XII. Mutagenesis by carcinogenic nitroso compounds, J. Cell Physiol., 78, 139 (1971).
10. F. T. Kao, L. Chasin, and T. T. Puck, Genetics of somatic mammalian cells. X. Complementation analysis of glycine-requiring mutants, Proc. Nat. Acad. Sci., 64, 1284 (1969).
11. F. T. Kao, R. T. Johnson, and T. T. Puck, Genetics of somatic mammalian cells. VIII. Complementation analysis on virus-fused Chinese hamster cells with nutritional markers, Science, 164, 312 (1969).
12. F. T. Kao and T. T. Puck, Genetics of somatic mammalian cells. XIV. Genetic analysis in vitro of auxotrophic mutants, J. Cell Physiol., 80, 41 (1972).
13. T. T. Puck, P. Wuthier, C. Jones, and F. T. Kao, Genetics of somatic mammalian cells: Lethal antigens as genetic markers for study of human linkage groups, Proc. Nat. Acad. Sci., 68, 3102 (1971).
14. C. Jones, P. Wuthier, F. T. Kao, and T. T. Puck, Genetics of somatic mammalian cells. XV. Evidence for linkage between human genes for lactic dehydrogenase B and serine hydroxymethylase, J. Cell Physiol., 80, 291 (1972).
15. F. T. Kao and T. T. Puck, Genetics of somatic mammalian cells: Demonstration of a human esterase activator gene linked to the adeB gene, Proc. Nat. Acad. Sci., 69, 3273 (1972).
16. C. Waldren, in preparation.

Chapter 30

INDUCTION OF VARIANTS BY NITROSOGUANIDINE IN DIPLOID AND TETRAPLOID LINES OF CHINESE HAMSTER CELLS

Morgan Harris

Department of Zoology
University of California
Berkeley, California

Tumors and permanent cell lines exhibit frequent de novo variations, in contrast with the relative stability of primary diploid cells in serial culture (see reviews in Refs. 1-3). Changes in drug sensitivity provide well-defined markers that may be used to analyze this phenomenon at the population level. Typical of such studies are experiments on the development of resistance to 8-azaguanine (4-8), amethopterin (9-11), cytosine arabinoside (12-14), and iododeoxyuridine (15).

The cellular changes that lead to drug resistance in these systems have a number of common properties. Such alterations can be detected even within clonally derived populations; typically, they are stable in the absence of selective agents and are mitotically transmissible in serial culture. Many or most of the variant properties have been subjected to fluctuation tests (16) in the investigations cited above. The results show, in general, that drug resistance arises by random and spontaneous changes in mammalian cells rather than by phenotypic adaptation at a population level. The mechanism of variation remains obscure. Although mutation at the gene or chromosome level has often been assumed as an implementing mechanism, direct proof is still lacking. Fluctuation tests do not resolve this problem since they cannot reveal the locus of variation in the cell or show whether the alteration is genetic or epigenetic in character.

Mutational hypotheses for de novo variation of somatic cells in culture can, however, be tested by other experimental procedures. One such method involves the use of matched polyploid lines, differing only in the number of chromosome sets (17). In this system a dominant mutation should appear in higher frequency as the ploidy level rises, owing to the increased number of loci available for change. Conversely, the expression of recessive mutations would be expected to decline sharply with the ploidy level since the probability of eliminating dominant wild-type alleles is progressively less. The predictions have been used to evaluate the "goodness of fit" of conventional genetic models for two variations arising spontaneously in Chinese hamster cells (7). Fluctuation tests were performed with diploid, tetraploid, and octaploid lines. Nominal mutation rates were calculated for resistance to 8-azaguanine as well as for changes in temperature sensitivity. Contrary to expectation, the mutation rates for both markers remained essentially constant for cells at all ploidy levels. This result is difficult to harmonize with concepts of gene or chromosome mutation, and suggests that additional studies are needed to establish the source of de novo variation in cultures of somatic cells.

The present experiments were designed to see whether the pattern of induced variation in cells at different ploidy levels is similar to the trend established for spontaneous changes. The potent mutagen N-methyl-N'-nitro-N-nitrosoguanidine (MNNG) is a useful agent for this purpose. MNNG along with other chemical mutagens is reported to induce large increases in mutation frequency in cultures of near-diploid Chinese hamster cells (18-20). We have accordingly exposed diploid and tetraploid lines of Chinese hamster cells to MNNG at graded dose levels, using changes in temperature sensitivity and resistance to 8-azaguanine as markers to compare the incidence of variants in derivative populations. The results show that under optimal conditions the frequency of both types of variants rises sharply with the concentration of mutagen. Further, the dose-response curves for these markers are substantially similar in diploid and tetraploid cells. A ploidy effect is thus absent for induced variation as well as for spontaneous variation in these marker systems.

MATERIALS AND METHODS

Cell Lines

All experiments were performed with clonal populations derived from V79 Chinese hamster cells (21). V79, clone 5 (hereafter referred to as V79) is a stable pseudodiploid line with modal chromosome number of 22-23 (7). Line 991, clone 2 (referred to in the present paper as 991) is a tetraploid derivative of these cells, obtained by treatment with colcemid following the procedure outlined in an earlier publication (17). Cells of line 991 show a well-defined chromosome mode at 44-45.

Chromosome counts were made on both lines at regular intervals; no changes were observed during the experiments to be described.

Culture Techniques

Procedures for the maintenance and handling of cell populations have been described previously (7, 17). All cultures were grown in a nutrient containing 10% fetal calf serum and 90% Dulbecco's modification of Eagle's medium (10FCSDB). In plating experiments, cells were cultivated in 60-mm petri dishes in a humidified CO_2 incubator. For colony counts, the petri dish cultures were rinsed briefly with 0.85% NaCl, stained 30 min in a saturated solution of crystal violet, and air dried.

Treatment of Cultures with MNNG

A 10^{-2} M stock solution of MNNG (Aldrich Chemicals) was prepared just before use by dissolving the compound in a small volume of 95% ethanol, followed by dilution with Hank's solution. Graded concentrations of MNNG were made as needed by serial dilution with 10FCSDB containing 5 mM HEPES buffer to stabilize the pH level. Cultures to be used for assays were established with 0.5 or 1.0×10^6 log phase cells in 16 oz prescription bottles in nutrient medium, and were incubated 2-3 hr to permit cell attachment. The supernatants were then replaced with MNNG at different concentrations for a 2 hr interval at 37 °C. Each culture was rinsed two times with 10FCSDB after mutagen treatment and incubated further.

Assays for Heat and Drug Sensitivity

Cultures receiving MNNG treatment were assayed for frequency of variants at two, three, or six days following exposure to the mutagen, since previous studies had shown that an interval of 42 hr or more is required for the phenotypic expression of azaguanine resistance (20). Determinations of heat or drug sensitivity, when made at two or three days, were performed with cells from the original recovery cultures. For assays to be performed at six days, subculture of the recovery cultures at three days was necessary, and determinations were carried out on second passage populations. Before use, the cultures were trypsinized and the cell number adjusted to 1.0×10^6/ml in 10FCSDB. For each series, a group of three to six petri dish cultures was then established at 20,000 cells in 10FCSDB containing 30 µg/ml 8-azaguanine. In addition, samples of 2.5×10^6 cells were placed in a water bath and heated to 44.5 °C for 60 min, according to procedures

TABLE 1

Relative Plating Efficiency of V79
Chinese Hamster Cells at Successive
Intervals after Exposure to MNNG[a]

MNNG treatment, M	Relative plating efficiency, days after treatment			
	0	3	6	7
—	100	100	100	100
1×10^{-7}	100	99	99	93
3×10^{-7}	76	69	93	87
1×10^{-6}	28	26	77	68
3×10^{-6}	8	9	49	57
1×10^{-5}	0	3	41	50

[a]All values shown represent mean colony counts for three replicate
petri dish cultures, normalized to 100% for untreated cells.

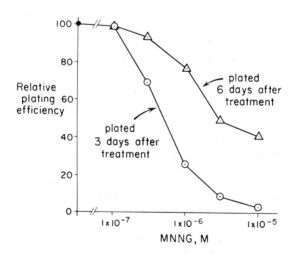

FIG. 1. Effect of nitrosoguanidine (MNNG) on plating efficiency
in V79 cells. Each point represents the average colony count for three
petri dish cultures, normalized to 100% for untreated cells.

outlined in detail in an earlier paper (7). After heating, the cells were plated at 37°C in fresh 10FCSDB to determine survival. Assay cultures for drug and heat resistance were maintained for 14 days with fluid changes twice per week, and were then terminated for colony counts. The plating efficiency of cells from recovery cultures was an important variable in these experiments and was determined in conjunction with each assay by inoculating groups of petri dishes at 100 cells in 10FCSDB. The plating efficiency immediately after MNNG treatment was measured in a few experiments by adding graded concentrations of mutagen directly to petri dish cultures containing 100 freshly attached cells. After the standard 2-hr exposure period to MNNG, these cultures were rinsed twice with 10FCSDB and incubated to determine colony formation by survivors.

RESULTS

Effect of MNNG Treatment on Plating Efficiency

Orkin and Littlefield (22) have called attention to the prolonged depression of plating efficiency that follows the treatment of mammalian cells with nitrosoguanidine. Since this phenomenon affects the observed incidence of variants significantly during drug resistance experiments, several studies were carried out to see how plating efficiency changes during the posttreatment period. The data shown in Table 1 are typical of the results obtained. V79 cells exposed to MNNG at 10^{-5} to 10^{-7} M show a sharp drop in plating efficiency when assayed immediately after exposure to the mutagen. In recovery cultures the plating efficiency gradually rises, but even in the second-passage populations tested at six days, there is a conspicuous depression in colony-forming potential (Fig. 1). These examples are derived from experiments with V79 cells, but similar data were obtained with 991 cultures. In general the dose-response curves for plating efficiency after MNNG treatment were similar for the two lines.

Changes in Resistance to 8-Azaguanine

Tables 2 and 3 summarize the data obtained from a number of experiments on the incidence of azaguanine-resistant variants among MNNG-treated cells. In both V79 and 991 cultures, there is an absolute increase in the frequency of resistant colonies as the concentration of mutagen rises. However, a different curve of response is obtained if the colony counts are adjusted for the relative plating efficiency of recovery cultures. When the data are normalized in

TABLE 2

Induction of Variants Resistant to 8-Azaguanine in
Cultures of Diploid V79 Chinese Hamster Cells[a]

Experiment	MNNG treatment, M	Interval before plating, days	Resistant colonies per culture, direct counts	Relative plating efficiency	Resistant colonies per 20,000 cells, adjusted for plating efficiency
1	—	2	7.7	100	7.7
	1×10^{-7}		11.7	95	12.3
	1×10^{-6}		25.0	49	51.0
	3×10^{-6}		24.0	29	82.8
	1×10^{-5}		8.3	3.4	244.0
2	—	2	4.0	100	4.0
	1×10^{-7}		10.3	100	10.3
	3×10^{-7}		11.3	83	13.6
	1×10^{-6}		17.6	79	22.3
	3×10^{-6}		11.3	41	27.6
	1×10^{-5}		9.0	27	33.3
3	—	6	3.5	100	3.5
	1×10^{-7}		3.5	96	3.7
	3×10^{-7}		11.0	83	13.2
	1×10^{-6}		17.5	71	24.6
	3×10^{-6}		36.5	59	61.9
	1×10^{-5}		21.5	32	67.4

[a]Aliquots of 2×10^4 cells were inoculated into 60-mm petri dishes and incubated in 10FCSDB containing 30 µg 8-azaguanine per milliliter. Survival data are based on colony counts for three to six petri dish cultures per sample.

TABLE 3
Induction of Variants Resistant to 8-Azaguanine in
Cultures of Tetraploid 991 Chinese Hamster Cells[a]

Experiment	MNNG treatment, M	Interval before plating, days	Resistant colonies per culture, direct counts	Relative plating efficiency	Resistant colonies per 20,000 cells, adjusted for plating efficiency
1	—	2	1.0	100	1.0
	1×10^{-7}		1.7	87	1.9
	1×10^{-6}		6.3	80	7.9
	3×10^{-6}		10.0	37	27.0
	1×10^{-5}		2.3	3.6	64.7
2	—	2	1.7	100	1.7
	1×10^{-7}		4.7	95	5.0
	1×10^{-6}		28.7	76	37.7
	3×10^{-6}		17.0	23	73.9
	1×10^{-5}		11.7	7	167.1
3	—	6	13.8	100	13.8
	1×10^{-7}		19.8	88	22.5
	3×10^{-7}		40.3	78	51.7
	1×10^{-6}		71.0	46	154.3
	3×10^{-6}		56.8	24	236.7
	1×10^{-5}		28.0	7.2	388.0

[a] Aliquots of 2×10^4 cells were inoculated into 60-mm petri dish cultures and incubated in 10FCSDB containing 30 μg 8-azaguanine per milliliter. Survival data are based on colony counts for three to six petri dish cultures per sample.

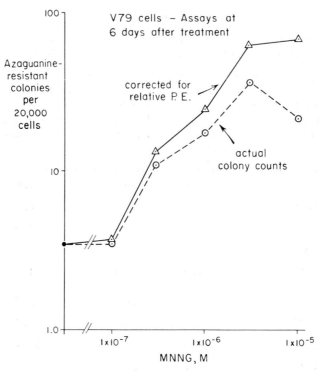

FIG. 2. Induction of variants resistant to 8-azaguanine in cultures of V79 (diploid) cells. Each point represents the average colony count for three petri dish cultures.

this fashion, the rise in frequency of variants with both lines appears to be approximately exponential with the mutagen concentrations used (Figs. 2 and 3). The true kinetics in this system are difficult to assess, since the baseline of plating efficiency used for correction may not reflect the actual colony-forming potential of cells in the mass population assays. However, it is obvious that nitrosoguanidine has a clear-cut inductive effect on azaguanine resistance in both diploid and tetraploid cells, and the two types of curves shown in Figs. 2 and 3 serve to define the limits within which this response occurs.

Induction of Heat Resistance with MNNG

For purposes of comparison, a number of assays for heat resistance were also carried out with MNNG-treated cells. The results obtained with cultures of V79 and 991 cells are tabulated in Table 4. The data show that the incidence of heat-resistant cells rises in populations of

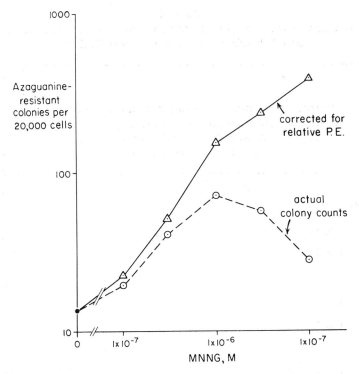

FIG. 3. Induction of variants resistant to 8-azaguanine in cultures of 991 (tetraploid) cells. Each point represents the average colony count for six petri dish cultures.

either cell type after exposure to graded level of mutagen. Figure 4 serves to illustrate a typical experiment with V79 cells. There is an absolute increase in the number of heat-resistant colonies from MNNG-treated cells, and if the data are adjusted to relative plating efficiency, a log-linear trend appears as in drug resistance studies. In Figs. 5 and 6 representative data for heat resistance have been plotted on the same grid with those for azaguanine resistance, using values that have been adjusted for plating efficiency. The slopes of the variant frequency curves are essentially similar in diploid and tetraploid cells. Although the data for heat resistance are more variable, there is no indication that the trend for variant frequency differs significantly between the two cell lines. Stated differently, a ploidy effect in the induction of variants by MNNG appears to be lacking; variants for the markers studied appear as readily in cells with four chromosome sets as in those with the usual diploid chromosome complement.

TABLE 4

Induction of Heat-Resistant Variants in Cultures of Diploid
and Tetraploid Chinese Hamster Cells[a]

Cell line	MNNG treatment, M	Interval before heat treatment, days	Heat-resistant colonies per 10^6 cells, actual counts	Relative plating efficiency	Resistant colonies per 10^6 cells, adjusted for plating efficiency
V79 (diploid)	—	2	1.3	100	1.3
	1×10^{-7}		1.7	85	2.0
	1×10^{-6}		7.7	52	14.8
	1×10^{-5}		12.0	6.2	193.5
991 (tetraploid)	—	2	1.3	100	1.3
	1×10^{-7}		2.0	87	2.3
	1×10^{-6}		2.3	80	2.5
	3×10^{-6}		3.0	37	8.1
	1×10^{-5}		3.3	3.6	92.5
991 (tetraploid)	—	2	0.3	100	0.3
	1×10^{-7}		1.3	95	1.4
	3×10^{-7}		2.3	73	3.2
	1×10^{-6}		1.0	17	5.9
	3×10^{-6}		0.7	7	9.4

[a] Samples of 2.5×10^6 cells were suspended in 10FCSDB, heated to 44.5°C for 60 min, and plated at 37°C to determine survival. Each point shown represents the average colony count from three to six petri dish cultures.

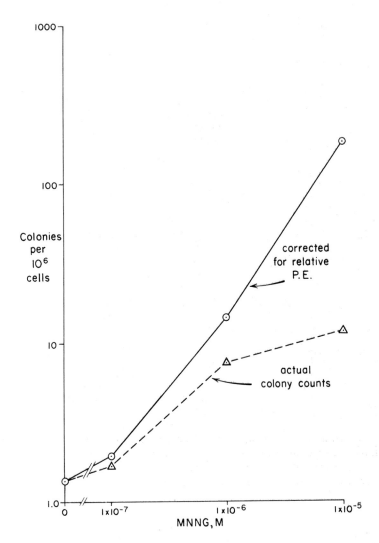

FIG. 4. Induction of heat-resistant variants in cultures of V79 (diploid) cells. Each point represents the average colony count for six petri dish cultures.

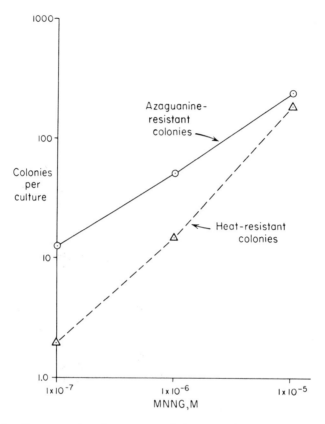

FIG. 5. Comparative frequency of drug- and heat-resistant variants after MNNG treatment in cultures of V79 (diploid) cells. All data have been adjusted for relative plating efficiency. Each point is based on counts from three to six petri dish cultures.

DISCUSSION

The present experiments suggest that nitrosoguanidine induces variation for specific markers at rates that do not differ significantly in diploid and tetraploid cell populations. This finding does not coincide with predictions based on the assumption of dominant or recessive gene mutation at the presumed loci in question, nor with hypotheses of random chromosomal loss. The results are, however, consistent with our earlier studies that showed that spontaneous mutation rates for the same two markers are essentially level in diploid, tetraploid, and octaploid cells (7). It is not unreasonable, therefore, to suggest that

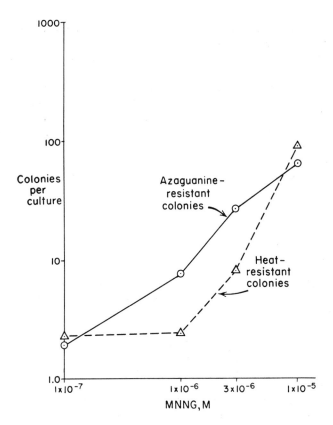

FIG. 6. Comparative frequency of drug- and heat-resistant variants after MNNG treatment in cultures of 991 (tetraploid) cells. All data have been adjusted for relative plating efficiency. Each point is based on counts from three to six petri dish cultures.

at least some types of de novo variations in somatic cells may be based on extrachromosomal changes.

The exact nature of these changes is necessarily speculative at this point. However, at least two types of models can be suggested as a basis for further analysis at the experimental level. One may assume, for example, that stable shifts. in phenotypic expression take place within clonal populations of somatic cells in culture, i. e., that de novo variations may be epigenetic rather than genetic in character (7). Alternatively, the same changes might be based on alterations in genetic information, but at a cytoplasmic rather than a nuclear locus, e.g., in mitochondria. In this connection it may be appropriate to point out that genetic determinants for resistance to erythromycin and chloramphenicol have recently been demonstrated in the mitochondria of Para-mecium (23, 24). Other recent papers described the presence of cytoplasmic DNA in membrane-associated fractions from plasma cells (25), and in nonmitochondrial particles from the cytoplasm of chick muscle cells (26). The latter have been designated I-somes, and are thought to include gene copies that function at a cytoplasmic level in the transfer and use of genetic information. It is not known whether any of these models based on extranuclear DNA are relevant to the problems of de novo variation in cultures of mammalian cells. However, until this possibility is excluded it may be best to keep a wide range of options open.

SUMMARY

Nitrosoguanidine (MNNG) has been used to increase the spontaneous frequency of variations in diploid and tetraploid lines of Chinese hamster cells. Cultures were exposed to graded concentrations of MNNG and assayed for changes in heat sensitivity and for resistance to 8-azaguanine. An absolute increase in variant frequency was observed for both markers, and the dose-response curves were approximately exponential with mutagen concentration when adjusted for relative plating efficiency. No significant differences between diploid and tetraploid cells were observed when the slopes of induced variations were compared for either of the two markers studied. A ploidy effect on induced variation thus seems to be lacking, in agreement with earlier studies that showed that spontaneous mutation rates for these markers are independent of ploidy level. These findings are not readily explained on the basis of conventional gene or chromosome changes. Models are discussed for nonchromosomal patterns of inheritance.

ACKNOWLEDGMENT

This work was supported by Grant CA 12130 from the National Cancer Institute, U.S. Public Health Service, and by Cancer Research Funds from the University of California.

REFERENCES

1. M. Harris, Cell Culture and Somatic Variation, Holt, Rinehart and Winston, New York, 1964.
2. S. M. Gartler and D. A. Pious, Genetics of mammalian cell cultures, Humangenetik, 2, 83 (1966).
3. J. Paul, Growth and differentiation of animal cells in culture, Symp. Soc. Gen. Microbiol., 19, 351 (1969).
4. W. Szybalski, Genetics of human cell lines. II. Method for determination of mutation rates to drug resistance, Exptl. Cell Res., 18, 588 (1959).
5. E. H. Y. Chu, P. Brimer, K. B. Jacobson, and E. V. Merriam, Mammalian cell genetics. I. Selection and characterization of mutations auxotrophic for L-glutamine or resistant to 8-azaguanine in Chinese hamster cells in vitro, Genetics, 62, 359 (1969).
6. J. Morrow, Genetic analysis of azaguanine resistance in an established mouse cell line, Genetics, 65, 279 (1970).
7. M. Harris, Mutation rates in cells at different ploidy levels, J. Cell Physiol., 78, 177 (1971).
8. N. I. Shapiro, A. E. Khalizev, E. V. Luss, M. I. Marshak, O. N. Petrova, and N. B. Varshav~r, Mutagenesis in cultured mammalian cells. I. Spontaneous gene mutations in human and Chinese hamster cells, Mutation Res., 15, 203 (1972).
9. M. T. Hakala, S. F. Zakrzewski, and C. A. Nicol, Relation of folic acid reductase to amethopterin resistance in cultured mammalian cells. J. Biol. Chem., 236, 952 (1961).
10. S. H. Orkin and J. W. Littlefield, Mutagenesis to amethopterin resistance in cultured hamster cells, Exptl. Cell Res., 69, 174 (1971).
11. J. L. Biedler, A. M. Albrecht, D. J. Hutchison, and B. A. Spengler, Drug response, dihydrofolate reductase, and cytogenetics of amethopterin-resistant Chinese hamster cells in vitro, Cancer Res., 32, 153 (1972).
12. M. K. Bach, Biochemical and genetic studies of a mutant strain of mouse leukemia L1210 resistant to 1-β-D-arabinofuranosylcytosine (Cytarabine) hydrochloride, Cancer Res., 29, 1036 (1969).
13. D. B. Smith and E. H. Y. Chu, A genetic approach to the study of cytotoxicity and resistance of cultured Chinese hamster cells in the presence of cytosine arabinoside, Cancer Res., 32, 1651 (1972).
14. M. Harris, Phenotypic expression of drug resistance in hybrid cells, J. Nat. Cancer Inst., 50, 423 (1973).
15. M. Fox, Spontaneous and X-ray-induced genotypic and phenotypic resistance to 5-iodo-2'-deoxyuridine in lymphoma cells in vitro, Mutation Res., 13, 403 (1971).

16. S. E. Luria and M. Delbrück, Mutations of bacteria from virus sensitivity to virus resistance, Genetics, 28, 491 (1943).

17. M. Harris, Polyploid series of mammalian cells, Exptl. Cell Res., 66, 329 (1971).

18. F. T. Kao and T. T. Puck, Genetics of somatic mammalian cells. VII. Induction and isolation of nutritional mutants in Chinese hamster cells, Proc. Nat. Acad. Sci., 60, 1275 (1968).

19. T. T. Puck, "Biochemical and Genetic Studies of Mammalian Cells in vitro," in Control Mechanisms in the Expression of Cellular Phenotypes, Academic, New York, 1970.

20. E. H. Y. Chu and H. V. Malling, Mammalian cell genetics. II. Chemical induction of specific locus mutations in Chinese hamster cells in vitro, Proc. Nat. Acad. Sci., 61, 1306 (1968).

21. C. K. Yu and W. K. Sinclair, Homogeneity and stability of chromosomes of Chinese hamster cells in vitro, Can. J. Genetics Cytol., 6, 109 (1964).

22. S. H. Orkin and J. W. Littlefield, Nitrosoguanidine mutagenesis in synchronized hamster cells, Exptl. Cell Res., 66, 69 (1971).

23. A. Adoutte and J. Beisson, Evolution of mixed populations of genetically different mitochondria in Paramecium aurelia, Nature, 235, 393 (1972).

24. G. H. Beale, J. K. C. Knowles, and A. Tait, Mitochondrial genetics in Paramecium, Nature, 235, 396 (1972).

25. M. R. Hall, W. Meinke, D. A. Goldstein, and R. A. Lerner, Synthesis of cytoplasmic membrane-associated DNA in lymphocyte nucleus, Nature New Biol., 234, 227 (1971).

26. E. Bell, C. Merrill, and C. B. Lawrence, Analysis of DNA-containing particles recovered from the cytoplasm of differentiating chick muscle cells, Europ. J. Biochem., 29, 444 (1972).

Chapter 31

EFFECT OF MUTAGENS ON BUdR RESISTANCE IN HAPLOID CELLS: GENETIC OR EPIGENETIC?

Liselotte Mezger-Freed

The Institute for Cancer Research
Fox Chase, Philadelphia, Pennsylvania

An increased frequency of drug-resistant or temperature-sensitive colonies in cell cultures exposed to mutagens is considered to be evidence that the new phenotype is the result of gene mutation (here defined as a change in DNA base sequence). Such tests are based on two assumptions: (a) that compounds known to produce mutations in one system, usually bacteria, will behave as mutagens in other systems; and (b) that the compounds elicit the phenotype in question by acting as a mutagen.

An internal control for possible nonmutagenic effects of a compound is present in comparisons of colony frequencies from haploid and diploid cell lines of similar origin. Factors such as the metabolism of the mutagen should be the same in all the lines, and the cultures should differ only in the frequency with which mutations can be detected. A recessive mutation would be expressed in diploid cells at a frequency equal to the square of that in the haploid; a dominant one should be twice as frequent in diploid cells.

The first vertebrate haploid cell lines were developed in collaboration with Freed (1). These lines were isolated from embryos of the frog, Rana pipiens, a species in which haploid material can be produced in quantity. The most useful haploid line, ICR 2A, was initiated in 1968; 95% of metaphases are haploid (Fig. 1). The amount of DNA per cell (5 pg), chromosome number (13), and volume (1200 μ^3) are half that of diploid cells. The chromosomes were found to be close to euploid when relative lengths were compared with karyotypes from embryos. Seven hundred generations after initiation, some of the ICR 2A lines still remain haploid with karyotypes that appear normal. The cells grow as monolayer cultures in L-15 medium modified for

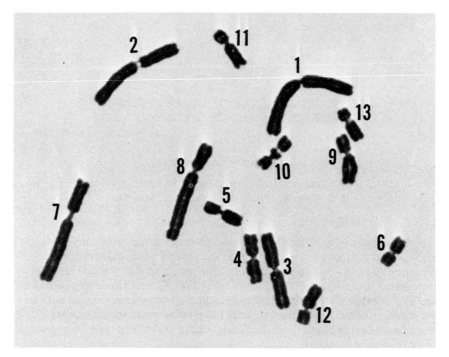

FIG. 1. Metaphase plate from line ICR 2A at subculture 32 (2).

amphibian cells plus 10% fetal calf serum; at their maintenance temperature, 25°C, the doubling time is 40 hr (2).

THYMIDINE TRANSPORT DEFICIENT (TT-) HAPLOID CELLS

Among the first variants isolated from ICR 2A were colonies that appeared at a frequency of about 1 colony per 10^8 cells in selective medium containing 5×10^{-5} M bromodeoxyuridine (BUdR). The progeny of these colonies multiplied in 3×10^{-4} M BUdR even after many generations in medium without BUdR. Resistance to BUdR was not the result of the classic thymidine kinase deficiency (3, 4), in which the absence of the enzyme prevents a lethal incorporation of BUdR into DNA. The average enzyme activity of nine haploid isolates was 67% of the value for ICR 2A. Instead, resistance was correlated with a greatly decreased uptake of thymidine or BUdR, a phenotype similar to that found in Chinese hamster cells (5). After two hours' exposure to tritiated thymidine, the resistant haploid cells contained only a few percent as much label as sensitive cells. Further

characterization of the resistant cells when compared with the
sensitive cells indicates that a facilitated diffusion system specific
for thymidine has been lost; this is shown in Fig. 2, where thymidine
uptake is plotted as a function of the concentration of thymidine in
the medium (6). The BUdR sensitive cells have a transport system
that saturates at about 2×10^{-4} M thymidine; in the resistant cells,
uptake is strictly proportional to concentration.

The facts presented thus far are consistent with the interpretation
that BUdR resistance at the 10^{-4} M level may be the result of a mutation at a "permease" locus, analogous to those in bacteria (7). The
stability of the phenotype and the low frequency at which it appears
might also be considered as evidence of a gene mutation; however,
stable phenotypes result from differentiation as well as mutation. It
is possible that the low frequency is due to the rare occurrence in
culture of the specific combination of cell competence and environment necessary for the development of a phenotype through processes
similar to those of differentiation.

To test, therefore, for the mutational origin of BUdR resistance
in the haploid cells, the effect of ploidy and of mutagens on the
appearance of 10^{-4} M BUdR resistance was studied (8). Colony frequencies were compared in: (a) cultures treated with mutagens before
selective medium (BUdR) was applied, and untreated cultures; (b)
haploid cultures and pseudodiploid cultures. The cultures were exposed to nitrosoguanidine, ethyl methane sulfonate, and three
acridine half-mustard ICR compounds, 372, 340, and 191, for one
generation time. To allow time for mutations to be expressed, at
least three generation times elapsed before BUdR was added to the
cultures. The following results were obtained:

1. Mutagens that increased the colony frequency in one haploid
   line did not increase the frequency in a second haploid line.

2. Whether the frequency of colony formation in BUdR was affected by mutagen treatment was dependent on the number of
   cell generations that elapsed between mutagen application
   and selection. This observation is not explained by selection
   against BUdR resistant variants during this period because
   isolated resistant strains have a normal doubling time in
   BUdR-free medium; in addition, colony frequency sometimes
   increased after a longer period between mutation treatment
   and selection.

3. The frequency of colonies in a pseudodiploid line was greater
   than in the haploid lines; this increase is not the result of
   dominant expression since mutagens decreased the frequency
   in the pseudodiploid cultures.

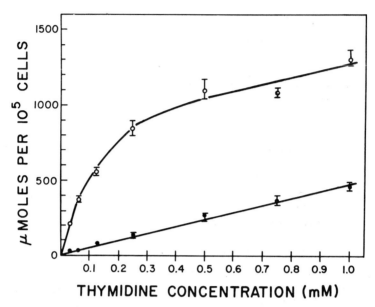

FIG. 2. The uptake of thymidine and its acid soluble derivatives
as a function of the external concentration of thymidine. Time of
exposure to thymidine was 5 min. O, wild-type ICR 2A haploid line;
●, ICR B20 haploid line resistant to 10^{-4} M BUdR.

Although treatment with mutagens apparently had an effect in
some of the experiments, it was not consistent with expectations for
mutation. Therefore, the genetic nature of the BUdR resistant variants
in these lines was questioned.

It should be noted that in the experiments summarized above, more
than 10^{8} haploid "wild-type" cells were treated with mutagens prior to
selection in 5×10^{-5} M BUdR, but that none of the 13 resistant isolates
tested was found to be thymidine kinase deficient. It is possible that
multiple gene copies for some proteins may be present even in haploid
eukaryotic cells; if this were true, then thymidine kinase mutations
would be expressed at a frequency so low as to be nearly undetectable.

THYMIDINE KINASE DEFICIENT (TK-) HAPLOID CELLS

Thymidine kinase deficient (TK-) isolates have recently been obtained from the transport-deficient haploid cells (6). These lines are
resistant to levels of BUdR (10^{-3} M) three to four times higher than for
the transport deficient (TT-) lines; thymidine kinase activity is about

5% of that in the parental ICR 2A line. The phenotype is also stable, i. e., cultures do not require maintence in BUdR to retain resistance. Further evidence for phenotypic stability is the observation that each of 40 clones derived from a TK- isolate was deficient in thymidine kinase activity. Also in accord with a mutational origin is the observation that the frequency of one per 10^6 cells with which TK- colonies appear in culture is increased 25 times by treatment with ICR 191, an acridine half-mustard compound known to act as a mutagen in bacteria (9).

The usefulness of phenotypic stability and low frequency of appearance of a phenotype as evidence for gene mutation has already been questioned; it should now be added that the effect of organic compounds (putative mutagens?) in promoting stable epigenetic changes has been extensively documented by the experimental embryology of the decades following the discovery of the amphibian organizer (10). It was not, however, such theoretical considerations but the following experimental observations that made me question gene mutation as the cause of thymidine kinase deficiency in the haploid cultures:

1. Thymidine kinase deficient cells have been obtained only from the transport deficient line and not from the wild-type. The transport deficiency is thus similar to the classic first-step drug resistance, which was attributed to heterozygosity at an enzyme locus (4). Such an explanation is untenable for the present case since both the ICR 2A and the transport deficient lines are not only haploid, but largely isogenic, since the TT- variant derives from the ICR 2A line.

2. A larger proportion of TT- cells than wild-type cells survive under the conditions of selection (10^{-3} M BUdR). For example, in Fig. 3, after two weeks in BUdR, a number of TT- cells proportional to 50% of the inoculum remains, compared with less than 10% of the ICR 2A. As a result, the TT- cultures would have more time and more cells in which the turning off of thymidine kinase expression could occur.

3. Related to point 2 is the observation that variants with thymidine kinase deficiency are apparently not present at the beginning of selection, since colonies of 50 cells do not appear until four weeks, indicating a lag of about two weeks before resistant cells start multiplying.

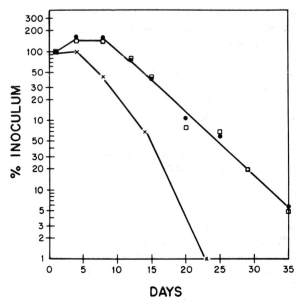

DAYS

FIG. 3. Comparison of the survival of sensitive and 10^{-4} M BUdR-resistant cells in medium containing 10^{-3} M. BUdR. The ordinate is the number of attached cells as a percent of the number present at zero time. X, ICR 2A; □, ICR B20; ●, ICR B20(191).

CLONAL ANALYSIS OF A THYMIDINE TRANSPORT VARIANT (11)

A clonal analysis of a population derived from a transport-deficient colony should establish whether the intervening cell divisions have resulted in heterogeneity with respect to specific properties such as BUdR resistance, viability in ICR 191, and frequency with which thymidine kinase deficient colonies appear. Since the clones are haploid and isogenic, one would expect the same frequency of thymidine kinase colonies for each clone. If the frequency is different for each clone, then any consistent correlation between the production of TK-colonies by clones in BUdR and one or more other characteristics of the clones would be additional evidence that the production of thymidine kinase deficiency in these cells is not genetic. The characteristics correlated with colony production would be concerned with the competence of a cell or culture to block translation or transcription at the thymidine kinase locus.

The transport-deficient variant chosen for this analysis was ICR B20; ICR B20(191), which had been exposed to 0.25 µg/ml ICR 191,

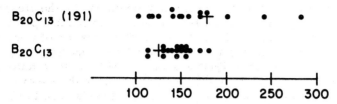

FIG. 4. Comparison of the survival of clones derived from ICR B20 and ICR B20(191) after 10 days in 10^{-3} M BUdR. The abscissa is the number of attached cells as a percent of the number present at zero time. +, parent population; ●, clone.

was also cloned. Clones were initiated by seeding wells in Microtest Plates and checking for the presence of single cells by microscopic examination. Thirty-three clones plus the two parent populations were examined for a number of properties.

All of the clones were found to have a low thymidine uptake and are assumed to be transport deficient. Although all showed thymidine kinase activity, the range from lowest to highest activity was several-fold. The heterogeneity of the B20 line was further confirmed by variations in the behavior of the clones in dense culture conditions. The degree to which thymidine kinase activity could be raised by exposing the cultures to high concentrations of thymidine or of BUdR were also different for each clone.

CLONAL ANALYSIS OF BUdR RESISTANCE

BUdR resistance in the form of thymidine transport deficiency is a prerequisite for thymidine kinase deficiency. If the B20 (TT⁻) line is heterogeneous in resistance to BUdR, one would like to know if the most resistant clones have the highest probability of forming TK⁻ colonies.

The degree of resistance of individual clones to BUdR was determined by adding 10^{-3} M BUdR medium to three 25 cm² Falcon flasks containing 2×10^5 cells each and counting the surviving (attached) cells at intervals thereafter (Fig. 4). After 10 days of BUdR treatment, clones derived from the B20 (TT⁻) population had from 114 to 180% of the inoculum number still remaining; clones from B20(191), the ICR 191-treated population, ranged from 103 to 283% of the inoculum. Among the 15 B20(191) clones were six (40% of the clones) that were as resistant, or even more resistant, to 10^{-3} M BUdR as the most resistant clones from the population before ICR 191 treatment. Thus, ICR 191 treatment increased the capacity of the parent population to

survive BUdR treatment, an observation confirmed by the greater
survival of the uncloned B20(191) compared with the B20 population
(180% compared with 128% at 10 days). The question of whether the
degree of BUdR resistance is correlated with colony frequency was
approached by keeping the cultures in 10^{-3} M BUdR for a total of six
weeks. Five of the 33 clones yielded colonies; only one of these
clones was among the seven with the highest resistance to BUdR.
Therefore, the capacity to survive BUdR treatment is not the only
requirement for the production of thymidine kinase deficiency from
transport deficient cells. (Eight colonies from these experiments were
tested for enzyme activity; all but one were deficient.)

CLONAL ANALYSIS OF ICR 191 RESISTANCE

Since the reaction of the TT⁻ cultures with ICR 191 also affects
the production of TK⁻ cells, correlations were sought between the
behavior of the clones in ICR 191 and their ability to form colonies.
The B20 and B20(191) populations, seventeen of their clones, and the
wild-type ICR 2A line were studied. ICR 191 was added to 2×10^5
cells/25 cm^2 Falcon flasks and after 48 hr, or about one generation
time, the medium was decanted and normal medium added. Cell counts
made over a period of a month indicated that the clones differed in
their survival after exposure to ICR 191. At a level of 1.5 μg/ml,
only the parent population previously exposed to ICR 191 had more
than 2% of the inoculum level of cells remaining in the flasks. The
kinds of survival curves obtained after 1.0 μg/ml ICR 191 treatment
were more complex than at the higher concentration and could be
divided into four phases (Fig. 5). Phase I takes place during the 48
hr of exposure to mutagen, when none of the cultures undergoes the
doubling expected for normal conditions. Only the ICR 2A cultures
increase in number (by 25%). The prior treatment of B20(191) with
ICR 191 apparently increases its resistance to this compound, since
it remained at 100% of inoculum compared with 80% for B20. The
clones at 48 hr ranged in cell number from 60 to 95% of the inoculum.
There are several reasons for believing that the cell death observed in
the clones during this first phase is unlikely to be the result of mutation: (a) it occurs before mutations would be expressed; (b) the haploid, isogenic clones differ in their reaction to the treatment; (c) cells
are made sensitive to short exposure to trypsin; (d) most of the clonal
populations increase in number and may even resume a normal doubling
time shortly after removal of ICR 191. This resumption of cell division
is Phase II; the clones again show a variety of reactions, from 45%
to 160% of inoculum number by the sixth day. In Phase III, the populations again decline at a time consistent with the expression of lethal

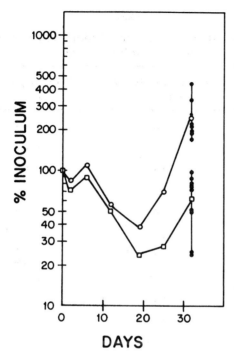

FIG. 5. The survival of B20 and B20(191) clones after a 48-hr
exposure to 1.0 μg/ml ICR 191 as a function of time. O, the average
of clones that at 32 days had a cell number equal to at least 170% of
the number at zero time; □, the average of clones that at 32 days had
a cell number of less than 100% at zero time; O, values for individual
clones.

recessive mutations (after three generations). There is some indication that those clones in which cell division (replication) was most
affected by the ICR 191 treatment show a delay before the decline in
cell number, as would be expected if replication is necessary for the
expression of mutation. The last phase (IV) in the reaction to ICR 191
treatment is a return to a normal doubling time, which occurs 19 days
or more (10 generation times) after ICR 191 treatment. When the data
were examined, it was noted that in this phase also there was a
heterogeneity in the behavior of the clonal populations. However, it
appeared that the cultures treated with ICR 191 fell into two categories,
one showing a relatively late recovery, the other group, a fast recovery
at Phase IV. The two groups were then averaged to give the curves in
Fig. 5. The early recovery group contained the two parent B20 populations and six of the clones; an important finding was that this group
included all seven clones that formed colonies resistant to 10^{-3} M

TABLE 1

Clonal Analysis of a Cell Line Which Yields Thymidine
Kinase Deficient Variants

Cell line or clone	BUdR resistance, % inoculum	Recovery from ICR 191	Colonies
ICR 2A	23	+ + + +	
ICR B20	128	+ + +	+
Clone B_2	148	+ +	
B_8	145	+ +	
B_{12}	152	+ + +	+
C_2	114	+ +	
C_8	170	+ + +	
D_5	180	+ +	
D_7	143	+ +	
E_{10}	131	+ + +	+
G_4	142	+	
ICR B20 (191)	180	+ + +	+
Clone A_{12}	283	+	
B_{10}	202	+ + +	+
B_{12}	142	+ + +	+
D_{12}	103	+	
C_4	175	−	
E_4	141	+ + +	+
E_6	242	−	
F_{12}	148	+ +	

BUdR. In Table 1, the data on BUdR resistance, recovery from ICR
191, and colony formation have been summarized. It appears that
only cultures that have both increased BUdR resistance and the
capacity to resume normal cell division rates in Phase IV are competent for the production of thymidine kinase deficiency. ICR 2A has
good recovery but low BUdR resistance and so does not form colonies.
At this time, one can only speculate about the basis of the recovery
from ICR 191. Since it occurs after the cells have been released from

the first, probably nonmutational, effects of ICR 191 and also after
the mutagenic action, it may be a measure of the DNA repair capacity
of a culture. Perhaps mutagen treatment selects cells with an efficient
repair system that is then able to erase the limited amounts of BUdR
that diffuse into the transport deficient cells. Such a combination of
resistance and repair might maintain cells in a viable but nondividing
state long enough for thymidine kinase deficiency to develop, or repair
may have a more specific role in the process.

EFFECT OF BUdR

The analysis of BUdR resistance is complicated by the possibility
that BUdR itself may have several functions. In addition to selecting
against sensitive cells, it may also be turning off the expression of
the thymidine kinase locus by the same unknown mechanisms by which
it dedifferentiates melanin (12), muscle (13), and cartilage cells (14).
Thymidine kinase, like the enzymes associated with differentiated
cells, has functions dispensable for normal cell division and growth.
In the case of cartilage, UDPG-epimerase is reduced to 5% of the
cartilage level by treatment with BUdR (15). If the thymidine kinase
deficiency of the haploid cells is similar to epimerase deficiency, the
expression of thymidine kinase could be studied as a model of dedifferentiation and perhaps differentiation in culture. Finally, there is a
possibility that BUdR is itself acting as a mutagen in bringing about
thymidine kinase deficiency. However, the evidence that the variants
are not present at the beginning of selection, the requirement for a
transport deficient precursor in a haploid system, the fact that haploid
clones derived from a single colony differ in their competence for
developing the enzyme deficiency, the correlation of this competence
with transport deficiency and ICR 191 recovery, all indicate that the
loss of thymidine kinase activity in these cells is epigenetic and not
genetic. If that is true, the lack of real thymidine kinase mutants
suggests that evolution may have provided somatic cells with effective
mechanisms against the expression of gene mutation.

The data on the effect of ICR 191 on cell populations have provided evidence that several different processes are involved in this
interaction. An early toxic effect on viability may range from a block
to cell division to cell death, depending both on the concentration of
ICR 191 and on the specific cell population being treated. At a time
when replication would be expected to allow mutation expression,
there is again a decrease in population. After this period, the return
to a normal multiplication rate is also different for each clone; since
this last phase takes place two weeks after the cells, by dividing,
have shown recovery from the toxic effects, it may be a measure of

the proportion of cells in a population able to recover from mutations, possibly of DNA repair capacity. Such a variety of effects and diversity of reactions must be taken into account not only in comparisons of the activity of mutagens, but also in comparisons of different cell populations in their reaction to a mutagen. These considerations, as well as the specific observation on thymidine kinase deficiency, question whether increased frequency of variants after mutagen treatment is evidence of a mutational origin, or indeed, whether an increase in frequency is a test for the mutagenicity of a molecule.

ACKNOWLEDGMENTS

This work was supported by U. S. P. H. S. grants CA-05959, CA-06927, and RR-05539 from the National Institutes of Health, contract AT(11-1)3110 with the U. S. Atomic Energy Commission (report no. COO-3110-7), and by an appropriation from the Commonwealth of Pennsylvania.

REFERENCES

1. J. J. Freed and L. Mezger-Freed, Stable haploid cultured cell lines from frog embryos, Proc. Nat. Acad. Sci. , 65, 337 (1970).
2. J. J. Freed and L. Mezger-Freed, Culture methods for anuran cells, in Methods in Cell Physiology, Vol. 4 (D. M. Prescott, ed.), Academic, New York, 1970, p. 19.
3. S. Kit, D. R. Dubbs, L. J. Piekarski, and T. C. Hsu, Deletion of thymidine kinase activity from L cells resistant to bromodeoxyuridine, Exptl. Cell Res. , 31, 297 (1963).
4. J. W. Littlefield, Studies on thymidine kinase in cultured mouse fibroblasts, Biochim. Biophys. Acta, 95, 14 (1965).
5. R. E. Breslow and R. A. Goldsby, Isolation and characterization of thymidine transport mutants of Chinese hamster cells, Exptl. Cell Res. , 55, 339 (1969).
6. J. J. Freed and L. Mezger-Freed, Origin of thymidine kinase deficient (TK-) haploid frog cells via an intermediate thymidine transport deficient (TT-) phenotype, J. Cell Physiol. , 82, 199 (1973).
7. G. N. Cohen and J. Monod, Bacterial permeases, Bacteriol. Rev. , 21, 169 (1957).

8. L. Mezger-Freed, Effect of ploidy and mutagens on bromodeoxy-uridine resistance in haploid and diploid frog cells, Nature, 235, 245 (1972).

9. B. N. Ames, and H. J. Whitfield, Jr., Frameshift mutagenesis in Salmonella, Cold Spring Harbor Symp., 31, 221 (1966).

10. J. Needham, Biochemistry and Morphogenesis, Cambridge University Press, Cambridge, 1942.

11. L. Mezger-Freed, unpublished observations.

12. S. Silagi and S. A. Bruce, Suppression of malignancy and differentiation in melanotic melanoma cells, Proc. Nat. Acad. Sci., 66, 72 (1970).

13. J. R. Coleman, A. W. Coleman, and E. J. H. Hartline, A clonal study of the reversible inhibition of muscle differentiation by the halogenated thymidine analog 5-BUdR, Develop. Biol., 19, 527 (1969).

14. J. Abbott and H. Holtzer, The loss of phenotypic traits by differentiated cells. V. The effect of 5-BUdR on cloned chondrocytes, Proc. Nat. Acad. Sci., 59, 1144 (1968).

15. G. Marzullo, Regulation of cartilage enzymes in cultured chondrocytes and the effect of 5-bromodeoxyuridine, Develop. Biol., 27, 20 (1972).

VI

VIRAL CARCINOGENESIS AS RELATED TO CHEMICAL CARCINOGENESIS

Chapter 32

ENHANCEMENT OF VIRAL ONCOGENESIS BY CHEMICAL CARCINOGENS

Bruce C. Casto

BioLabs, Inc.
Northbrook, Illinois

The stimulation of viral-induced tumors by chemical carcinogens was first reported in 1938 by Rous and Kidd (29), who demonstrated an increase in viral papillomas in rabbits treated jointly with chemicals and Shope papilloma virus. These studies were later confirmed and extended by Rogers and Rous (27) and by Rous and Friedewald (28). Subsequently, several investigators reported the enhancement of viral oncogenesis in vivo by the combined action of fibroma (1, 3), polyoma (31), or murine leukemia (4, 12) viruses and chemical carcinogens.

Pretreatment of cells in vitro with X irradiation (14, 22, 32), thymidine analogs (9, 14, 33), or UV irradiation (9) has been shown to increase the frequency of cell transformation by oncogenic DNA viruses. Several explanations have been offered to account for the observed increase. Stoker (32) concluded that cells surviving X irradiation appeared to have an increased susceptibility to transformation by polyoma virus, but cautioned that certain radiation-resistant, but virus-sensitive, cells may have been selected by treatment.

Pollack and Todaro (22) showed that selection of a virus-sensitive cell population by X irradiation was not the explanation for the enhancement of SV40 transformation since low doses of irradiation resulted not only in an increase in the transformation frequency but also in an increase in the absolute number of viral-transformed cell foci.

It has been suggested (9, 14, 22) that the enhancement of viral transformation by physical and chemical agents may be due to the availability of additional sites for integration of viral DNA into cell DNA during host cell repair synthesis of induced lesions in the cell DNA. Cleaver (13) has postulated that regions for incorporation of viral DNA may also be created in cell DNA during scheduled DNA synthesis at sites of unrepaired DNA damage. Under these conditions gaps would appear in the newly synthesized strand opposite the un-repaired lesions in the parental strand. If the gaps are repaired prior to the introduction of virus, then an increase in viral transformation would not be expected. Therefore, it is necessary for viral DNA to be present at the time when a large number of lesions are present in the cell DNA or at times of maximal host cell repair synthesis.

If the above is true, certain predictions can be made concerning the interaction between viruses and physical or chemical agents which leads to the enhancement of viral transformation. First, if the oncogenic virus has the capacity to replicate in the host cell, then enhancement might be expected if the damage to cell DNA were initiated shortly before or at any time after virus inoculation. However, if the virus is defective for replication and does not persist in the host cell, then enhancement would be expected only if DNA lesions were induced immediately before, or shortly after, virus addition. Second, those chemicals that induce damage that is rapidly repaired by the excision-repair system of the cell should enhance viral transformation for only brief periods after treatment, whereas those compounds that are incorporated into cell DNA in a stable manner would cause enhance-ment for extended periods after treatment.

In this discussion, data are presented that show that hamster embryo cells treated with chemical carcinogens are more susceptible to transformation by an oncogenic simian adenovirus, SA7. The in-crease in transformation frequency resulting from the combined action of SA7 and chemical carcinogens cannot be attributed to the appearance of foci transformed by chemical alone, since the foci scored are typi-cal for SA7 (6, 7) and do not resemble chemically transformed cells (5, 10, 16, 21). Furthermore, attempts to induce colonies resembling SA7 foci with chemical treatment alone were unsuccessful.

Primary hamster embryo cell cultures (HEC) were treated for 18 hr before virus inoculation with the polycyclic hydrocarbons 3-methyl-cholanthrene (MC), benzo(a)pyrene (BP), dibenz(a, h)anthracene [DB(a, h)A], dibenz(a, c)anthracene [DB(a, c)A], 7, 12-dimethylbenz(a)-anthracene (DMBA), phenanthrene, pyrene, and perylene.

HEC were also treated with methyl methanesulfonate (MMS), methylazoxymethanol acetate (MAM-Ac), N-2-acetylaminofluorene (AAF), acetoxy-AAF (Ac-AAF), N-nitrosodiethylamine (DEN), N-nitroso-dimethylamine (DMN), or N-methyl-N'-nitro-N-nitrosoguanidine (MNNG) for 2 or 18 hr before, or 5 hr after, virus addition.

Immediately after treatment, the cell cultures were rinsed with medium and 200 to 300 focus-forming units (FFU) of SA7 were added to each of three plates of treated and control cells. After virus adsorption, the cells were removed with trypsin, centrifuged, and

TABLE 1

Enhancement of SA7 Transformation of Hamster Embryo Cells
by Carcinogenic Polycyclic Hydrocarbons

Chemical[a]	Chemical dilution				Acetone control
	1:1	1:5	1:25	1:125	
MC	2.1[b]	9.1	3.8	2.3	0.9
BP	5.8	7.7	3.7	1.9	1.1
DB(a,h)A	4.3	2.3	2.5	2.2	0.9
DMBA	2.5	6.5	1.8	1.1	0.9

[a] Chemical and initial concentration: MC (3-methylcholanthrene),
10 μg/ml; BP [benzo(a)pyrene], 10 μg/ml; DB(a,h)A [dibenz(a,h)-
anthracene], 10 μg/ml; and DMBA [dimethylbenz(a)anthracene], 0.1
μg/ml. HEC were pretreated for 18 hr, virus adsorbed for 3 hr, and
the cells were then transferred to each of five plates at 2×10^5
(transformation assays) and 1×10^3 (survival assays) cells/plate.

[b] Enhancement was determined by dividing the SA7 transformation
frequency from treated cells by that obtained from SA7-inoculated
control cells. Underlined values are statistically significant
$(p < 0.01)$

resuspended to 10^6 cells/ml in an enriched Eagle's medium supplemented with 10% fetal bovine serum. For virus transformation assays,
2×10^5 cells were seeded onto each of five plates, fed after three
days with medium containing 0.1 mM $CaCl_2$, and covered with medium
containing 0.5% agar after five to six days. Additional feedings, con-
sisting of the 0.5% agar medium, were at intervals of five to six days.
Final focus counts were made after 25 to 30 days' incubation at 37°C.
Cell survival was determined by plating 1000 virus-inoculated, treated
or control cells onto each of five dishes. The cell colonies were fixed
and stained after nine days' incubation. Enhancement was calculated
by dividing the viral transformation frequency among surviving treated
cells by that obtained from virus-inoculated control cells (32).

Several polycyclic hydrocarbons have been shown to transform
cells in culture (5, 11, 15, 21) and to act synergistically with murine
leukemia virus in vitro to transform rat and mouse cells (18, 20, 23-26).
Pretreatment of HEC with MC, BP, DB(a,h)A, DB(a,c)A, and DMBA
were shown to increase the frequency of SA7 transformation (Table 1),
but treatment with phenanthrene, perylene, or pyrene did not (Table 2).
Concentrations of MC, BP, and DMBA above those necessary to

TABLE 2

Effect of Treatment of Hamster Embryo Cells with DB(a, c)A
and Certain Noncarcinogenic Polycyclic Hydrocarbons
on Transformation by SA7

Chemical[a]	μg/ml				Acetone control
	20	10	5	2.5	
Pyrene	1.1[b]	1.2	1.1	1.0	1.0
Perylene	1.1	0.9	1.2	1.2	1.0
Phenanthrene	1.4	1.4	1.3	0.8	1.0
DB(a, c)A	ND[c]	6.3	4.6	4.1	1.1

[a] HEC were pretreated for 18 hr, virus adsorbed for 3 hr, and the cells were then transferred to each of five plates at 2×10^5 (transformation assays) and 1×10^3 (survival assays) cells/plate. SA7 foci were counted after 25 to 30 days and colonies of surviving cells were fixed, stained, and counted after nine days.

[b] Enhancement was determined by dividing the SA7 transformation frequency from treated cells by that obtained from SA7-inoculated control cells. Underlined values are statistically significant ($p < 0.01$).

[c] ND, not done.

demonstrate maximal enhancement often reduced the frequency of transformation relative to that observed with lower doses. Addition of these three polycyclic hydrocarbons 5 hr after virus inoculation resulted in a dramatic inhibition of virus transformation in contrast with the enhancement obtained when the chemical was added prior to virus inoculation (Table 3).

The inhibition of transformation by high concentrations of MC, BP, and DMBA, or by the addition of these chemicals after virus addition, may be due to a delay in scheduled DNA synthesis, which is necessary for expression of adenovirus transformation (8). Inhibition of cell DNA synthesis after treatment of hamster cells with DMBA has been observed by Alfred and DiPaolo (2).

Pretreatment of HEC for 2 or 18 hr with MMS, MNNG, or Ac-AAF also resulted in an enhancement of SA7 transformation (Table 4), whereas treatment with MAM-Ac caused a stimulation of transformation when added 18 hr prior to virus, but did not do so when added 2 hr before virus inoculation (Table 5). Enhancement of viral transformation

TABLE 3

Effect of Time of Addition of DMBA on the
Transformation of Hamster Embryo Cells by SA7

Time of treatment, hr[a]	μg/ml				Acetone control
	0.1	0.05	0.025	0.01	
-18	<0.1[b]	3.7	2.9	2.1	1.4
+ 5	0.06	0.2	0.2	0.7	1.1

[a] HEC were treated for 18 hr prior to, or 5 hr after, virus inoculation. Following 18 hr treatment, the HEC were inoculated with SA7 and transferred at 2×10^5 (transformation assays) and 1×10^3 (survival assays) cells/plate. Other cultures (+ 5 hr) were inoculated with virus, transferred as above, and chemical added approximately 2 hr after cell transfer.

[b] Enhancement was determined by dividing the transformation frequency from treated cells by that obtained from SA7 inoculated control cells. Underlined values are statistically significant ($p < 0.01$).

TABLE 4

Enhancement of SA7 Transformation of Hamster Embryo
Cells by MMS, MNNG, and Ac-AAF

Chemical[a]	Time of treatment, hr	Chemical dilution				Acetone control
		1:1	1:2	1:4	1:8	
MMS	- 2	9.1[b]	3.1	1.8	2.1	1.8
MNNG	- 2	4.6	4.1	1.4	0.9	0.7
Ac-AAF	- 2	21.8	7.2	3.2	2.6	1.5

[a] Chemical and initial concentration: MMS (methyl methanesulfonate) 50 μg/ml; MNNG (N-methyl-N'-nitro-N-nitrosoguanidine) 0.5 μg/ml; Ac-AAF (N-acetoxy-acetylaminofluorene) 10 μg/ml. HEC were pretreated for 2 hr, rinsed once, virus adsorbed for 3 hr, and the cells then transferred at 2×10^5 (transformation assays) and 1×10^3 (survival assays) cells/plate.

[b] Enhancement was determined by dividing the SA7 transformation frequency from treated cells by that obtained from SA7-inoculated control cells. Underlined values are statistically significant ($p < 0.01$).

was also demonstrated when MMS, Ac-AAF, or MNNG were added 5 hr after virus inoculation and cell transfer (Table 6).

In contrast to the synergistic action observed between DEN and murine leukemia virus in rat embryo cells (19), treatment of hamster cells for up to 18 hr with 5 to 1000 μg/ml of DEN did not lead to an enhancement of SA7 transformation. Similar results were observed when HEC were treated with DMN under the same conditions of time and chemical concentration (Table 7). Treatment with AAF also failed to enhance SA7 transformation at concentrations up to 20 μg/ml. The failure of these latter compounds to stimulate viral transformation of hamster cells may be due to an inability of these cells to metabolize the chemical to an active carcinogen. Supportive evidence for this possibility has been obtained by DiPaolo et al. (17), who found that DEN did not transform hamster embryo cell cultures, but did cause transformation when administered in utero. In addition, Ac-AAF was shown to be 30 times more effective in transforming hamster embryo cells than the parent compound AAF (17).

As outlined previously, those agents that induce DNA lesions that are rapidly corrected by the excision-repair system of the cell would be expected to enhance transformation only if virus were already present or were added shortly after treatment. On the other hand, chemicals that become more stably associated with the host cell DNA would be expected to cause enhancement for a prolonged period after treatment.

Coggin (14) has shown that the enhancement of SV40 transformation declines by 70%, if the addition of virus is delayed until 10 hr after treatment. Similarly, Stich and Casto (34) have found that enhancement of SA7 transformation by 4-nitroquinoline-1-oxide (4NQO) was reduced from 25- to 1.5-fold if the period between 4NQO treatment and virus inoculation was extended to 12 hr. Other experiments with MMS (Table 8) suggest that virus must be added soon after MMS treatment in order to obtain maximal enhancement of viral transformation.

In contrast to the results obtained with X irradiation, 4NQO, and MMS, treatment of HEC with 5-bromodeoxycytidine (BCdR) resulted in an enhancement of SA7 transformation for at least 48 hr following treatment (Table 9). The similarity in the degree of enhancement, when virus was added at 0, 24, and 48 hr after treatment, suggests that most of the BCdR remains associated with the cell DNA.

In summary, the role of chemical carcinogens in promoting viral transformation may be due to the creation of gaps in cell DNA, thereby providing additional sites for incorporation of viral genetic material into cell DNA.

TABLE 5

Effect of Time of Addition of MAM-Ac on the
Transformation of Hamster Embryo Cells by SA7

Time of treatment, hr[a]	μg/ml				Acetone control
	10	5	2.5	1.25	
- 2	1.2[b]	1.3	1.2	1.3	1.1
-18	0.4	3.2	1.7	0.7	0.8

[a] HEC were treated for 2 or 18 hr prior to virus inoculation, rinsed once, virus was adsorbed for 3 hr, and the cells then transferred at 2×10^5 (transformation assays) and 1×10^3 (survival assays) cells/plate. SA7 foci were counted after 25 to 30 days. Colonies of surviving cells were fixed, stained, and counted after nine days.

[b] Enhancement was determined by dividing the transformation frequency from treated cells by that obtained from control cells. Underlined values are statistically significant ($p < 0.01$).

TABLE 6

Enhancement of SA7 Transformation by Treatment of Hamster Embryo
Cells with MMS, MNNG, or Ac-AAF 5 hr after Virus Inoculation

Chemical[a]	Chemical dilution				Acetone control
	1:1	1:2	1:4	1:8	
MMS	0.3[b]	7.5	2.7	1.9	1.1
MNNG	<0.1	14.6	4.5	1.9	1.1
Ac-AAF	2.3	2.2	2.0	ND	0.9

[a] Chemical and initial concentration: MMS (methyl methanesulfonate) 50 μg/ml; MNNG (N-methyl-N'-nitro-N-nitrosoguanidine) 1.0 μg/ml; Ac-AAF (N-acetoxy-acetylaminofluorene) 5 μg/ml. HEC were inoculated with SA7, the virus was adsorbed for 3 hr, and the cells then transferred at 2×10^5 (transformation assays) and 1×10^3 (survival assays) cells/plate.

[b] Enhancement was determined by dividing the SA7 transformation frequency of treated cells by that obtained from SA7-inoculated control cells. Underlined values are statistically significant ($p < 0.01$).

The gaps may be created either as a result of the excision-repair system of the cell (9, 14, 22) or during scheduled DNA synthesis in

TABLE 7

Effect of Treatment of Hamster Embryo Cells
with DMN or DEN on Transformation by SA7

Chemical[a]	Time of treatment, hr	µg/ml				Acetone control
		1000	500	250	125	
DEN	- 2	0. 6[b]	0. 8	0. 7	0. 8	0. 7
	-18	1. 1	1. 3	1. 4	1. 1	0. 8
DMN	- 2	0. 6	0. 6	0. 7	0. 8	0. 7
	-18	1. 4	0. 9	1. 2	1. 5	1. 2

[a] HEC were pretreated for 2 or 18 hr with DEN (N-nitrosodiethylamine) or DMN (N-nitrosodimethylamine), virus was adsorbed for 3 hr, and the cells then transferred at 2×10^5 (transformation assays) or 1×10^3 (survival assays) cells/plate.

[b] Enhancement was determined by dividing the SA7 transformation frequency of treated cells by that obtained from SA7-inoculated control cells. HEC treated with lower doses of either chemical were similarly negative for enhancement of SA7 transformation.

TABLE 8

Effect of Time of Virus Addition on Enhancement of SA7 Transformation after Treatment of Hamster Embryo Cells with MMS

Time after treatment, hr[a]	µg/ml			Acetone control
	25	5	1	
2	4. 0[b]	2. 0	1. 1	1. 3
8	1. 7	1. 2	1. 6	0. 6
12	0. 8	0. 7	1. 2	0. 6
24	1. 3	1. 3	1. 0	1. 7

[a] HEC were treated for 2 hr with MMS (methyl methanesulfonate). The cultures were rinsed once with medium, after which the treated and control cultures were fed with medium containing 0. 5% fetal bovine serum. SA7 was added to each of three cultures of treated or control cells at 2, 8, 12, or 24 hr after initiation of chemical treatment. The cultures were transferred, following 3 hr virus adsorption, at 2×10^5 (transformation assays) or 1×10^3 (survival assays) cells/plate.

[b] Enhancement was determined by dividing the SA7 transformation frequency of treated cells by that obtained from SA7-inoculated control cells. Underlined values are statistically significant (p < 0. 01).

TABLE 9

Effect of Time of Virus Addition on Enhancement of SA7
Transformation after Treatment of Hamster Embryo Cells
with 5-Bromodeoxycytidine

Time after treatment, hr[a]	μg/ml		SA7 Control
	50	100	
0	59.0[b]	89.0	1.0
24	56.0	81.0	1.0
48	54.0	91.0	1.0

[a] BCdR was added to primary cultures of HEC 24 hr after plating. The cells were incubated in the presence of BCdR for 48 hr, after which the cultures were changed with medium containing 0.5% fetal bovine serum, but free of BCdR. At 0, 24, and 48 hr after removal of the BCdR, the cells were inoculated with SA7 and transferred at 2×10^5 (transformation assays) and 1×10^3 (survival assays) cells/plate.

[b] Enhancement was determined by dividing the SA7 transformation frequency of treated cells by that obtained from SA7-inoculated control cells. At each concentration of BCdR the actual number of SA7 foci per plate increased five- to eight-fold.

areas opposite unrepaired lesions in the parental DNA strand (13). If viral genetic material is available during the time that lesions are present in the cell DNA, then an increase in viral transformation might be expected. Repair of these lesions, either by excision-repair mechanisms or by recombinational processes (30) before the availability of viral genetic material, should abolish any expected stimulation of viral transformation.

ACKNOWLEDGMENT

The work upon which this publication is based was performed pursuant to Contract No. NIH-NCI-E-71-2164 with the National Cancer Institute, Department of Health, Education, and Welfare.

REFERENCES

1. C. G. Ahlström and C. H. Andrewes, Fibroma virus infection in tarred rabbits, J. Pathol. Bacteriol., 47, 65 (1938).
2. L. J. Alfred and J. A. DiPaolo, Reversible inhibition of DNA synthesis in hamster embryo cells in culture: Action of 1, 2-benzanthracene and 7, 12-dimethylbenz(a)anthracene, Cancer Res., 28, 60 (1968).
3. C. H. Andrewes, C. G. Ahlström, L. Foulds, and W. E. Gye, Reaction of tarred rabbits to the infectious fibroma virus, Lancet, 2, 893 (1937).
4. I. Berenblum, "The Possible Role of a Transmissible Factor in Leukemia Induction by Radiation plus Urethan, " in Viruses, Nucleic Acids, and Cancer, 17th Annual Symposium on Fundamental Cancer Research, University of Texas M. D. Anderson Tumor Institute, Williams and Wilkins, Baltimore, 1963, pp. 529-543.
5. Y. Berwald and L. Sachs, In vitro cell transformation with chemical carcinogens, Nature, 200, 1182 (1963).
6. B. C. Casto, Adenovirus transformation of hamster embryo cells, J. Virol., 2, 376 (1968).
7. B. C. Casto, Transformation of hamster embryo cells and tumor induction in newborn hamsters by simian adenovirus SV11, J. Virol., 3, 513 (1969).
8. B. C. Casto, Biologic parameters of adenovirus transformation, Progr. Exptl. Tumor Res., 18, 167 (1972).
9. B. C. Casto, Enhancement of adenovirus transformation by treatment of hamster cells with ultraviolet-irradiation, DNA base analogs, and dibenz(a, h)anthracene, Cancer Res., 33, 402 (1973).
10. T. T. Chen and C. Heidelberger, In vitro malignant transformation of cells derived from mouse prostate in the presence of 3-methylcholanthrene, J. Nat. Cancer Inst., 42, 915 (1969).
11. T. T. Chen and C. Heidelberger, Quantitative studies on the malignant transformation of mouse prostate cells by carcinogenic hydrocarbons in vitro. Intern J. Cancer, 4, 166 (1969).
12. L. Chieco-Bianchi, L. Fiore-Donati, G. deBenedictus, and G. Tridente, Influence of urethan on susceptibility to leukemia induction by Graffi virus in adult mice, Nature, 199, 292 (1963).
13. J. E. Cleaver, "Repair of Damaged DNA in Human and Other Eukaryotic Cells, " in Nucleic Acid-Proteins Interactions — Nucleic Acid Synthesis in Viral Infections (D. W. Ribbons, J. F. Woessner, and J. Schultz, eds.), North Holland, Amsterdam/London, 1971, pp. 87-112.

14. J. H. Coggin, Jr., Enhanced virus transformation of hamster embryo cells in vitro, J. Virol., 3, 458 (1969).
15. J. A. DiPaolo, P. Donovan, and R. Nelson, Quantitative studies of in vitro transformation by chemical carcinogens, J. Nat. Cancer Inst., 42, 867 (1969).
16. J. A. DiPaolo, R. L. Nelson, and P. J. Donovan, Morphological, oncogenic, and karyological characteristics of Syrian hamster embryo cells transformed in vitro by carcinogenic polycyclic hydrocarbons, Cancer Res., 31, 1118 (1971).
17. J. A. DiPaolo, R. L. Nelson, and P. J. Donovan, In vitro transformation of Syrian hamster embryo cells by diverse chemical carcinogens, Nature, 235, 278 (1972).
18. A. E. Freeman, P. J. Price, R. J. Bryan, R. J. Gordan, R. V. Gilden, G. J. Kelloff, and R. J. Huebner, Transformation of rat and hamster embryo cells by extracts of city smog, Proc. Nat. Acad. Sci., 68, 445 (1971).
19. A. E. Freeman, P. J. Price, H. J. Igel, J. C. Young, J. M. Maryak, and R. J. Huebner, Morphological transformation of rat embryo cells induced by diethylnitrosamine and murine leukemia viruses, J. Nat. Cancer Inst., 44, 65 (1970).
20. A. E. Freeman, P. J. Price, E. M. Zimmerman, G. J. Kelloff, and R. J. Huebner, RNA tumor virus genomes as determinants of chemically-induced transformation in vitro, Intern. Symp. Comp. Leukemia Res., Padua/Venice, 1971.
21. E. Huberman and L. Sachs, Cell susceptibility to transformation and cytotoxicity by the carcinogenic hydrocarbon benzo(a)pyrene. Proc. Nat. Acad. Sci., 56, 1123 (1966).
22. E. J. Pollack and G. J. Todaro, Radiation enhancement of SV40 transformation in 3T3 and human cells, Nature, 219, 520 (1968).
23. P. J. Price, A. E. Freeman, W. T. Lane, and R. J. Huebner, Morphological transformation of rat embryo cells by the combined action of 3-methylcholanthrene and Rauscher leukemia virus, Nature New Biol., 230, 144 (1971).
24. P. J. Price, W. A. Suk, and A. E. Freeman, Type C RNA tumor viruses as determinants of chemical carcinogenesis: effects of sequence of treatment, Science, 177, 1003 (1972).
25. J. S. Rhim, H. Y. Cho, M. H. Joglekar, and R. J. Huebner, Comparison of the transforming effect of benzo(a)pyrene of mammalian cell lines in vitro, J. Nat. Cancer Inst., 48, 949 (1972).
26. J. S. Rhim, B. Creasy, and R. J. Huebner, Production of altered cell foci by 3-methylcholanthrene in mouse cells infected with AKR leukemia virus, Proc. Nat. Acad. Sci., 68, 2212 (1971).
27. S. Rogers and P. Rous, Joint action of a chemical carcinogen and a neoplastic virus to induce cancer in rabbits; results of exposing epidermal cells to a carcinogenic hydrocarbon at time of infection with the Shope papilloma virus, J. Exptl. Med., 93, 459 (1951).

28. P. Rous and W. F. Friedewald, The effect of chemical carcinogens on virus-induced rabbit papillomas, J. Exptl. Med., 79, 511 (1944).

29. P. Rous and J. G. Kidd, The carcinogenic effect of a papilloma virus on the tarred skin of rabbits. I. Description of the phenomenon, J. Exptl. Med., 67, 399 (1938).

30. W. D. Rupp and P. Howard-Flanders, Discontinuities in the DNA synthesized in an excision-defective strain of Escherichia coli following ultraviolet irradiation, J. Mol. Biol., 31, 291 (1968).

31. M. H. Salaman, K. E. K. Rowson, F. J. C. Roe, J. K. Ball, J. J. Harvey, and G. deBenedictus, "The Combined Action of Viruses and Other Carcinogens," in Viruses, Nucleic Acids, and Cancer, 17th Annual Symposium on Fundamental Cancer Research, University of Texas M. D. Anderson Tumor Institute, Williams and Wilkins, Baltimore, 1963, pp. 544-558.

32. M. Stoker, Effect of X irradiation on susceptibility of cells to transformation by polyoma virus, Nature, 200, 756 (1963).

33. G. J. Todaro and H. Green, Enhancement by thymidine analogs of susceptibility of cells to transformation by SV40, Virology, 24, 393 (1964).

34. H. F. Stich and B. C. Casto, unpublished data.

Chapter 33

GENETICS OF AVIAN RNA TUMOR VIRUSES:
A REVIEW OF RECENT DEVELOPMENTS

Peter K. Vogt, Maxine Linial,[*] W. S. Mason,
Robin A. Weiss,[+] John A. Wyke,[+] and Robert R. Friis

Department of Microbiology
University of Southern California School of Medicine
Los Angeles, California

INTRODUCTION

Mutants and markers of avian RNA tumor viruses are now available in sufficient numbers to allow genetic studies of selected problems in tumor virus biology. Temperature-sensitive mutants can be used to define viral genetic functions. Deletion mutants may prove useful in constructing a genetic map (37). Avian RNA tumor viruses also show various forms of genetic and nongenetic interactions including phenotypic mixing, complementation, and genetic recombination (12, 17, 18, 35, 37). This chapter gives a brief review of recent results obtained with temperature-sensitive mutants of avian sarcoma viruses and with endogenous RNA tumor viruses.

TEMPERATURE-SENSITIVE MUTANTS

Temperature-sensitive mutants of avian sarcoma viruses can be divided into three classes (Table 1). Class T mutants are defective in their cell-transforming ability at the nonpermissive temperature (41°) but produce normal quantities of infectious viral progeny. Class R

---

[*] Current address: Department of Genetics, University of Washington, Seattle, Washington.

[+] Current address: Imperial Cancer Research Fund, Lincoln's Inn Fields, London, England.

TABLE 1

Classes of Avian Sarcoma Virus ts Mutants

Class	Functions at 41°	
	Production of progeny virus	Transformation of host cell
Transformation (T)	+	-
Replication (R)	-	+
Coordinate (C)	-	-

mutants show the reciprocal defect; they transform cells under restrictive conditions but synthesize only small quantities of progeny virus. Class C mutants neither transform nor produce progeny at the nonpermissive temperature. This physiologic classification is useful in pointing out similarities between mutants, but it represents an oversimplification. For instance, virus-induced neoplastic transformation includes changes in a number of cellular properties, and different tests for transformation do not always detect the same cellular change. Thus some temperature-sensitive mutants are unable to produce foci in monolayers at 41° but have an unaltered ability to produce colonies in agar (10). Although such mutants are not absolutely transformation negative, they are included among the T or C classes because they are affected in one of their transforming functions.

The three classes of temperature-sensitive mutants can be further subdivided according to several biologic and biochemical characteristics (42). For example, late mutants are usually able to initiate infection and enter a stable union with the cell at the nonpermissive temperature. After shift to the permissive conditions (35°), complete recovery of all viral functions is observed. Early mutants, on the other hand, often fail to establish stable focus forming or infectious centers under restrictive conditions. If infection with such a mutant is carried out at 41° and cells are maintained at this temperature, the fraction of viruses that can resume normal functions after shift to 35° decreases with the length of time spent at 41°.

There are several other physiologic and genetic criteria by which temperature-sensitive mutants of avian sarcoma viruses may be characterized. Some mutants, notably those of class R, can be complemented by wild-type avian leukosis virus; others, among them all class T mutants, cannot (44). Most mutations do not result in enhanced heat lability of the virion, but some early mutations have this effect (21). Further physiologic markers are provided by the ability or inability of mutants to synthesize viral DNA, RNA, or virus structural proteins at 41°.

Most of the avian sarcoma virus temperature-sensitive mutants isolated so far belong to class T (Table 2) (3, 6, 16, 23, 43). They are unable to induce focus or agar colony formation at 41°. Furthermore, cells transformed by these mutants at 35° lose at least some of their transformed characteristics if shifted to 41°, indicating that the mutants are unable to maintain transformation under nonpermissive conditions. Transformation appears, therefore, to depend on the continuous genetic action of the virus.

The mutants of class T have been studied in complementation tests and can be assigned to at least four complementation groups (37, 44). Within each group there is minimal complementation, whereas members of different groups are able to complement each other effectively. This observation suggests that more than one viral gene is important for the transformation process. Similar conclusions have been reached with another set of class T mutants (17).

It is not clear why class T mutants are isolated more frequently than class R or class C mutants. Some intentional and unintentional selection may take place; mutations belonging to class T are easily recognized because of their effect on focus formation. However, even strenuous efforts to obtain class C or class R mutants yield comparatively few usable isolates, and the possibility that class T mutants occur more frequently must be left open.

The literature contains several reports on physiologic and genetic experiments with avian sarcoma virus temperature-sensitive mutants of class T and of class C (3, 7, 8, 10, 15, 16, 18, 23, 24). In the present review two recently isolated mutants of class C will serve as illustration for such studies. These mutants, ts335 and ts337, are of particular interest because the temperature-sensitive lesion has been located early in the infection and possibly affects RNA-directed DNA synthesis (21).

Both ts335 and ts337 fail to produce foci of transformed cells at 41° (focus counts at 41° are about 10^{-2} to 10^{-3} of the counts at 35°). The production of infectious progeny virus is likewise suppressed at 41° to 3 to 10% of the control levels at 35°. Both mutants have a virion that shows increased heat lability; the half-life of the mutants at 41° is less than half that of the wild type. One of the mutants, ts337, also appears to have an alteration in the envelope antigens as compared with wild type. This alteration may be due to a second mutation. Temperature shift experiments indicate that the temperature-sensitive step in ts335 and ts337 occurs early in infection. In these shifts, three viral functions have been measured: induction of foci in

TABLE 2

Avian Sarcoma Virus ts Mutants: Distribution
of Isolates in Three Mutant Classes

Class	Number of isolates[a]
T	23[a]
C	7
R	14[b]

[a] Mutants isolated in the laboratory of the authors. Published reports from other laboratories would bring the number of class T mutants to 30.

[b] Some of the class R isolates may prove too "leaky" for genetic or physiologic analysis.

monolayer cultures, formation of cell colonies in agar suspension, and synthesis of infectious progeny virus. The effects of shifts on these three viral functions are similar: initiating infection at 35° allows both mutants to pass through the temperature-sensitive phase within a relatively short time, after which a shift to 41° no longer affects transformation or virus production. For instance, if infection with ts335 for 8 hr at 35° is followed by a shift to 41°, as much as 10% of the number of foci obtained in the 35° control are found on the experimental plate. If infection with ts335 is followed by a 24-hr reprieve at 35° before shift to 41°, the effect of the nonpermissive conditions on focus formation in monolayers or colony formation in agar is virtually abolished. Virus production also becomes refractory to restrictive conditions if the first 2 to 5 hr following inoculation are spent at 35°. These observations indicate that the temperature-sensitive phase of ts335 and ts337 lies within the first 24 hr after infection. Shift down experiments support this conclusion. Cultures infected and maintained for increasing lengths of time at 41° become less and less able to express viral functions when shifted to 35°. Infection followed by 24 hr at 41° results in a decay of 99% of the potential focus-forming or colony-forming centers of ts335 or ts337. The ability of cells to yield infectious virus after shift to 35° also decays in cultures infected and maintained at 41°. These experiments suggest that the early viral function suppressed at 41° in ts335 and ts337 is required to establish a stable union between cell and virus. Similar observations have been made with a previously described class C mutant, ts336 (formerly referred to as ts149) (10). ts335 and ts337 also fail to produce viral group specific (gs) antigen at 41°

which is in accord with the proposed early location of the temperature-sensitive lesion, as gs antigen is the first viral protein detectable by fluorescent staining after infection (26).

Neither of the mutants can be complemented by wild-type leukosis virus at 41°, yet double infections at 35° with a mutant and wild-type leukosis virus yield progeny that contain wild-type recombinants combining the temperature insensitivity of the leukosis virus with the focus forming ability of the sarcoma virus. Leukosis viruses must therefore have the viral gene that is mutated in ts335 and ts337. The lack of complementation between wild-type leukosis virus and mutant sarcoma virus at 41° can be explained by assuming that the active gene products of the wild-type virus cannot rescue temperature-sensitive mutants which are blocked at an early state of the infection.

The early expression of the temperature-sensitive lesion in ts335 and ts337 may indicate a deficiency in the adsorption of the mutants to the host cell or in penetration. However, both ts335 and ts337 become resistant to pH 2 after adsorption at about the same rate as wild type. The mutations thus appear to affect a function that follows adsorption and penetration. The temperature-sensitive phase of ts335 and ts337 coincides with a period of infection during which the viral RNA is transcribed into DNA by a virion-associated enzyme (2, 4, 33). It was therefore of interest to test the effect of the nonpermissive temperature on the RNA-directed DNA polymerase carried by the mutants. The endogenous reaction of ts335 directed by virion RNA showed no significant DNA synthesis at 41° while incorporation of [^{3}H]thymidine was found at 35°. ts337 had a very low endogenous enzyme activity at both temperatures. Since the inhibition of the ts335 enzyme at 41° could be caused by a defect in the template rather than in the enzyme, tests were also performed with rA:dT as added template. Under these conditions the rates of thymidine incorporation with ts335 and ts337 were reduced two- to fourfold at 41° as compared with the 35° control, while the wild type incorporated at the same rate at both temperatures. The results suggest that the mutations in ts335 and ts337 affect the virion DNA polymerase. However, definitive proof of this point will require studies with purified enzymes and isolation of genetic revertants to wild type. In these revertants normal enzyme activities should be restored together with transforming and replicating ability.

ENDOGENOUS VIRUSES

Many normal cells harbor genetic information for the synthesis of an RNA tumor virus (5, 9, 13, 25, 27, 34, 38, 41). This information can be activated by exposing cells to physical or chemical carcinogens (1, 22, 39). Complete synthesis of the endogenous virus ensues; in some cases the cells become permanent virus producers, while in others virus synthesis stops spontaneously some time after induction. These observations confirm and extend the classic studies by Kaplan and his associates, who showed that X-ray induced leukemia in mice could be transmitted by a virus that was probably activated by the X-ray treatment (20).

In studies with avian cells, endogenous virus was induced in cultures derived from several chicken lines of Europe, America, and Asia as well as in cultures from feral jungle fowl, the ancestral form of the domestic chicken. The viruses produced by these diverse chicken cells are rather similar; they all belong to subgroup E of avian RNA tumor viruses (39). This uniformity of induced viruses in the chicken system has no obvious explanation. Perhaps subgroup E viruses have a greater probability of becoming repressed in normal cells as compared with other subgroups of avian RNA tumor viruses in which overt virus synthesis may predominate.

The induction of endogenous RNA tumor viruses has raised several questions that remain to be answered. The most urgent one of these concerns the oncogenic potential of the induced viruses. The earlier studies in mice suggest that the endogenous viruses isolated from X-ray induced leukemias can be oncogenic (14, 20). Tests with the agents obtained from normal fibroblasts have not yet been completed. In the chicken system these tests are complicated by the fact that most chicken lines are resistant to exogenous infection with subgroup E viruses, and that the readily infectable ringneck pheasants as well as Japanese quail may not respond with tumor formation despite abundant virus production.

A second question that has not yet been answered concerns the ubiquity of endogenous viruses. Virus synthesis can be induced in all chicken lines tested so far but has not been detected in cultures of Japanese quail. In mice, inducibility of virus is a characteristic of certain mouse strains and appears to be controlled by chromosomal genes. At least some of these genes may be identical with an integrated viral genome (28-32). Whether the noninducible mouse strains or quail cells lack viral genetic information altogether is not known.

Recent investigations with endogenous avian tumor viruses have concentrated on genetic interactions between endogenous viral genomes and exogenous superinfecting virus. As an introduction to these studies, genetic recombination between two exogenous avian tumor viruses will be summarized. In order to study genetic recombination, stable genetic markers that can be easily scored are needed.

The markers selected for recombination tests with avian RNA tumor viruses are host range and focus forming ability in fibroblast cultures. Avian RNA tumor viruses belonging to different subgroups differ in their host range, and selectively resistant chicken cells are available that allow plating of one subgroup to the complete exclusion of another. Focus formation in fibroblast cultures is generally a property of sarcoma viruses. Leukosis viruses do not form foci, although they replicate. In a typical genetic cross, avian sarcoma virus of subgroup A may be grown together with leukosis virus of subgroup B. A large fraction of the yield from such a culture is phenotypically mixed, combining the host range property of both parental viruses on the same particle. Upon cloning, the phenotypically mixed particles produce mostly parental-type virus. However, the mixed yield also contains genetically stable recombinants. In the particular cross mentioned, these are sarcoma viruses of subgroup B (36, 37). These recombinants unite the focus forming ability of the sarcoma parent with the host range of the leukemia parent. The reciprocal recombinants combining the host range marker of the sarcoma virus with the inability to form foci characteristic of leukosis virus probably occur but for technical reasons have not been looked for. Table 3 gives a survey of several such host range crosses. Host range recombinants occur in very high frequencies except in crosses involving the defective Bryan high titer strain of Rous sarcoma virus, which appears to be unable to recombine with the host range marker of any leukosis virus.

The crosses between exogenous and endogenous virus are in principle the same as those described for exogenous viruses. Focus formation in fibroblasts and host range are again used as markers (40). The exogenous parent is focus forming, nondefective sarcoma virus of subgroup B. The endogenous parent has the host range of subgroup E and exists in a "repressed" state in uninfected cells. It cannot form foci. After passage of the exogenous virus in various kinds of uninfected cells, the progeny is tested for recombinants that induce foci but have subgroup E host range. Selective plating on cells susceptible to subgroup E but resistant to subgroup B reveals the occurrence of such recombinants that can be cloned repeatedly and are genetically stable. Recombinants with endogenous virus information have been found only after passage of exogenous sarcoma virus in normal cells that showed partial expression of the endogenous viral genome as manifested in the synthesis of avian tumor virus gs antigen and in the ability to produce a helper factor that can complement the defective Bryan high titer strain of Rous sarcoma virus. Cells that are free of gs antigen and fail to complement defective Rous sarcoma virus do not give rise to recombinants between exogenous and endogenous virus. Since endogenous virus can be induced in these antigen and helper factor negative cells (39), failure to yield recombinants cannot

TABLE 3

Recombination of Host Range and Transformation Markers

| Parental viruses | | Recombinants[a] | Total number |
Sarcoma	Leukosis		of clones
PR RSV-A[b]	RAV-2[c]	10	24
PR RSV-A	Td B77[d]	12	20
BH RSV[e]	RAV-1	0	41
BH RSV	RAV-3	0	12
BH RSV	Td PR-A[f]	0	48
PR RSV-B[g]	RAV-1	11	25
PR RSV-B	RAV-3	8	34
PR RSV-B	Td PR-A	17	39

[a] Recombinants combine the transformation marker of the sarcoma virus and the host range marker of the leukosis virus in genetically stable form.

[b] Prague strain RSV, subgroup A.

[c] RAV, Rous associated virus.

[d] Transformation defective derivative of sarcoma virus B77.

[e] Bryan high titer strain of Rous sarcoma virus.

[f] Transformation defective derivative of PR RSV-A.

[g] Prague strain RSV, subgroup B.

be due to the lack of an endogenous viral genome but appears to be related to the transcription of this genome into RNA. Recombination seems to require RNA synthesis by both viral parents.

Stocks of subgroup B sarcoma virus grown up in cells that contain group specific antigen and helper factor not only include recombinants but also particles that give rise to progeny with host ranges of subgroups B and E. These particles are probably not virus clumps, because they persist through sonication of the virus stocks. They are also absent from similarly grown stocks of the Bryan high titer strain of Rous sarcoma virus, which does not recombine with other avian tumor viruses but is known to form virus clumps (11). These particles that can give rise to progeny of both parental host ranges are therefore probably heterozygotes, but more work is required to confirm this interpretation.

SUMMARY AND CONCLUSIONS

A beginning has been made toward defining viral genetic function with temperature-sensitive mutants. There is now ample genetic support for the conclusion that transformation by RNA tumor viruses requires the continuous activity of genes carried by the virus. However, it seems important to point out that genes carried by a virus are not necessarily viral genes. Viruses that become integrated in cellular DNA may also incorporate cellular genes (19), and these may be of importance in transformation. It is still too early to tell whether the two coordinate mutants reviewed in this communication have a lesion in their DNA polymerase. If they do, they could answer many questions concerning the role and mode of action of this unusual enzyme.

The discovery of genetic recombination between exogenous and endogenous RNA tumor viruses offers an explanation for some forms of apparent host-induced modification of RNA tumor viruses. Recombinants with endogenous virus can be selected for in certain host cells. For instance, a subgroup B virus stock containing a small fraction of endogenous subgroup E recombinant would become entirely subgroup E through selection if grown on cells that exclude subgroup B but admit subgroup E. Much remains to be learned about endogenous RNA tumor viruses. They are obviously subject to cellular genetic regulation, but the mechanisms of repression and of induction are obscure. Genetic variations among these viruses and their oncogenic potential also remain to be demonstrated. Studies now in progress may provide answers to some of these questions.

ACKNOWLEDGMENTS

This work was supported by U. S. Public Health Service Research Grant No. CA-13213 from the National Cancer Institute, Contract No. NIH-NCI 72-2032 under the Virus Program, and the Robert E. and May R. Wright Foundation.

Maxine Linial is a fellow of the Jane Coffin Childs Memorial Fund for Medical Research.

William S. Mason and John A. Wyke are fellows of the Leukemia Society of America, Inc.

VOGT ET AL.

REFERENCES

1. S. A. Aaronson, G. J. Todaro, and E. M. Scolnick, Induction of murine C-type viruses from clonal lines of virus free BALB/3T3 cells, Science, 174, 157 (1971).
2. J. P. Bader, Metabolic requirements for infection by Rous sarcoma virus. I. The transient requirement for DNA synthesis, Virology, 29, 444 (1966).
3. J. P. Bader, Temperature-dependent transformation of cells infected with a mutant of Bryan Rous sarcoma virus, J. Virology, 10, 267 (1972).
4. D. Baltimore, RNA-dependent DNA polymerase in virions of RNA tumor viruses, Nature, 226, 1209 (1970).
5. M. A. Baluda, Widespread presence, in chickens, of DNA complementary to the RNA genome of avian leukosis viruses, Proc. Nat. Acad. Sci., 69, 576 (1972).
6. J. Biquard and P. Vigier, Isolement et étude d'un mutant conditionnel du virus de Rous à capacité transformante thermosensible, Comptes Rend. [D]271, 2430 (1970).
7. J. Biquard and P. Vigier, Characteristics of a conditional mutant of Rous sarcoma virus defective in ability to transform cells at high temperature, Virology, 47, 444 (1972).
8. M. M. Burger and G. S. Martin, Agglutination of cells transformed by Rous sarcoma virus by wheat germ agglutinin and concanavalin A, Nature New Biol., 237, 9 (1972).
9. R. M. Dougherty, H. S. DiStefano, and F. K. Roth, Virus particles and viral antigens in chicken tissues free of infectious avian leukosis virus, Proc. Nat. Acad. Sci., 58, 808 (1967).
10. R. R. Friis, K. Toyoshima, and P. K. Vogt, Conditional lethal mutants of avian sarcoma viruses. I. Physiology of ts 75 and ts 149, Virology, 43, 375 (1971).
11. H. Hanafusa, T. Hanafusa, and H. Rubin, Analysis of the defectiveness of Rous sarcoma virus. I. Characterization of the helper virus, Virology, 22, 591 (1964).
12. H. Hanafusa, T. Hanafusa, and H. Rubin, Analysis of the defectiveness of Rous sarcoma virus. II. Specification of RSV antigenicity by helper virus, Proc. Nat. Acad. Sci., 51, 41 (1964).
13. H. Hanafusa, T. Miyamoto, and T. Hanafusa, A cell-associated factor essential for formation of an infectious form of Rous sarcoma virus, Proc. Nat. Acad. Sci., 66, 314 (1970).
14. N. Haran-Ghera, Leukemogenic activity of centrifugates from irradiated mouse thymus and bone marrow, Intern. J. Cancer, 1, 81 (1966).

15. E. Katz and P. K. Vogt, Conditional lethal mutants of avian sarcoma viruses. II. Analysis of the temperature sensitive lesion in ts 75, Virology, 46, 745 (1971).
16. S. Kawai and H. Hanafusa, The effects of reciprocal changes in temperature on the transformed state of cells infected with a Rous sarcoma virus mutant, Virology, 46, 470 (1971).
17. S. Kawai, C. E. Metroka, and H. Hanafusa, Complementation of functions required for cell transformation by double infection with RSV mutants, Virology, 49, 302 (1972).
18. S. Kawai and H. Hanafusa, Plaque assay for some strains of avian leukosis virus, Virology, 48, 126 (1972).
19. S. Lavi and E. Winocour, Acquisition of sequences homologous to host deoxyribonucleic acid by closed circular simian virus 40 deoxyribonucleic acid, J. Virology, 9, 309 (1972).
20. M. Lieberman and H. S. Kaplan, Leukemogenic activity of filtrates from radiation-induced lymphoid tumors of mice, Science, 130, 387 (1959).
21. M. Linial and W. S. Mason, Characterization of two conditional early mutants of Rous sarcoma virus, Virology, 53, 258 (1973).
22. D. R. Lowy, W. P. Rowe, N. Teich, and J. W. Hartley, Murine leukemia virus: high frequency activation in vitro by 5-iododeoxyuridine and 5-bromodeoxyuridine, Science, 174, 155 (1971).
23. G. S. Martin, Rous sarcoma virus: a function required for the maintenance of the transformed state, Nature, 227, 1021 (1970).
24. G. S. Martin, S. Venuta, M. Weber, and H. Rubin, Temperature-dependent alterations in sugar transport in cells infected by a temperature-sensitive mutant of Rous sarcoma virus, Proc. Nat. Acad. Sci., 68, 2739 (1971).
25. L. N. Payne and R. C. Chubb, Studies on the nature and genetic control of an antigen in normal chick embryos which reacts in the COFAL test, J. Gen. Virol., 3, 379 (1968).
26. F. E. Payne, J. J. Solomon, and H. G. Purchase, Immunofluorescent studies of group-specific antigen of the avian sarcoma-leukosis viruses, Proc. Nat. Acad. Sci., 55, 341 (1966).
27. P. N. Rosenthal, H. L. Robinson, W. S. Robinson, T. Hanafusa, and H. Hanafusa, DNA in uninfected and virus-infected cells complementary to avian tumor virus RNA, Proc. Nat. Acad. Sci., 68, 2336 (1971).
28. W. Rowe, J. W. Hartley, and T. Bremmer, Genetic mapping of a murine leukemia virus-inducing locus of AKR mice, Science, 178, 860 (1972).
29. W. Rowe, Studies of genetic transmission of murine leukemia virus by AKR mice. I. Crosses with Fv-1[n] strains of mice, J. Exptl. Med., 136, 1272 (1972).
30. W. Rowe and J. W. Hartley, Studies of genetic transmission of murine leukemia virus by AKR mice. II. Crosses with Fv-1[b] strains of mice, J. Exptl. Med., 136, 1286 (1972).

31. J. R. Stephenson and S. A. Aaronson, A genetic locus for inducibility of C-type virus in Balb/c cells: The effect of a nonlinked regulatory gene on detection of virus after chemical activation, Proc. Nat. Acad. Sci., 69, 2798 (1972).
32. J. R. Stephenson and S. A. Aaronson, Genetic factors influencing C-type RNA virus induction, J. Exptl. Med., 136, 175 (1972).
33. H. M. Temin and S. Mizutani, RNA-dependent DNA polymerase in virions of Rous sarcoma virus, Nature, 226, 1211 (1970).
34. H. E. Varmus, R. A. Weiss, R. R. Friis, W. Levinson, and J. M. Bishop, Detection of avian tumor virus-specific nucleotide sequences in avian cell DNAs, Proc. Nat. Acad. Sci., 69, 20 (1971).
35. P. K. Vogt, Phenotypic mixing in the avian tumor virus group, Virology, 32, 708 (1967).
36. P. K. Vogt, Genetically stable reassortment of markers during mixed infection with avian tumor viruses, Virology, 46, 947 (1971).
37. P. K. Vogt, J. A. Wyke, R. A. Weiss, R. R. Friis, E. Katz, and M. Linial, Avian RNA tumor viruses: mutants, markers and genotypic mixing, M. D. Anderson Symposium, Houston, Texas, 1972, in press.
38. R. A. Weiss, The host range of Bryan strain Rous sarcoma virus synthesized in the absence of helper virus, J. Gen. Virol., 5, 511 (1969).
39. R. A. Weiss, R. R. Friis, E. Katz, and P. K. Vogt, Induction of avian tumor viruses in normal cells by physical and chemical carcinogens, Virology, 46, 920 (1971).
40. R. A. Weiss, W. S. Mason, and P. K. Vogt, Genetic recombination between endogenous and exogenous avian RNA tumor viruses, Virology, 52, 535 (1973).
41. D. E. Wilson and H. Bauer, Hybridization of avian myeloblastosis RNA with DNA from chick embryo cells, Virology, 33, 754 (1967).
42. J. A. Wyke and M. Linial, Temperature sensitive avian sarcoma viruses: A physiological comparison of twenty mutants, Virology, 53, 152 (1973).
43. J. A. Wyke, The selective isolation of temperature sensitive mutants of Rous sarcoma virus, Virology, 52, 587 (1973).
44. J. A. Wyke, Complementation among avian sarcoma virus temperature sensitive mutants, Virology, 54, 28 (1973).

Chapter 34

STUDIES ON THE COMBINED EFFECTS OF ONCORNA VIRUSES AND CHEMICAL CARCINOGENS IN MICE

J. A. McCarter and J. K. Ball
University of Western Ontario
Cancer Research Laboratory
London, Canada

Studies of the combined effects of viruses and chemical carcinogens have been made for many years. The subject has been recognized to be a complex one, full of uncertainties in interpretation of results [for review, see Roe and Rowson (1)]. Recently there has been renewed interest in the possibility that chemical carcinogens exert their effects through interaction with viral, oncogenic information. This renewed interest stems from the hypothesis of Huebner and Todaro (2) that the cells of many, and possibly all, vertebrates contain viral and oncogenic information in a covert or repressed form. Carcinogenic agents may allow the partial or complete expression of this information, that is, the formation of gene products characteristic of the virogenes or oncogenes, and sometimes, the production of complete, infectious virus.

Several examples are now known of the activation of latent infectious, oncogenic RNA-containing viruses by X irradiation and chemical carcinogens. The best known such virus is Rad-LV (3) from X-irradiated C57B1/Ka mice, which produces thymic lymphoma in mice of that strain. We have described the recovery of a similar virus from thymic lymphomas and from fibrosarcomas induced in inbred mice by 7, 12-dimethylbenz(a)anthracene (DMBA) (4). This virus, called DMBA-LV in analogy with Rad-LV, produces thymic lymphomas in CFW mice but, despite its occurrence in fibrosarcomas induced by chemical carcinogens, it does not by itself produce fibrosarcomas. What, then, is the role of this virus, endogenous in CFW mice, in the induction of fibrosarcomas and other tumors by DMBA? By itself it is inactive in this respect but possibly it is the interaction of chemical carcinogen with DMBA-LV that produces sarcomas in CFW mice. To test this possibility we might increase the load of presumed oncogenic information by giving DMBA-LV to mice and then treat them with chemical carcinogen.

DMBA-LV used in our experiments was prepared by Moloney's procedure (5) as an extract of thymic lymphomas produced by serial passage in CFW/D inbred mice of virus originally isolated from a DMBA-induced thymic lymphoma (4). The virus was assayed by injection into a newborn thymus gland implanted under the kidney capsule of a normal adult mouse (6). The potency of the preparations was such that 0.05 ml of a phosphate-buffered saline extract, equivalent to 5 mg of tumor, produced tumors in 60% of the thymic grafts (extract used in Experiment 1, Table 1) or 90% (extract used in Experiment 2, Table 1).

Rad-LV was obtained from Dr. H.S. Kaplan. It was prepared and assayed as described above and produced tumors in 85% of thymic grafts in C57Bl/Ka mice. In CFW/D mice it was completely inactive and, in our experiments, was used as a control.

The data of Table 1 show that DMBA injected into newborn CFW/D mice induced thymic lymphomas. When given to newborn CFW/D mice, DMBA produces a long-lasting immunosuppression (7), and one might have expected to see a significant increase in yield of tumors in the situation where DMBA-LV was given 24 hr after DMBA but there was not.

DMBA injected into CFW/D mice 21 days of age induces subcutaneous fibrosarcomas at the site of injection of the hydrocarbon. As shown in Table 1, the number of mice that developed tumors appeared to be greater in the group that received both virus and DMBA than in the group that received DMBA alone, but the difference is not significant. In any event, if a difference did occur, the data indicate that it would be small. In the experiment using Rad-LV, the combination of chemical carcinogen and virus was not more effective than the chemical alone. Not only were the yields of tumors not affected by treatment with virus and chemical carcinogen, but the types of tumors produced and the average latent periods for tumor production were also unaffected.

We then decided to see if DMBA-LV could initiate the production of papillomas of mouse skin employing the sensitive technique of two-stage carcinogenesis (8). DMBA-LV was vaccinated (0.02 ml) on the skins of mice, and the mice were then painted twice weekly for 20 weeks with a solution of croton oil, 2% in liquid paraffin. In Fig. 1 are shown the cumulative yields of papillomas produced per mouse with time. More papillomas per mouse were produced in the animals that received DMBA-LV than in mock-vaccinated controls, but the variation was such that the difference was not significant ($P \approx 0.1$).

TABLE 1

Effect of DMBA plus Murine Leukemia Virus on the Tumor
Incidence in Inbred CFW/D Mice[a]

Virus	Dose DMBA, μg	Dose Virus, ml	Order-interval	Tumor incidence	Tumor type L[b]	Tumor type S[b]	Latent period[c] L	Latent period[c] S
1. DMBALV	20	0.1	D - 24 hr - V	19/43	18	1	22.4	14.5
	20	—	—	13/43	13		22.2	
2. DMBALV	200	0.1	V - 21 days - D	5/12	1	4	18.0	22.5
	200	—	—	4/23		4		20.5
	—	0.1	—	0/25				
3. RadLV	200	0.1	V - 21 days - D	2/17	2		20.5	
	—	0.1	—	0/15				

[a] Mice were injected at birth with either 0.1 ml virus or DMBA. Virus (undiluted-10% PBS tumor extract) was administered intraperitoneally and 0.01 ml DMBA in trioctanoin was injected subcutaneously into the intrascapular region.

[b] L, leukemia; S, sarcoma.

[c] Time to death of tumor bearing animal (weeks).

However, in all these experiments, the dose of DMBA-LV might have been too small to allow an effect to be seen. The experiment was repeated using four intraperitoneal injections of 0.1 ml of DMBA-LV a week apart. The control group for this experiment received four injections of the same preparation of DMBA-LV that had been heated at 56 °C for 30 min to inactivate the virus. Croton oil was applied to the skin of the mice as described above. As shown in Fig. 2, the yield of papillomas in the virus-treated group was larger than in the control groups, but the difference was only of borderline significance $(0.1 > P > 0.05)$. We have, therefore, no good evidence that DMBA-LV can do other than induce lymphomas. Possibly had we used larger numbers of animals or treated them differently, another conclusion might have been reached, but we now think that in DMBA-LV we may have been studying a virus that has only part of the endogenous oncogenic information available in the mouse.

That there is additional oncogenic information available in the mouse emerged from studies of the combined effects of a chemical

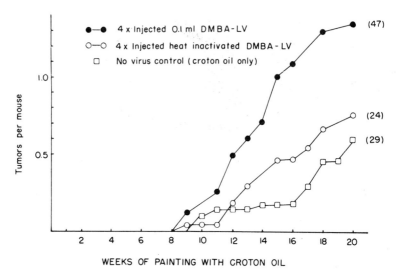

FIG. 1. Test of activity of DMBA-LV as an initiating agent for production of papillomas in skin of CFW/D mice. Hair was plucked from skin of backs of anesthetized male mice, four to six weeks old. Corium was stripped using adhesive cellulose tape. DMBA-LV was applied to treated area of 50 mice. Phosphate-buffered saline was applied to treated area of 29 mice. All mice were painted twice weekly with croton oil, 2% in liquid paraffin, and the numbers of papillomas found per mouse were recorded weekly.

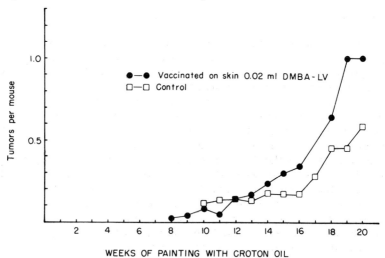

FIG. 2. As for Fig. 1, except that skin of the back was not vaccinated. Instead, mice were given four weekly intraperitoneal injections of DMBA-LV or heat-inactivated DMBA-LV and treatment with croton oil was begun after the last injection. The numbers in brackets are numbers of aninals in the test.

TABLE 2

Effect of DMBA and JLSV9MuLV on Tumor
Incidence in Inbred CFW/D Mice[a]

Dose DMBA, µg	Virus	Order-interval	Tumor incidence	Tumor type L[b]	S[b]	Latent period[c] L	S
25	0.10(10⁻¹)	V - 4 days - D	22/26	0	22		8.8
	0.10(10⁻¹)	—	32/34	0	32		9.6
25	0.10(10⁻³)	V - 4 days - D	7/23	7	0	13.0	
	0.10(10⁻³)	—	3/26	0	3		12.1
25	—	—	4/27	4	0	15.6	

[a] Mice were injected with virus or DMBA at birth. Virus (tissue culture supernatant of virus-infected cells) was administered intraperitoneally and 0.01 ml DMBA in trioctanoin was injected subcutaneously in the intrascapular region.

[b] L, leukemia; S, sarcoma.

[c] Time to appearance of tumor (weeks).

carcinogen and another virus. In the course of routine passage in tissue culture of a clone derived from JLSV9 cells (9), an RNA-containing C-type particle virus appeared spontaneously (10). This virus grows to high titers (1 to 2×10^8 infectious units/ml) in various mouse cell cultures as measured by the XC assay (11).

In Table 2 are shown the results of experiments in which JLSV9-MuLV, at two concentrations, was given to mice at birth, with or without concomitant treatment with DMBA given four days after the virus. The combined treatment was no more effective in producing tumors than the sum of the separate treatments for either dose. With the smaller dose of virus, the tumors produced by combined treatment were leukemias, whereas with the higher dose of virus, all the tumors were sarcomas, but we do not know what significance to attach to this alteration of tumor type.

The significant information obtained in these experiments is that JLSV9MuLV by itself produced sarcomas, all of which were rhabdomyosarcomas. These arose in the muscles of the face, head, chest, abdomen, limbs, and feet. Multiple sarcomas are induced by JLSV9MuLV given to newborn mice of all strains tested. These sarcomas, and the

TABLE 3

Summary of the Properties of JLSV9MuLV

	Titration of JLSV9MuLV in CFW newborn mice		
Virus dilution	Infectious units injected/0.1 ml undiluted virus	Tumor yield, %	Latent period, wk[a]
Undiluted	2×10^7	100	8.3
1:10	2×10^6	94	9.6
1:100	2×10^5	26	9.7
1:1000	2×10^4	12	12.1

[a] To time of appearance of tumor.
Originated in JLSV9 cells in tissue culture
Titer of virus in tissue culture medium by XC assay = 2×10^8 i.f./ml.
No detectable focus-forming activity in vitro.
Clone purified virus induces habdomyosarcomas in newborn CFW mice
and in NIH-Swiss, C3H/Bi, C57Bl/6J, CBA/H.
Ineffective in newborn W/Fu rats and normal adult mice.
All sarcomas contain MuSV.

plasmas of mice bearing them, contain murine sarcoma virus as well
as viruses having the properties of JLSV9MuLV. However, exhaustive
tests, to be described in detail elsewhere (12), have shown that
JLSV9MuLV purified by cloning is not a "transforming virus" and contains no murine sarcoma virus. Some properties of JLSV9MuLV are
summarized in Table 3. As shown by these data, the virus is very
effective in eliciting the production of sarcomas. Under the circumstances, it is difficult to decide if JLSV9MuLV possesses oncogenic
information of its own or if it acts only through eliciting the activity of
an endogenous, latent sarcoma virus. Alternatively, JLSV9MuLV may
be particularly effective in picking up sarcomagenic information from
the mouse. We take it that the failure of combined treatment with
chemical carcinogen and JLSV9MuLV to be more than additive, points
to the conclusion that the oncogenic information is not in the JLSV9MuLV,
but in the mouse. Our data also indicate that the oncogenic information in the mouse can be rescued by JLSV9MuLV. In tissue culture,
JLSV9MuLV can rescue murine sarcoma virus from nonproducer cell
lines transformed by Moloney murine sarcoma virus but no focus-
forming virus is produced by passage of JLSV9MuLV in primary or
secondary cultures of mouse embryo fibroblasts nor any established
line of mouse cells in culture tested to date. We do not yet know if

murine sarcoma virus can be rescued by JLSV9MuLV from sarcomas induced by chemical carcinogens, but we are testing this possibility.

REFERENCES

1. F. J. C. Roe and K. E. K. Rowson, The induction of cancer by combinations of viruses and other agents, Intern. Rev. Exptl. Pathol., 6, 181 (1968).
2. R. J. Huebner and G. J. Todaro, Oncogenes of RNA tumor viruses as determinants of cancer, Proc. Nat. Acad. Sci., 64, 1087 (1969).
3. H. S. Kaplan, On the natural history of the murine leukemias: Presidential address, Cancer Res., 27, 1325 (1967).
4. J. K. Ball and J. A. McCarter, Repeated demonstration of a mouse leukemia virus after treatment with chemical carcinogens, J. Nat. Cancer Inst., 46, 751 (1971).
5. J. B. Moloney, Biological studies on a lymphoid-leukemia virus extracted from Sarcoma 37. 1. Origin and introductory investigations, J. Nat. Cancer Inst., 24, 933 (1960).
6. N. Haran-Ghera and A. Peled, The mechanism of radiation action in leukaemogenesis. Isolation of a leukaemogenic filtrable agent from tissues of irradiated and normal C57Bl mice, Brit. J. Cancer, 21, 730 (1967).
7. J. K. Ball, N. R. Sinclair, and J. A. McCarter, Prolonged immunosuppression and tumor induction by a chemical carcinogen injected at birth, Science, 152, 650 (1966).
8. I. Berenblum and P. Shubik, An experimental study of the initiating stage of carcinogenesis, and a re-examination of the somatic cell mutation theory of cancer, Brit. J. Cancer, 3, 109 (1949).
9. B. S. Wright, P. A. O'Brien, G. P. Shibley, S. A. Mayyasi, and J. C. Lasfarques, Infection of an established bone marrow cell line (JLS-V9) with Rauscher and Moloney leukemia viruses, Cancer Res., 27, 1672 (1967).
10. S. A. Aaronson, J. W. Hartley, and G. J. Todaro, Mouse leukemia virus: "Spontaneous" release by mouse embryo cells after long-term in vitro cultivation, Proc. Nat. Acad. Sci., 64, 87 (1969).
11. W. Klement, W. P. Rowe, J. W. Hartley, and W. E. Pugh, Mixed culture cytopathogenicity: A new test for murine leukemia viruses in tissue culture, Proc. Nat. Acad. Sci., 63, 753 (1969).

12. J. K. Ball, D. A. Harvey, and J. A. McCarter, Evidence for naturally occurring murine sarcoma virus, Nature, 241, 272 (1973).

Chapter 35

UPTAKE OF T7 DNA BY HAMSTER EMBRYO CELLS
IN TISSUE CULTURE

J. C. Leavitt, L. M. Schechtman, and P. O. P. Ts'o

The Johns Hopkins University
Department of Biochemical and Biophysical Sciences
Baltimore, Maryland

E. Borenfreund and A. Bendich

Memorial Sloan-Kettering Cancer Center
New York, New York

The conversion of a normal mammalian cell to a cancer cell and the persistence of the change through many cell generations would appear to require some qualitative or quantitative alteration in the genetic information of the cell. Heritable acquisition of malignant potential has resulted from the "infection" of mammalian cells by DNA isolated from oncogenic viruses (1, 2) and from tumor cells (3, 4). To elucidate some of the complex molecular events involved in viral- or chemical-induced cancer, it would help to develop efficient model systems with which to study cell-DNA interactions. Uptake of foreign DNA by cells of higher organisms has been investigated in this regard (4, 5). Cells in culture can incorporate exogenous DNA from widely heterologous sources with apparent preservation of structural or functional integrity of DNA in some instances (6, 7, 14, 15). However, little is known about the process of incorporation, the amount of foreign DNA that can enter the nucleus of recipient cells, and its replication and function within the heterologous host.

In this chapter an experimental model is described using embryo cells from the Golden Syrian hamster in culture as recipient cells to exogenous coliphage T7 or its DNA. Experiments have been performed to answer the following basic questions about this phage DNA-mammalian cell interaction: (a) the location of the cell-associated exogenous DNA with respect to the cell membrane—development of an assay to distinguish the extracellular and intracellular DNA attached to the cell; (b) the extent of conservation and degradation of exogenous DNA inside the cell; (c) the localization of the exogenous DNA conserved within the cell; and (d) the functional state of the exogenous DNA with regard to its replication and its expression within the recipient cell.

ABBREVIATIONS

GSHE, Golden Syrian hamster embryo; DEAE-D, diethylaminoethyldextran; EDTA, ethylenediamine tetraacetate; PBS, phosphate-buffered saline; SDS, sodium dodecylsulfate.

MATERIALS AND METHODS

Cell Culture Methods

Embryo cells from the Golden Syrian hamster (GSHE cells) were derived from stocks between second and tenth passages and grown in Dulbecco's modified Eagle's medium with 10% fetal calf serum, 100 units penicillin/ml, and 100 μg streptomycin/ml (Gibco) in 60 mm plastic petri dishes (Falcon), some of which contained microscope coverslips. DEAE-D, mol. wt. about 2×10^6, was purchased from Pharmacia, and pancreatic DNase I, specific activity 2100 to 2500 units/mg, from Worthington. A stock of T7 phage lysate was a gift of Dr. W. Studier. $[^3H]$ T7 phage was grown by the procedure of Englund (8) and $[^{32}P]$ T7 phage by the procedure of Grossman (9). T7 phage was purified according to Englund (8). T7 DNA was isolated and purified by three phenol extractions, one extraction with 96% chloroform—4% isoamyl alcohol, three ether extractions, and extensive dialysis in 0.02 M Tris-HCl, pH 7.9. The specific activity of $[^3H]$ T7 DNA was $1.2 - 2.6 \times 10^5$ cpm/μg, and that of $[^{32}P]$ T7 DNA was $1.0 - 6.0 \times 10^5$ cpm/μg at the time of preparation. Aseptic technique was used from the final step in the purification of phage or DNA. Cell cultures were negative for mycoplasma.

Standard Five-Step Experimental Procedure

1. Into each plate, 1.5 to 5×10^5 GSHE cells were seeded and incubated overnight at 37° in a humidified atmosphere of 10% CO_2 and 90% air.

2. The culture fluid was replaced with 3 ml fresh growth medium

containing 10 μg DEAE-D/ml, and the cells were incubated 15 min at 37°.

3. Medium containing DEAE-D was then replaced with fresh serum-free medium to which $10^{5.5}$ to 10^6 radioactive T7 phage per cell or 10 to 50 μg of radioactive T7 DNA was added. After 1 hr at 37°, fetal calf serum was added to 10% and incubation continued for two more hours; the medium was then replaced with fresh growth medium.

4. After appropriate incubation times up to 72 hr, cells were treated with 20 μg of DNase I for 30 min at 37° and washed twice with 3 ml of PBS. Average GSHE cell generation times were approximately 12-15 hr.

5. For assays of cellular uptake of T7 DNA, PBS-washed cells were solubilized in 1 ml 0.5% SDS containing 0.001 M EDTA and 0.01 M Tris-HCl, pH 7.9. Aliquots were counted in a Beckman LS-200B scintillation counter in 10 ml Aquasol (New England Nuclear). Other methods of analysis are given with each individual experiment.

Autoradiography (4)

Coverslips with methanol-fixed cells were mounted on microscope slides with Kaiser's gel and extracted with cold 5% trichloroacetic acid for 10 min (to remove acid-soluble radioactivity), washed, and dried. Slides were then dipped in 1:1 diluted Kodak NTB$_3$ photograph emulsion, kept in the dark for 1-2 weeks, developed with Kodak D-19 and stained with Giemsa.

Reassociation Kinetics

Hydroxyapatite techniques used for DNA reassociation kinetic analysis are described in detail by Kohne and Britten (22).

RESULTS

Coliphage T7 was chosen as a source of DNA "foreign" to embryo cells from the Golden Syrian hamster because this phage is genetically well described, and its vegetative cycle during infection in E. coli is relatively well understood at the molecular level. The T7 genome does not integrate into the host genome nor require DNA synthesis prior to vegetative gene expression. Its genes are transcribed from one DNA strand (10), which offers an immediate test for specificity in transcription by the host cell. Large quantities of the duplex genome can be isolated with a minimal amount of structural damage, and the relatively shear-resistant genome allows greater experimental manipulation without loss of biologic activity. Routine analytical ultracentrifugation (11) revealed that DNA preparations (32S; mol wt, 25×10^6) had less than one single-strand break for every three copies of the genome.

Kinetics of Cellular Attachment of T7 DNA and Virus,
and Development of Resistance to Release by DNase

The attachment of $[^{32}P]$ T7 DNA and virus to GSHE cells was nearly complete between 3 and 6 hr (Fig. 1) and was almost entirely dependent on pretreatment of the cells with DEAE-D (12). The naked DNA attached more efficiently than did the phage itself. For example, after 24 hr 15.8% of the exogenous DNA attached while only 4.0% of the intact phage did. Nearly all of the T7 DNA (97%) was released from attachment to the cells when treated with DNase after 3 hr of incubation with DNA. However, after medium change at 3 hr without DNase treatment and further cell growth, there was a steady increase in the amount of attached T7 DNA isotope that was not released by subsequent DNase treatment. In this experiment (Fig. 1) 50% of the T7 DNA that had become attached to the cells after 3 hr of initial incubation was converted to a DNase-resistant form after 34 hr of cell growth. This amount is equivalent to 3.8 nmoles of $[^{32}P]$ T7 DNA nucleotide for 6×10^5 cells or 4.45×10^4 genome equivalents of T7 DNA per GSHE cell. In the following sections studies using techniques of autoradiography, sedimentation analysis, DNA–DNA hybridization, and DNA reassociation kinetics indicate that conversion of exogenous DNA to this protected form is the result of uptake of T7 DNA as well as the reutilization of its degradation products.

Autoradiographic Examination of
Cellular Uptake of $[^3H]$ T7 DNA

Autoradiography was used to assess the validity of DNase treatment for measurement of true intracellular T7 DNA. However, it cannot be assumed that intracellular localization of the isotope of $[^3H]$ T7 DNA by this technique alone reflects the conservation of T7 nucleotide sequences. The most obvious alternative to the conservation of $[^3H]$ thymine in T7 DNA sequences is degradation and reutilization of the products in the synthesis of cellular macromolecules.

Autoradiographs were developed from cells grown on coverslips that were incubated for either 3 or 24 hr with $[^3H]$ T7 DNA (Fig. 2) or $[^3H]$ T7 virus. Duplicate coverslips were prepared with and without DNase treatment. After 3 hr, when 2% of the $[^3H]$ T7 DNA associated

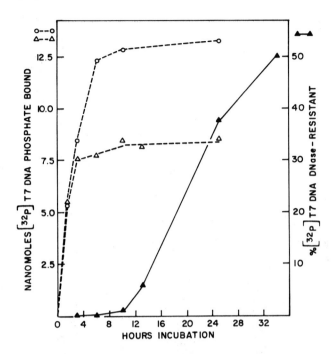

FIG. 1. Kinetics of attachment of T7 virus and DNA to GSHE cells
and the development of resistance of T7 DNA to release from cells by
exogenous DNase. In 28 hr of incubation with T7 DNA, GSHE cells
multiplied from 1.7 to 5.0 × 10⁵ cells per dish. Either 338 nmoles of
[³²P] T7 DNA per dish in the form of intact phage or 57 nmoles of
deproteinized [³²P] T7 DNA per dish were incubated with GSHE cells.
For determination of total binding, cells were incubated without medium
change, washed with PBS at the times indicated omitting DNase treatment, and analyzed after SDS solubilization. o---o represents the
binding of T7 phage, and △---△ the binding of T7 DNA, both expressed
in nanomoles [³²P] T7 DNA nucleotide. When sensitivity to added DNase
was assayed, binding of [³²P] T7 DNA was allowed for 3 hr and unbound
DNA removed by medium change. The cells were then incubated further
and DNase treated at various times. [³²P] T7 DNA that remained bound
to cells after DNase treatment is represented by ▲——▲ and is expressed
in terms of the percentage of total [³²P] T7 DNA that had attached to
cells in 3 hr.

with the cells had become resistant to release by DNase treatment,
about one-third of the nuclei of the cell population were labeled. Of
293 cells counted, the labeled nuclei showed 10-99 silver grains.
After 24 hr of incubation, 28 % of the [³H] T7 DNA had become resistant

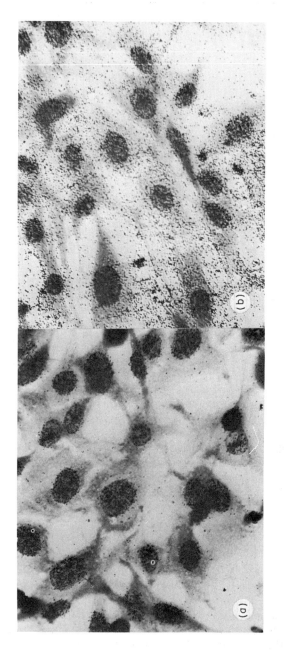

FIG. 2. Autoradiographs of GSHE cells that were exposed to [³H]T7 DNA for 24 hr (see text); X 530. (a) With DNase treatment. (b) Without DNase treatment.

to release by DNase and 98% of the nuclei were heavily labeled, and the extranuclear background of silver grains (after DNase treatment) was well below 1%. The average number of grains per nucleus increased by about 230%. Indistinguishable results were obtained with cells incubated with either T7 DNA or T7 phage after 24 hr and DNase treatment. The result was obtained in a typical experiment [Fig. 2(a)] in which 2.85×10^5 cells on a coverslip had incorporated the equivalent of 0.112 μg of [^{3}H]T7 DNA after 24 hr. This equals 9200 T7 genome equivalents per cell for the 98% of the cells that were labeled. Cells not treated with DNase [Fig. 2(b)] showed the same degree of nuclear labeling as those treated with the DNase. A considerable quantity of radioactivity, which was insoluble in trichloroacetic acid, apparently was associated with cells but not incorporated.

Autoradiography routinely confirmed that DNase treatment of cells in monolayer was a reliable method of measurement for uptake of [^{3}H] T7 DNA into the cell. Interestingly, pretreatment of cells with increasing levels of DEAE-D up to 50 μg/ml did not reduce the efficiency of degradation of extracellular T7 DNA by DNase. When T7 phage were used, the presence of the phage coat did not inhibit the degradation of extracellular T7 DNA by DNase after the phage had been incubated with GSHE cells for 10 hr.

Stability of T7 DNA in Cell Cultures

Because of the apparent lability of T7 phage in cell cultures, the stability of the intact phage in culture medium in the absence of cells was examined. After the intact T7 phage was incubated in the culture medium containing 10% fetal calf serum for 24 hr, the deproteinized T7 DNA from the phage was found to be intact since the DNA cosedimented with the native, untreated T7 DNA (32S) in a neutral sucrose gradient (Fig. 3). On the other hand, after the deproteinized DNA was incubated under the same conditions, this incubated DNA was found to be so highly degraded that it barely sedimented (Fig. 3). These findings together with the observation that the T7 DNA in the intact T7 phage incubated with GSHE cells for 10 hr became sensitive to exogenous DNase suggest that the T7 DNA in the phage was exposed by the proteolytic enzyme(s) originating from the GSHE cells.

Suppression of Reutilization of T7 DNA Degradation Products

The quantitative study on the fate of T7 DNA in the cell is complicated by the observation that T7 DNA was degraded to products that were then reutilized in the synthesis of cellular DNA and RNA. It seemed reasonable to assume that the reutilization of [^{3}H]thymine

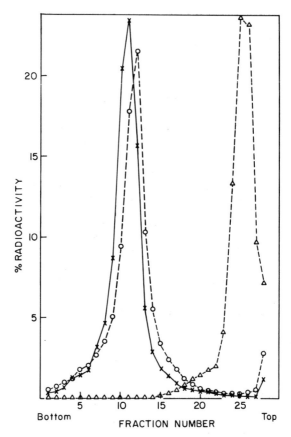

FIG. 3. Stability of T7 phage in cell culture medium. Thirty-four
micrograms of [^{32}P]T7 DNA in the form in intact phage or 20 µg extracted
[^{32}P]T7 DNA were incubated in complete medium for 24 hr in the absence
of GSHE cells. The incubation mixture was then adjusted to 0.6% SDS
and the buffered phenol-extracted [^{32}P]T7 DNA analyzed by sedimentation in 5-20% sucrose gradients (0.1% SDS, 0.01 M Tris-HCl, pH 7.9
and 0.001 M EDTA) in a SW 27.1 rotor at 23,000 rpm for 18 hr (11 °C);
fractions were collected and counted in 10 ml Aquasol. Sedimentation
of a control [^{3}H]T7 DNA marker is shown by ✕—✕; [^{32}P]T7 DNA incubated as phage is shown by o- - -o; [^{32}P]T7 DNA incubated in naked
form is shown by ∆- - -∆. Sedimentation is expressed as the percentage
of the total radioactivity in the gradient.

from the T7 DNA labeled with [^{3}H]thymine should be suppressed substantially by adding thymidine to the cell culture. The amount of
radioactivity from T7 DNA, which after 24 hr of incubation became

TABLE 1

Intracellular Localization of $[^3H]T7$ DNA by
Autoradiographic Examination of GSHE Cells[a]

Incubation time[b]	$[^3H]T7$ genome equivalents per cell[c]	Percent grains localized with nucleus	Percent Extra-cellular grains	Percent nuclei labeled with grains	Average grains per nucleus
24	118	> 97%	< 1%	75	10
48	560	> 97%	< 1%	95	30

[a]GSHE cells were grown on coverslips: 3.7×10^4 cells per coverslip at time of addition of T7 DNA (zero time); 10.6×10^4 cells per coverslip at 24 hr; 28.9×10^4 cells per coverslip at 48 hr. Three coverslips of cells were incubated with 20 µg $[^3H]T7$ DNA (82,258 cpm/nmole); autoradiographs were exposed 25 days. Culture medium contained thymidine, 6.8×10^{-5} M.

[b]See standard procedure outlined in the methods; all coverslips were DNase-treated.

[c]Calculated from the amount of radioactivity associated with cells after DNase treatment.

resistant to DNase treatment, was reduced by 60-80% due to the addition of 17 nmoles thymidine per milliliter of culture medium. This observation is in accord with the expectation that the presence of thymidine in the culture medium suppresses the reutilization of degradation products of T7 DNA in synthesis of cellular macromolecules. Addition of thymidine to higher concentrations did not further diminish the amount of $[^3H]T7$ DNA resistant to DNase. This amount of radioactivity from T7 DNA is thought to represent the amount of $[^3H]T7$ DNA that has been transported inside the cell without extensive degradation and reutilization. Autoradiographic examination of GSHE cells that have been incubated with $[^3H]T7$ DNA or $[^3H]$-phage in the presence of thymidine (6.8×10^{-5} M) revealed that the radioactive DNA was localized only with the cell nuclei. A summary of such an autoradiographic experiment is presented in Table 1.

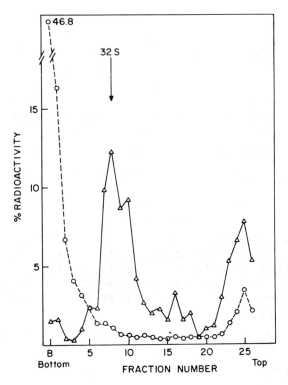

FIG. 4. Sedimentation analysis of intracellular T7 DNA isotopes. [$^{32}_2$P] T7 phage (1. 48 μg DNA) attached to 1. 8 × 10^5 GSHE cells in 3 hr. After replacement of the medium and cell growth to 7. 0 × 10^5 cells in 24 hr followed by DNase treatment of the cells, 10. 4% of the T7 DNA became resistant to the exogenous DNase. During the 24-hr incubation, replicating GSHE cellular DNA was labeled with 0.5 μCi [^{3}H] thymidine (20 Ci/mm). DNA was extracted and analyzed by sedimentation (see Fig. 3); Δ---Δ, [^{32}P] DNA; o---o, [^{3}H] DNA. A T7 DNA marker sedimented to fraction 8 (32S).

Fragmentation of T7 DNA during the Cellular Uptake

Sedimentation studies provide additional information about the degradation of T7 DNA and the reutilization of the radioactive degradation products during cellular uptake. Figure 4 demonstrates that the newly labeled hamster DNA with [^{3}H] thymidine can be separated from native [^{32}P] T7 DNA (32S) in the sucrose gradient sedimentation pattern. When [^{32}P] T7 DNA was taken up by GSHE cells during their incorporation of [^{3}H] thymidine into the hamster DNA, less than 4% of the [^{32}P] T7 DNA

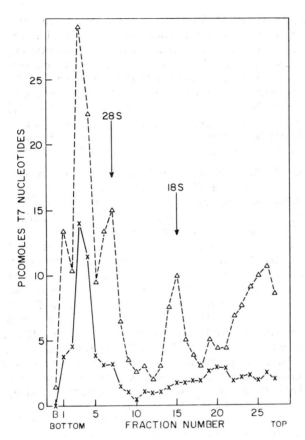

FIG. 5. Sedimentation analysis of intracellular T7 DNA isotopes. [^{3}H]T7 phage (48.7 μg DNA) and [^{32}P]T7 phage (79.5 μg DNA) were simultaneously incubated with 2.3×10^5 GSHE cells according to the procedure outlined in the Methods. Cells were cultivated for 30 hr in the presence of 67 nmoles thymidine/ml. At termination of cell growth, the monolayer was treated with DNase (see Methods). By 30 hr of cell growth, the cell population had increased to 6.6×10^5 cells. Cell lysates were analyzed by sedimentation (see Fig. 3). Specific activities of ^{32}P and [^{3}H]T7 DNA were adjusted to represent the total amount of T7 DNA present in the culture; X—X, [^{3}H]T7 DNA Δ---Δ [^{32}P]T7 DNA. 43.5 pmoles [^{3}H]T7 DNA nucleotide and 231.1 pmoles ^{32}P T7 DNA nucleotide became resistant to release from cells by DNase in this cell culture.

sedimented with GSHE [^{3}H]DNA, which was found at the bottom of the centrifuge tube (Fig. 4). This result suggested that the ^{32}P from T7 DNA was not reutilized by the GSHE cells for synthesis of the hamster DNA. Then, the major peak in the sedimentation profile labeled by ^{32}P was tested for homology to T7 DNA by the hybridization technique (13). In this experiment the authentic T7 DNA was immobilized onto the nitrocellulose filters (13). With the control [^{32}P] T7 DNA, 76% was hybridized, while under the same conditions only 26% of the ^{32}P isolated from this sedimentation peak was hybridized. This result indicates that only a portion of [^{32}P] T7 DNA taken up by the cell still has the original nucleotide sequence of the viral genome, while a major portion of the [^{32}P] T7 DNA was degraded and probably reutilized for the synthesis of RNA.

The fate of T7 DNA within the cell was better shown in the sedimentation study presented in Fig. 5. In this experiment a mixture of two T7 phage preparations, the DNA in one labeled with ^{32}P and the other with [^{3}H] thymine, was incubated with the GSHE cells for 30 hr together with thymidine (6.8×10^{-5} M) added in the medium. After deproteinization, the ^{32}P-containing nucleic acid in the cells sedimented in five separate peaks, two of which sedimented with S values of 28S and 18S as did the ribosomal RNA, while the major peak sedimented with an S value of 32S as did the native T7 DNA. On the other hand, the [^{3}H] T7 DNA was found to sediment mainly with 32S. The difference in the fate of [^{3}H] T7 DNA and the [^{32}P] T7 DNA within the hamster cells clearly is due to the difference in the reutilization of the degradation products of T7 DNA. While the reutilization of the [^{3}H] thymidine-containing products was suppressed by the addition of 6.8×10^{-5} M nonradioactive thymidine in the cell culture, the reutilization of [^{32}P] PO$_4$-containing products was not suppressed by the 9×10^{-4} M phosphate present in the medium. This observation suggests that the degradation of T7 DNA and the reutilization of the ^{32}P phosphate product may be compartmentalized within the cell and kept away from the pool of inorganic phosphate available in the medium. The presence of T7 DNA (32S) labeled with [^{3}H] thymidine or ^{32}P as a major peak in the sedimentation profile indicates that substantial quantities of T7 DNA, when supplied as intact phages, can be transported into the cell without fragmentation.

When the GSHE cells were incubated with the deproteinized [^{3}H] T7 DNA instead of the intact phage, the intracellular [^{3}H] T7 DNA which was not released from the cells by DNase treatment was found to be highly fragmented as shown in Fig. 6. This fragmentation can be due to either the action of serum nuclease, the process of uptake and intracellular nuclease, or the action of added DNase that might enter the cells. Reutilization of [^{3}H] thymine containing degradation products in this experiment had been suppressed by the addition of thymidine (6.8×10^{-5} M) in the culture. This suppression is indicated

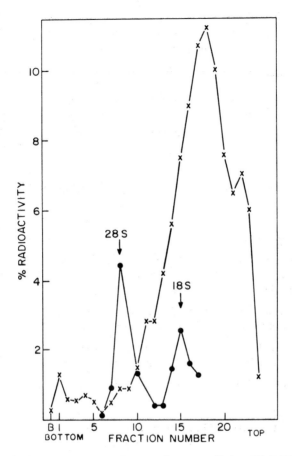

FIG. 6. Sedimentation analysis of intracellular T7 DNA. Twenty-five micrograms [³H]T7 DNA was incubated with 1.5 × 10⁵ cells according to the procedure outlined in the Methods. Cells were cultivated 24 hr in the presence of 67 nmoles thymidine/1 ml. At termination of cell growth the monolayer was treated with DNase (see Methods). By 24 hr of cell growth, the cell population had increased to 4.8 × 10⁵ cells. Cell lysates were analyzed by sedimentation (see Fig. 3); x—x, [³H]T7 DNA; •—•, [³²P]ribosomal RNA marker.

by the absence of a large incorporation of [³H]thymidine into the hamster DNA sedimented at the bottom (Fig. 6).

TABLE 2

Amount of T7 DNA Associated with Hamster Embryo Cells
after DNase Treatment

Infecting agent[a]	Hours of incubation	Final cell number	T7 DNA resistant to DNase, pmoles	T7 genome[d] equivalents/ hamster cell
[^{3}H] T7[b] DNA	26	6.2×10^5	109.8	1426
[^{3}H] T7[c] phage	30	6.6×10^5	112.8	1367

[a] Sixty-seven nanomoles thymidine/1 ml was present during the entire incubation of cells with T7 DNA or phage; [^{3}H] T7 DNA specific activity was 48,498 cpm/nmole.

[b] [^{3}H] T7 DNA, 20 µg, was incubated with 2.2×10^5 GSHE cells; at 26 hr of incubation the cell number increased to 6.2×10^5 cells.

[c] [^{3}H] T7 phage, 128 µg DNA, was incubated with 2.3×10^5 GSHE cells; at 30 hr of incubation the cell number increased to 6.6×10^5 cells.

[d] Molecular weight of the T7 genome is 2.5×10^7 daltons DNA.

Quantitative Measurement of Uptake of T7 DNA by Hamster Cells

Table 2 summarizes an experiment in which the amount of [^{3}H] T7 DNA taken up by the hamster cells has been quantitatively measured. In this experiment, the T7 DNA was supplied either as intact phage or as deproteinized DNA together with 6.7×10^{-5} M of thymidine; the criterion for uptake was based on the continuous attachment to the cell even after DNase treatment. In general, cells in the mass cultures under the present conditions took up about 1200-1500 T7 genomes per cell during one to two cell generations.

Fate of T7 DNA in GSHE Cells after Long-Term Culture

It is of fundamental importance to know whether the T7 DNA can replicate inside the GSHE cells after long-term culture. This information can be obtained through quantitative measurements of the copies of T7 DNA existing inside the cells over many generations and the multiplication factors of the cells during this period.

Reassociation kinetic analysis of DNA extracted from cells transformed to neoplasia with oncogenic viruses has proven to be a highly sensitive and reliable technique for quantitative and qualitative determination of persistence of viral genes in mammalian cells (23, 24). This technique has been used in this study to determine the persistence of T7 DNA within GSHE cells and the extent to which T7 DNA is replicated over many generations of cell growth.

The protocol for this experiment required three stages: (a) incubation of T7 DNA (or phage) with GSHE cells and subsequent cultivation of the cells in continuous stocks; (b) extraction of total DNA from cells taken at various times from these continuous stocks; and (c) denaturation and reassociation of a known concentration of $[^{32}P]$ T7 DNA "probe" in the presence of DNA from GSHE cells. An increase in the rate of reassociation of $[^{32}P]$ T7 DNA in the presence of these DNA extracts [assayed by hydroxyapatite chromatography (22)] would indicate the presence of T7 DNA sequences in that extract.

Figure 7 depicts log cot plots of a typical reassociation kinetic experiment that demonstrates the presence of T7 DNA sequences in GSHE cells cultivated for 36 days after exposure to T7 DNA phage. These cells had been subcultured seven times at a 10:1 split ratio. Between passages one and seven (33 days), cells had gone through 21 average cell generations and progeny had increased by 8×10^5-fold. Sheared and denatured DNA extracted from cells initially exposed to either T7 DNA or T7 phage increased the rate of reassociation of the $[^{32}P]$ T7 DNA probe 8- to 16-fold, indicating the presence of T7 DNA base sequence in the DNA from these GSHE cell extracts. DNA extracted from control cells, which were never incubated with T7 DNA or phage, did not alter the kinetics of reassociation of the $[^{32}P]$ T7 DNA probe from that observed in the absence of GSHE DNA.

Table 3 summarizes results obtained from a series of T7 DNA reassociation kinetic analyses of GSHE DNA at various times after initial exposure of the cells to T7 DNA. In every reassociation kinetic analysis, $[^{32}P]$ T7 DNA was reassociated in the presence of DNA extracted from control GSHE cells grown simultaneously but not incubated with T7 DNA. As indicated in Fig. 7, the cot 1/2 value in these controls was routinely found to be 2.3×10^{-3} (68 °C and 0.72 M phosphate), nearly identical to that of $[^{32}P]$ T7 DNA reassociated in the absence of GSHE DNA. That control GSHE DNA had no effect on the reassociation kinetics of T7 DNA confirmed, as expected, that no DNA with sequence homology to T7 DNA is present in normal hamster cells. GSHE cells that were exposed to T7 DNA or to T7 phage contained between 220 and 580 T7 genome equivalents at the end of three days. Most of the

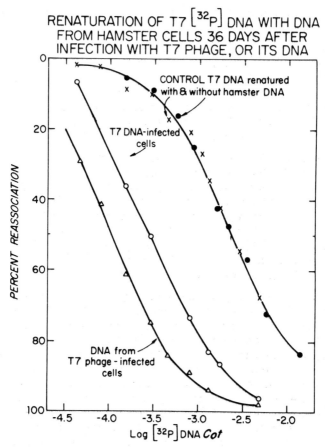

FIG. 7. Reassociation of [^{32}P] T7 DNA with DNA from GSHE cells
36 days after "infection" with T7 phage or T7 DNA. Six falcon flasks
(75 cm^2) containing 4×10^6 GSHE cells in passage 4 were pretreated
with 20 μg DEAE-D/ml (see Methods). Duplicate flasks were divided
into three sets: (a) control cells not exposed to T7 DNA or phage;
(b) cells incubated with deproteinized T7 DNA (165 μg); (c) cells incubated with T7 phage (350 μg DNA). Cultures were incubated in medium
without serum, 1 hr after which the FCS was adjusted to 10%. At 3 hr
medium was removed and replaced with fresh medium containing serum,
thereby removing T7 phage or DNA that had not become associated with
cells in the monolayer. These cell stocks were then cultured continuously making 10:1 splits when cells reached confluency: confluent
monolayers were trypsinized, 10% of the cell population reseeded in
flasks, and 90% of the cell population collected by centrifugation and
extracted for DNA. In this manner cells were collected from seven

passages by 36 days during which time cells doubled an average of 24 times. Total GSHE cell DNA was extracted from these stocks by lysis and solubilization of the lysate in 8 M urea, 1% SDS, 1 M NaClO$_4$, 0.01 M Tris-HCl pH 7.9, and 0.001 M EDTA. Total cellular DNA was prepared for reassociation studies by sonication of the lysate, extraction with chloroform-octanol (95:5), alkaline hydrolysis in 0.2 M NaOH, reextraction with organic solvents, and precipitation. The DNA extract was then dissolved in 0.4% SDS and heated in boiling water bath (5 min) prior to adjustment to 4 ml of 0.72 M sodium phosphate (pH 7.0) and 0.4% SDS, and initiation of the renaturation process at 68 °C. The effect of the GSHE cellular DNA from cells 36 days after infection was measured on the reassociation kinetics of 3.82×10^{-8} M [^{32}P] T7 DNA (nucleotide) in 4 ml. The probe [^{32}P] T7 DNA and GSHE DNA had been sheared to an average length of 700 nucleotides. The extent of reassociation at 68 ° and 0.72 M phosphate and 0.4% SDS was measured by hydroxyapatite chromatography (22). The percent of [^{32}P] T7 DNA reassociation is plotted versus the logarithm of cot (molarity [^{32}P] T7 DNA × seconds of reassociation): ●——●, [^{32}P] T7 DNA without added GSHE DNA; ×——×, [^{32}P] T7 DNA with DNA from 3.74×10^7 control GSHE cells not incubated with T7 DNA; o——o, [^{32}P] T7 DNA with DNA from 4.22×10^7 T7 DNA-incubated GSHE cells; ▵——▵, [^{32}P] T7 DNA with DNA from 3.29×10^7 T7 phage-incubated GSHE cells.

Calculation of the average number genome equivalents per cell from the reassociation kinetic data: The control cot 1/2 value, 2.29×10^{-3}, was divided by the time at which 50% reassociation took place to obtain the molarity of T7 DNA in the renaturing solution; the molarity of the [^{32}P] T7 DNA probe was subtracted from the calculated molarity of T7 DNA; from the adjusted molarity of T7 DNA, the number of genome equivalents T7 DNA in 4 ml renaturing solution (or the extract) was calculated using 2.5×10^7 daltons as the molecular weight of the T7 genome; the number of molecular equivalents of the T7 genome in the extract was divided by the number of GSHE cells extracted in preparation of the DNA extract to determine the average number of T7 genome equivalents per cell. It was assumed that 100% of the total GSHE cell DNA was recovered during extraction since recovery of [^{3}H] GSHE cell DNA by this same procedure was > 95%.

TABLE 3

Bacteriophage T7 DNA in Syrian Hamster Embryo Cells
as Determined by Reassociation Kinetics

Infecting agent	Days after infection	Cell generations	Multiplication	T7 genome equivalents/ hamster cell
None (control)	3	4	1	0
	7	7	9	0
	10	10	50	0
	15	14	1,120	0
	36	24	782,000	0
T7 DNA	3	4	1	576
	7	7	8	62
	10	10	59	18
	15	15	2,200	63
	36	24	839,000	182
T7 bacterio-phage	3	4	1	223
	7	7	9	80
	10	10	63	29
	15	14	1,220	97
	36	24	786,000	682

cell-bound DNA was believed to be intracellular because it remained associated with cells after trypsinization and centrifugation of the cells. Replating of these cells and analysis of later passages showed that after seven and 10 generations of cell growth, copies of intracellular T7 DNA dissipated from both "infected" cell stocks to 18-29 T7 genome equivalents per cell. However, this loss of cellular T7 DNA was not at a rate that would be expected from the serial dilution of T7 DNA during cell division without replication of viral genome. Between 10 and 24 cell generations, a dramatic increase in the number of copies of T7 DNA per cell was observed in both "infected" cell stocks. An increase from 29 to 682 T7 genome equivalents in "phage infected" cells and from 18 to 186 T7 genome equivalents in "DNA infected" cells occurred during the 14 cell generations. The explanation for this apparent increase of T7 DNA in these cells is as yet undetermined. Assays for bacterial of micoplasma contamination have repeatedly proved negative. Two other explanations that are presently being explored are the following: (a) T7 DNA conserved in GSHE cells is

replicated more often than GSHE chromosomal DNA, perhaps through
the expression of its own T7 replicase; and (b) a select population of
GSHE cells that conserve and replicate T7 DNA eventually outgrow
other cells in the mass culture.

DISCUSSION

These studies indicate that mammalian cells, when appropriately
treated, can take up extraordinarily large quantities of DNA offered
either in isolated form or as bacterial virus particles. Much of what
is taken in is degraded and reutilized by the cells. However, a significant amount of T7 DNA is conserved within the cell in an apparently
unaltered form even after 24 generations. After ten days, the replication of intracellular T7 DNA was detected resulting not only in persistence but in a dramatic increase in the average cell content of T7 DNA
during the next 14 cell generations (26 days). Methods are available
to determine the intracellular fate of heterologous genomes, their
genetic expression, their interaction with chromosomes, and whether
they will exert a physiologic or genetic effect on their foreign host.
Reports of the functional acquisition of new genetic activities following
the exposure of cultured cells to DNA from appropriate sources lead to
the expectation that improved methods for study of cellular gene activity will be developed (4, 5, 7, 14-16). A preliminary study by immunofluorescence technique suggested the presence of T7 viral antigens in
a significant number of GSHE cells from a culture. This culture had
taken up naked T7 DNA in a manner described in this paper and had
since grown continuously for four months with 20 passages. Such T7
viral antigens were not found in the control cells (unpublished results).

It has been reported that the infection of human galactosemic cells
with bacteriophage (or its DNA), which carries the gene for galactose
phosphate uridyltransferase, leads to the restoration of the enzyme
activity (14) and persistent synthesis of specified RNA (15). Other
demonstrations of the ability of the genes of one species to function
in the cells (or cell-free system) of another have also appeared in the
literature (17-19). It is now feasible to insert new genetic activity (20),
or carcinogenic agents (21), into easily available specimens of DNA.
The characteristic property of mammalian cells to take up DNA encour-
ages the hope that studies employing these techniques, taken together,
may provide a further understanding of the role that DNA plays in
oncogenesis.

SUMMARY

Syrian hamster embryo cells in tissue culture were pretreated with diethylaminoethyl-dextran and were exposed either to bacteriophage T7 or to the DNA isolated therefrom at a multiplicity of about $10^{5.5-6}$ per cell. In 3 hr, 10^5 phage genome equivalents were bound per cell regardless of whether DNA or virus was used. Most of the DNA (or virus) that was bound after short incubation was released from cells by added DNase; on longer incubation 30-50% became resistant to DNase. As indicated by [^{3}H] autoradiography, all the extracellular T7 DNA was removed by DNase treatment, and 99% of the intracellular viral isotope was localized in the nuclei. After four generations of cell growth (71 hr), the intracellular viral isotopes were shown to have a high molecular weight by sedimentation study and to contain the original viral DNA sequence by DNA hybridization techniques. The amount of intracellular T7 genome conserved was estimated to be at 1500 viral equivalents per cell. During this same period a considerable amount of T7 DNA taken up by the cell was degraded and reutilized for synthesis of macromolecules. Reassociation kinetic analysis showed that DNA from continuous stocks of cells that had taken up T7 DNA contained sequences homologous to the entire T7 genome 24 generations or 36 days later. The amount of T7 DNA present in these cells indicated that efficient replication of this foreign DNA had taken place.

ACKNOWLEDGMENT

This work was supported in part by Atomic Energy Commission Contract AT(11-1)-3280 and by the National Institutes of Health Grant No. GM-16066-05 awarded to The Johns Hopkins University, and in part by the National Cancer Institute Grant CA08748, Atomic Energy Commission Contract AT(30-1)910, and the American Cancer Society Grant IC-20M awarded to the Sloan-Kettering Institute for Cancer Research. JCL is a postdoctoral fellow of the National Cancer Institute.

REFERENCES

1. K. Habel, Cancer Res., 28, 1825 (1968).
2. R. Dulbecco, Science, 166, 962 (1969).
3. A. Bendich, E. Borenfreund, Y. Honda, and M. Steinglass, Arch. Environ. Health, 19, 157 (1969).

4. E. Borenfreund, Y. Honda, M. Steinglass, and A. Bendich, J. Exptl. Med., 132, 1071 (1970).
5. M. Hill and J. Hillova, Nature New Biol., 237, 35 (1972).
6. P. M. Bhargava and G. Shanmugam, Progr. Nucl. Acid Res. Mol. Biol., 11, 103 (1971).
7. L. G. H. Ledoux (ed.), Informative Molecules in Biological Systems, American Elsevier, New York, 1971.
8. P. Englund, J. Mol. Biol., 66, 209 (1972).
9. L. Grossman in Methods in Enzymology, Vol. 12A (L. Grossman and K. Moldave, eds.), Academic, New York, 1967, p. 700.
10. W. F. Studier, Science, 176, 367 (1972).
11. W. F. Studier, J. Mol. Biol., 11, 373 (1965).
12. J. H. McCutchan and J. S. Pagano, J. Nat. Cancer Inst., 41, 351 (1968).
13. S. Gillespie and D. Gillespie, Biochem. J., 124, 481 (1971).
14. C. R. Merril, M. R. Geier, and J. C. Petricciani, Nature New Biol., 233, 398 (1971).
15. M. R. Geier and C. R. Merril, Virology, 47, 638 (1972).
16. E. Ottolenghi-Nightingale, Proc. Nat. Acad. Sci., 64, 184 (1969).
17. B. Ephrussi, "Interspecific Somatic Hybrids, " in Phenotypic Expression in Vitro, vol. 2, The Williams & Wilkins Co., Baltimore, 1967, p. 40.
18. C. D. Lane, G. Marbaix, and J. B. Gurdon, J. Mol. Biol., 61, 73 (1971).
19. H. Aviv, I. Boime, B. Loyd, and P. Leder, Science, 178, 1293 (1972).
20. D. A. Jackson, R. H. Symons, and P. Berg, Proc. Nat. Acad. Sci., 69, 2904 (1972).
21. V. M. Maher, S. A. Lesko, Jr., P. A. Straat, and P. O. P. Ts'o, J. Bacteriol., 108, 202 (1971).
22. D. E. Kohne and R. J. Britten in Procedures in Nucleic Acid Research (G. L. Cantoni and D. R. Davies, eds.), Harper and Row, New York, 1971, Vol. 2, p. 500.
23. D. D. Gelb, D. E. Kohne, and M. A. Martin, J. Mol. Biol., 57, 129 (1971).
24. U. Pettersson and J. Sambrook, J. Mol. Biol., 73, 125 (1973).

Chapter 36

CONDITIONAL TRANSFORMATION OF CELLS INFECTED WITH A MUTANT OF ROUS SARCOMA VIRUS

John P. Bader

Chemistry Branch
National Cancer Institute
Bethesda, Maryland

INTRODUCTION

Perhaps the central issue in carcinogenesis today is the nature of the basic biochemical defect responsible for the conversion of a functional responsible cell to a malignant irresponsible form. If this issue is discussed with a biochemist of any single specialty, one hears a convincing argument, based on explicit experimental data, that a defect in his molecule of interest could result in cancer. After several discussions with biochemists of differing specialties, each biochemist in turn expressing a different conviction, one cannot help but conclude that either (a) a functional change in any one of many specific cellular molecules can result in a malignant conversion, or (b) the biochemists strain the relevance of their molecules to obtain support for extension of their experiments.

The issue, as presented, does not deal with the genetic origin of the defect, whether due to a mutation, gene activity, gene amplification, etc. Nonetheless, one might consider that if a carcinogen induces mutations in a certain cellular gene at an efficiency of 10^{-5} (not an unusual mutagenic efficiency) and the carcinogen induces malignant transformation in the same cells at an efficiency of 10^{-2} (an efficiency similar to that described in this volume by Dr. DiPaolo) (1), then a mutation in the specific gene cannot be the only mutation leading to malignancy, and mutations in any one of 1000 similar genes could lead to the malignant state.

One popular thesis holds that no single genetic event leads to malignancy, but that tumor cells arise after accumulating many genetic changes requiring several to many cellular generations. This process seems unlikely, at least in some cases, in view of the rapidity of transformation noted with certain viruses (2, 3), and the observation that cells infected with Rous sarcoma virus can become transformed even in the absence of an intervening cellular division (3).

Much of the difficulty in resolving the nature of a basic biochemical defect stems from the multiplicity of metabolic changes accompanying the change to malignancy. There is hardly an exception to the proposition that if an investigator looks for a biochemical difference between tumor cells and their nonmalignant counterparts, he will find it. Whether the difference is the cause of the malignancy, or a result of it, is another matter. And, in most cases, the attempt to resolve the cause-effect relationship would be, and has been, futile.

TEMPERATURE-DEPENDENT TRANSFORMATION OF CELLS

Our approach to defining the basic biochemical defect responsible for malignancy is to attempt to describe the basic defect in one reproducible system, and then see if the same defect is basic to other malignancies. The Bryan strain of Rous sarcoma virus (RSV-BH) induces a characteristic morphologic change that accompanies a change to malignancy in infected cells. A mutant, called RSV-BH-Ta, has been isolated that is capable of full cycles of reproduction in chick embryo cells at temperatures between 36° and 41° (5, 6). However, cells infected by this mutant become transformed at 36°, but at 41° appear morphologically normal (Fig. 1). When cultures of infected cells grown at 41° are shifted to 36° the transformed phenotype appears, and shifting transformed cells from 36° to 41° results in disappearance of the transformed morphology. Cultures of infected cells can be redistributed many times, allowing more than 50 generations, and changes in temperature still effect a change in morphology.

When RSV-BH-Ta infected cells were grown at 41° and shifted to 36°, morphologic changes were observed within 10 min. These changes consisted of vacuolization in the perinuclear region of the cytoplasm detectable by phase contrast microscopy. The number of cells becoming vacuolated, and the numbers of vacuoles per cell, increased with time, accompanied by a general alteration in cell shape to a more rounded form. Disappearance of vacuoles and the return to elongated fibroblasts occurred when transformed cells were shifted from 36° to 41°, but this reversal required several hours, in some instances more than a day.

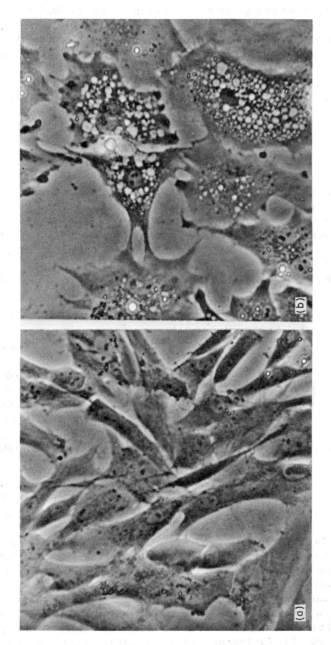

FIG. 1. (a) Chick embryo cells infected with the mutant of Rous sarcoma virus, RSV-BH-Ta, and grown at 41°. (b) A similar culture was incubated for 20 hr at 36°. Note the vacuolization and change in cell shape in cells incubated at 36°.

Requirements for macromolecular synthesis in the transformation process were examined using cytosine arabinoside to inhibit DNA synthesis, actinomycin D to inhibit RNA synthesis, and either cycloheximide or puromycin to inhibit protein synthesis. None of these compounds had any effect on the change in morphology after shifting cells from 41° to 36°. These results demonstrate that all macromolecular requirements up through protein synthesis had been fulfilled at 41° and suggest that the morphologic change at 36° is due to a temperature-sensitive enzyme or structural protein.

BIOCHEMICAL CHANGES IN TRANSFORMED CELLS

We then examined some biochemical alterations known to occur in transformed cells. A likely candidate for the basic biochemical defect was hyaluronic acid or a substance involved in its metabolism. Rous sarcomas had been recognized as high hyaluronate producers (7) for many years (many other malignancies had not been so recognized, and when we examined a few, they were not), and there was sufficient documentation and speculation in the literature to implicate hyaluronic acid in carcinogenesis.

Indeed, RSV-BH-Ta infected cells produced 3 to 10 times as much hyaluronate at 36° as they did at 41°, which favorably compared with amounts of hyaluronate produced by noninfected cells and the larger amounts by cells transformed by the wild type, RSV-BH. However, when RSV-BH-Ta infected cells were shifted from 41° to 36°, no increase in hyaluronate synthesis was found if actinomycin D or cycloheximide were included in the medium. Therefore, increased hyaluronate synthesis was dependent upon transcription of new RNA and synthesis of new protein, events that were not required for the morphologic change. It was clear that increased hyaluronate synthesis was not responsible for the morphologic change.

Another biochemical parameter that increases with transformation is hexose uptake (8, 9), and RSV-BH-Ta infected cells grown at 36° behave like wild type-transformed cells with higher rates of hexose (e. g., glucose, glucosamine, deoxyglucose) incorporation than noninfected cells or RSV-BH-Ta cells grown at 41°. These latter cells responded to a shift to 36° after 2 to 3 hr by slowly increasing the rate of hexose uptake over the next several hours. But, as in the case of hyaluronate, exposure of the cells to actinomycin D or cycloheximide during this time prevented the increased capacity to incorporate hexose. RNA synthesis and protein synthesis are required and morphologic transformation can be attributed neither to the factors directly responsible for increased hexose uptake, nor to the increased availability of glucose resulting from increased uptake.

ROLE OF CYCLIC ADENOSINE-3'5'-MONOPHOSPHATE

Studies on cyclic adenosine-3', 5'-monophosphate (cAMP) showed that RSV-BH-transformed cells contained lower levels of this nucleotide than noninfected cells, and that RSV-BH-Ta cells contained lower levels of cAMP at 36° than at 40.5° (10). Quantitation of shift-down experiments, and the effects of antimetabolites on cAMP levels are in progress. An interesting corollary is the effect of exogenous dibutyryl cAMP and theophylline, an inhibitor of phosphodiesterase, on morphologic transformation. This combination inhibited the morphologic change occurring after shifting cells from 41° to 36°, but (a) had no effect on the increase in rate of hexose uptake and (b) stimulated hyaluronate production. These results show that increased hexose uptake and increased hyaluronate production are not induced merely by the morphologic change, and that the biochemical changes may be independent of the morphologic change.

EFFECTS OF pH

The change to transformed phenotype upon shifting cells from 41° to 36° also can be prevented by low pH. At levels below 6.8 no change is detectable, and above pH 7.6 no increase in rate or extent of change is noted. Intermediate pH levels bring increasing morphologic change with increasing pH.

The induction of increased hexose uptake at 37° is not prevented by low pH, although levels of uptake at pH 6.6 do not attain those in cultures at pH 7.8. In contrast, induction of increased hyaluronate synthesis is prevented by low pH. So, while dissociation of biochemical and morphologic changes are apparent in pH experiments also, the dissociation is not as complete as in experiments using dibutyryl cAMP and theophylline.

PERSPECTIVES

The experiments outlined in this discussion show that there are temperature-dependent events occurring in cells infected with the mutant sarcoma virus that no longer depend on RNA or protein synthesis, and which are independent of at least two biochemical changes that occur regularly in transformed cells. It is tempting to consider that the transformed morphology is caused by structural changes in the cell membrane, perhaps mediated by a temperature-sensitive enzyme, and influenced by cAMP. The change in cell shape is consistent with a membrane alteration, and vacuolization can be explained in this context.

It is now feasible to examine changes in the cell membrane, or other cellular organelles for that matter, in the absence of secondary metabolic occurrences induced at transcriptional or translational levels. We feel that the likelihood of attaining a biochemical definition of events leading to malignancy are enhanced by elimination of the secondary changes that under other circumstances make the problem unresolvable.

REFERENCES

1. J. DiPaolo, Quantitative aspects of in vitro chemical carcinogenesis, 1972, unpublished.
2. H. Hanafusa, Rapid transformation of cells by Rous sarcoma virus, Proc. Nat. Acad. Sci., 63, 318 (1972).
3. J. P. Bader and A. V. Bader, Evidence for a DNA replicative genome for RNA-containing tumor viruses, Proc. Nat. Acad. Sci., 67, 843 (1970).
4. J. P. Bader, Metabolic requirements for infection by Rous sarcoma virus. IV. Virus reproduction and cellular transformation without cellular divisions, Virology, 48 494 (1972).
5. J. P. Bader, Induction of mutations in an RNA tumor virus by an analogue of a DNA precursor, Nature New Biol., 234, 11 (1971).
6. J. P. Bader, Temperature-dependent transformation of cells infected with a mutant of Bryan Rous sarcoma virus, J. Virol., 10, 267 (1972).
7. E. A. Kabat, A polysaccharide in tumors due to a virus of leucosis and sarcoma of fowls, J. Biol. Chem., 130, 143 (1939).
8. T. L. Steck, S. Kaufman, and J. P. Bader, Glycolysis in chick embryo cell cultures transformed by Rous sarcoma virus, Cancer Res., 28, 1611 (1968).
9. M. Hatanaka, R. J. Huebner, and R. V. Gilden: Alterations in the characteristics of sugar uptake by mouse cells transformed by murine sarcoma viruses, J. Nat. Cancer Inst., 43, 1091 (1969).
10. J. Otten, J. P. Bader, G. J. Johnson, and I. Pastan, A mutation in a Rous sarcoma virus gene that controls adenosine 3'5'-monophosphate levels and transformation, J. Biol. Chem., 247, 1632 (1972).

VII

CANCER IMMUNOLOGY AND IMMUNOTHERAPY

Chapter 37

RELATIONSHIP OF SIALIC ACID TO THE EXPRESSION OF FETAL ANTIGENS IN THE DEVELOPING HAMSTER FETUS

W. H. Hannon, N. G. Anderson, and J. H. Coggin, Jr.

The Molecular Anatomy (MAN) Program
Oak Ridge National Laboratory
Oak Ridge, Tennessee
and
The University of Tennessee
Department of Microbiology
Knoxville, Tennessee

INTRODUCTION

One hypothesis for the cancerous properties of transformed cells is that a partial or complete retrogression of the normal adult cell is induced by the carcinogen, resulting in a reversion of critical processes to an embryonic state (2, 17, 27). Extensive immunochemical research is being performed to characterize and to delineate the possible differences among antigens found in the embryonic state and those expressed in various cancerous and noncancerous conditions. Since cancer-associated embryonic antigens show promise of diagnostic and monitoring values, characterization of their phase-specific expression and chemical composition is of immediate concern.

The alterations in the deposition of sialic acid in glycoprotein and glycolipid components of mammalian cell membranes are increasingly related to the modification of membranes that occur with the transformation of cells. Ohta et al. (25) reported that malignant cells contained lower levels of sialic acid than "normal" cells. Spontaneous and virally transformed hamster fibroblast cells have been shown to contain glycolipids and glycoproteins with incomplete carbohydrate chains (20). Levels of sialic acid in SV40 or polyoma virus transformed mouse cell lines are reduced; this reduction was most pronounced in the plasma membrane and endoplasmic reticulum (19, 31). Additionally, the removal of sialic acid from cellular surfaces by enzymic treatment has been reported to produce an uncovering of transplantation antigens (12), to alter the response of tumor cells to phytoagglutinins used to monitor changes in surface membranes (6), and to reduce the rate of cellular adhesion (21). The concentration of sialic acid has been shown also to decrease with the morphologic progression of tumors (28).

Previous reports from our laboratory have indicated that membrane antigens that are cross-reactive with the SV40-induced membrane antigens of tumor cells are expressed during fetal development of the hamster (8, 9). The transient nature of the expression of the fetal antigens suggested that a "masking" of antigens might occur during embryogenesis. We investigated the possibility that the deposition of sialic acid in fetal cells may be responsible for the alterations in the antigenicity of these cells.

MATERIALS AND METHODS

Cell Lines and Tissue Sources

A cell line [(F5-1)(15)] derived from an SV40-induced tumor produced in the LVG/LAK Syrian golden hamsters (Lakeview Hamster Colony, Newfield, N. J.) was grown in Bellco roller bottles (100-ml cultures seeded at 4×10^7 cells) in medium 199 containing 10% inactivated calf serum at 37°. Cells were studied between tissue culture passages 52 and 55. When a dense, confluent cellular layer was achieved, the cells were harvested by scraping with a rubber-tipped spatula, resuspended in Hank's balanced salt solution (HBSS), pelleted by centrifugation, and washed twice with HBSS. The pellets of cells were stored at −20°.

Pregnant animals were obtained from trial meetings conducted under observation. Fetuses were harvested from the LVG/LAK hamster 3 hr prior to days 10, 11, 12, 14, and 15 of gestation. The fetuses of each age were rinsed several times with HBSS and stored at −20°. Neonatal and two-day suckling hamsters were collected and frozen.

Fibrosarcomas were induced by injection of F5-1 cells (10^4 cells/0. 5 ml) into adults and by the injection of SV40 into neonatal hamsters (2×10^5 TCID$_{50}$). The tumors were removed when they were 2 cm in size. Pooled tumors were rinsed several times in HBSS and stored at −20°.

PREPARATION AND FRACTIONATION OF HOMOGENATES

The cellular pellets, hamster fetuses, or tumors were suspended in a buffered salt solution (3 ml/g net weight) containing 1 mM potassium phosphate buffer, pH 7.4, 160 mM NaCl, 1 mM $MgSO_4$, 6.7 mM KCl, and 1 mM $CaCl_2$. A motorized stirrer fitted with a slip chuck for glass rods was employed to drive the glass pestle for the homogenization of the chilled tissues to a fine suspension. The homogenate was centrifuged at 600 g for 10 min. The pellet was washed with 2-5 ml of buffered salt solution (BSS) and resedimented by centrifugation. The pellet was resuspended in 5 ml of BSS and designated the membrane fraction. The pooled supernatant solutions combined with the wash solutions were centrifuged at 20,000 g for 15 min. The pellet, designated mitochondrial fraction, was washed with 2-5 ml of BSS, resedimented and resuspended in 2.5 ml of BSS. The wash solutions were combined with the supernatant solutions and subjected to centrifugation at 100,000 g for 1 hr. The pooled supernatant solution was designated the soluble fraction and the pellet, resuspended in 2.5 ml of BSS, was designated the microsomal fraction. Since no part of the homogenate was discarded in the preparation of the fractions, the complete homogenate is contained within the four fractions. This procedure for the fractionation of homogenates is a modification of the method reported by Grimes (19) and Wu et al. (31). Microscopic examination of the membrane and mitochondrial fractions indicated an absence of intact cells in these fractions. The concentration of protein for the membrane fraction was three- to fourfold greater than the concentration for each of the other fractions. All fractions were stored frozen until determinations for sialic acid were made. The membrane fractions routinely required rehomogenization to break up clumps (DNase insensitive) that possibly resulted from the agglutination of membranous material during the freezing and thawing process.

The purity of the various subcellular components within a fraction and the degree of cross-contamination of these fractions have not yet been established.

Measurement of Sialic Acid

The method described by Warren (29) was employed for the determination of sialic acid. Since this method only detects free sialic acid, a hydrolysis step is necessary for release of bound sialic acid. Aliquots of 0.9 ml of the tissue suspensions were added to 0.1 ml of 1 N H_2SO_4. The tubes were capped and heated in a waterbath for 1 hr at 85°. These conditions have been shown to

produce the maximum release of bound sialic acid (19). After the
tubes had cooled to ambient temperature, the denatured protein was
removed by centrifugation. Aliquots of the supernatant solution were
used in the assays along with solutions of N-acetylneuraminic acid
(crystalline) for determination of standard curves. The absorbance
of the samples was measured at both 532 and 549 nm. The procedure
described by Warren (29) was employed to correct for chromophores
not derived from sialic acid.

Determination of Protein

The procedure of Lowry et al. (23) was used for the assay of
protein and was performed prior to the previously described hydrolysis step. Bovine serum albumin (fraction V) was used for the generation of standard curves.

Tumor Immunity Assays

The SV40 tumor cell line [F5-1 (15)] was derived in the LVG/LAK
hamster strain from tumors induced by injection into neonates with
SV40 and was subsequently cultured in vitro in medium 199 containing 10% heat-inactivated calf serum. The cell line is virus free and
possesses tumor or T antigen, surface or S antigen, cytostatic or C
antigen in the plasma membrane, SV40 tumor-specific transplantation
antigen (TSTA), and fetal or phase-specific antigen (PSA) (1, 3, 8, 9).

The prevention of viral oncogenesis was tested by immunizing
with either tumor cells or fetal tissues of the hamster inactivated by
X irradiation as antigen administered intraperitoneally (5×10^6 viable
cells) between three and six weeks of age to hamsters infected at
birth with 10 $TCID_{50}$ of SV40 in the subscapular space. The SV40-
induced malignant fibrosarcomas characteristically appear 90-200
days after infection at the site of SV40 injection. Irradiated SV40
tumor cells prevent SV40 tumorigenesis (10, 18) and irradiated hamster
fetal cells (9-10 days of gestation) retard tumor development (9)
when used as vaccines in adult hamsters prior to tumor appearance.

Similarly, immunization of normal adult male hamsters with
irradiated SV40 tumor cells or syngeneic 10-day-old fetal cells
prevents tumor development induced by subsequent challenge with
living SV40 tumor cells propagated in vitro (2, 3, 8). Passive transfer
of tumor immunity by syngeneic peritoneal exudate cells (PEC) from
hamsters immunized against SV40 or syngeneic 10-day-old fetal
tissue has been demonstrated (2). In vitro cytotoxicity of the hamster
lymph node cell (LNC) or PEC sensitized against SV40 or irradiated

TABLE 1

Phasing of Fetal Antigens as Demonstrated by Various
Immunologic Tests against SV40 Tumor Cells

Immune reaction	Fetal age, days past coitus							
	9	10	11	12	13	14	15	Birth
Induction of cyto- static antibody[a]	+	+	−	−	−	−	−	−
Induction of cellu- lar-mediated immunity								
in vivo[b]	+	+	−	−	−	−	−	−
in vitro[c]	+	+	−	−	−	−	−	−
Induction of tumor resistance[d]	+	+	−	−	−	−	−	−
Interruption of oncogenesis[e]	+	+	−	−	−	−	−	−

The techniques employed to obtain this data are described in detail in
the references cited below.

[a] By diffusion chambers (1).

[b] By adoptive transfer test (14).

[c] By microcytotoxicity test – colony inhibition (14).

[d] By transplantation immunity (8).

[e] By prevention of SV40 tumor induction in neonatally infected animals
(9).

10-day-old hamster fetal cells against SV40 tumor target cells has
been demonstrated (2), employing the microcytotoxicity technique
described by Brawn (5). Detailed procedures for conducting all the
tests listed above are described in the cited publication.

RESULTS

The expression of a fetal antigen cross-reactive with the SV40-
induced tumor resistance antigen appeared to occur transiently at a
definite time in embryogenesis of the hamster. Coggin et al (8) reported that this antigen was expressed at the 9th day of gestation,

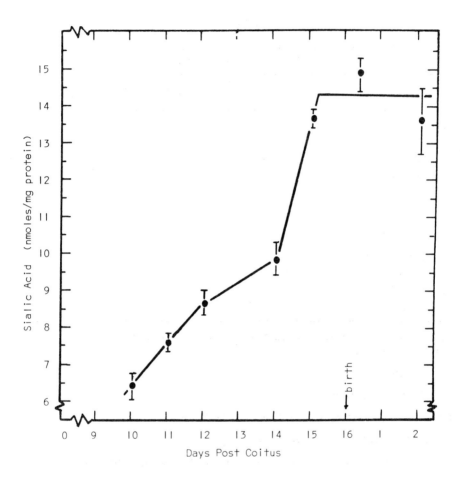

FIG. 1. Concentrations of total sialic acid during the development of the hamster fetus. The data represent mean values for sialic
acid determined on at least two separate homogenates of fetus from
each day examined. The homogenates were assayed in duplicate for
each analysis. The ranges for the mean values are indicated.

whereas with 14-day-old fetal tissue the antigen could not be demonstrated. In Table 1, the abruptness of the "phasing out" of the fetal
antigen is indicated. The expression was shown to occur on the 9th
and 10th days of gestation, while the antigen could not be detected
on the 11th and subsequent days of gestation employing a variety of
tests to measure antitumor reactivity. Since it was not possible to
obtain sufficient material for a vaccine at the 8th days of gestation,
the nature of the phase-specific fetal antigen prior to the 9th days is
not known.

The concentrations of total bound sialic acid in the developing
fetus were examined to ascertain what relation it might have with the
"phasing out" or "masking" of antigens in embryogenesis. Figure 1
illustrates the alterations in the levels of total sialic acid with
development of the fetus. A marked increase occurred from the 10th
day through the 15th day of gestation; the level then remained constant from the 15th day through two days after birth. The initial
increase was gradual and produced a 45% increase in the period from
10 to 14 days, whereas in one day, between the 14th and 15th days,
a 52% increase was evident. The monitoring of levels of sialic acid
was not performed in fetus prior to the 10th day of gestation because
of difficulties in obtaining sufficient fetuses. Free sialic acid was
also examined over these same days of development and the values
represented 1% or less of the total sialic acid. Since the values for
free (unbound) sialic acid were low and detection was at the limit of
the assay, a trend in the levels for free sialic acid could not be
definitely established; however, the concentrations appeared to be
relatively constant.

The homogenates of fetus were separated by fractional centrifugation to establish the extent of the contribution of particular fractions
to the total sialic acid (Fig. 2). The membrane, microsomal, and
soluble fractions contained increasing levels of sialic acid from the
10th day through the 15th day followed by constant levels through
two days after birth. The patterns of change seen in these three
fractions are similar to that for the total sialic acid (Fig. 1). The
concentration of sialic acid in the mitochondrial fraction was constant over the range of gestation examined (Fig. 2), while a four- to
fivefold change is seen in the other three fractions. In all fractions,
the amount of sialic acid appeared to be constant after the 15th day.

The question as to whether the changes in concentrations of sialic
acid observed in Figs. 1 and 2 were representative of the complete
fetus or the result of organogenesis of specific components at particular times in gestation (4) prompted the investigation of the contribution
of blood, liver, and brain to the levels of sialic acid in fetus. The
results in Table 2 for homogenates of 15-day-old fetuses, which were
exsanguinated, hepatectomized and exsanguinated, and decapitated
and exsanguinated revealed essentially the same values for total
sialic acid. Additionally, no difference was found in the levels for
each of the fractions with possible exception of the microsomal
preparation, which indicated a slight elevation with the hepatectomized
and decapitated fetus. These data demonstrated that changes in the
volume of blood, or in the tissue mass of liver and brain, did not
contribute in a major way to the relative content of sialic acid in the
fetus.

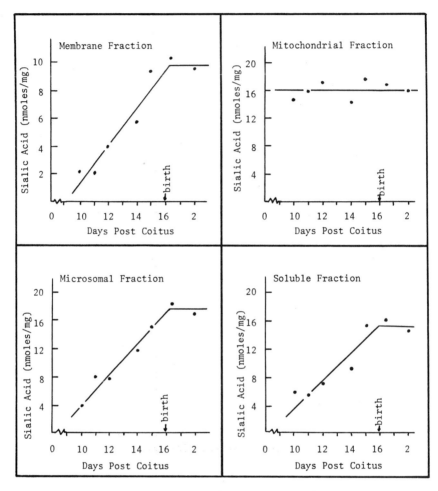

FIG. 2. Concentrations of sialic acid in fractionated preparations from homogenates of hamster fetus. Fractionations were carried
out on at least two homogenates for each day examined. The plotted
data represent the mean values of at least two assays in duplicate
for each of the fractions.

Since the correlation has been suggested in the present study
that tumorigenic "unmasking" and differentiative "masking" of antigens may involve the same processes, the concentrations of sialic
acid were examined for SV40-induced tumor cells to attempt an
evaluation of this implication (Table 3). The total levels of sialic
acid for the SV40-transformed tissues were lower than the total levels

TABLE 2

Influence of Blood, Liver, and Brain on the Concentration
of Sialic Acid in Hamster Fetus

Treatment of 15-day-old fetus	Concentration of sialic acid,[a] nmoles/mg of protein				
	Membrane fraction	Mitochondrial fraction	Microsomal fraction	Soluble fraction	Total[b]
Untreated	9.68 ± 0.26	18.23 ± 0.26	15.82 ± 0.09	15.91 ± 0.52	13.37
Exsanguinated	9.80 ± 1.25	18.15 ± 0.52	14.79 ± 0.69	16.99 ± 0.65	13.89
Exsanguinated and hepatectomized	8.90 ± .43	17.67 ± 0.26	17.42 ± 0.73	16.68 ± 0.04	13.67
Exsanguinated and decapitated	10.10 ± 0.99	16.86 ± 1.29	17.24 ± 0.69	16.90 ± 0.22	13.93

[a] The reported values represent means and ranges for duplicate assays on the fractionated homogenates.

[b] The total represents the average concentration of sialic acid for the complete homogenate.

HANNON, ANDERSON, AND COGGIN

TABLE 3

Levels of Sialic Acid in Homogenates of SV40
Fibrosarcoma and SV40 Cells[a]

| Homogenate | Concentration of sialic acid, nmoles/mg of protein | | | | |
	Membrane fraction	Mitochondrial fraction	Microsomal fraction	Soluble fraction	Total[b]
SV40 fibrosarcoma	7.31 ± 2.10	13.33 ± 2.58	9.89 ± 2.10	6.88 ± 0.86	9.37
Cultured SV40 tumor cells (F5-1)	3.87 ± 0.47	18.92 ± 0.43	8.60 ± 1.29	3.23 ± 0.65	8.64

[a] The data represent mean values for sialic acid determined on at least two separate homogenates of tissue from each source examined. The fractions were assayed in duplicate for each analysis. The ranges for the mean values are indicated.

[b] The total represents the average concentration of sialic acid for the complete homogenate.

found for neonatal and suckling hamsters (Fig. 1). Values for total
sialic acid in the SV40-transformed systems were similar to the values
obtained for the 12-day-old fetus (Fig. 1 and Table 3). Significant
changes appeared to occur in the membrane and soluble fractions of
the SV40 tumor tissue homogenates. The levels of sialic acid for SV40
tumor cells in culture were less than those for SV40 fibrosarcoma in
both of these fractions (Table 3). These data may reflect changes in
the levels of sialic acid that occur possibly with the continuous
passage of the SV40 tumor cells in culture. Cells of at least 50
passages in tissue culture were used. The mitochondrial fractions
yielded concentrations similar to those seen throughout development
(Fig. 2), while the microsomal fractions for both tissues (Table 3)
indicated low levels of sialic acid comparable with those of the 12-
day-old fetus. Note that, in Table 3, the values for sialic acid with
the SV40-induced fibrosarcomas showed large ranges around the
reported mean value.

DISCUSSION

A relationship was observed between the expression of fetal
antigens and the content of bound sialic acid in the developing fetus
of hamsters. The embryonic, fetal, or phase-specific antigen present
in syngeneic hamsters was expressed on the 9th and 10th days of
gestation but not thereafter. The fetal antigen(s) present elicited
both humoral and cell-mediated immune responses in vaccinated
syngeneic male hamsters. Girardi and Reppucci (16) recently reported
that nonimmunogenic fetus from the 14th day of gestation could be
rendered immunogenic following trypsinization to expose fetal antigens. The exact nature of the events that produce this "unmasking"
of antigens is not known. The treatment of cells with trypsin has
been demonstrated to liberate sialylated glycoproteins, in addition
to other proteins from the surface of cells (24, 25). The removal of
sialoglycoproteins by trypsinization could permit the "unmasking" of
fetal antigen determinants in situ, or might cause the formation of
these determinants by conformational rearrangement.

These correlations suggest a role for sialic acid in the matura-
tional traits of the plasma membrane and implicate the deposition of
sialic acid in the "masking" of fetal antigens. The abrupt nature of
the "masking" process in fetal development suggests that a "switching-
on" of specific genes involved in the synthesis and incorporation of
sialic acid may occur at this interval in gestation. The malfunction,
or the "switching-off," of the enzymic system of glycosyltransferase
has been employed to explain the reduction of sialic acid and other
surface changes of transformed cells (11, 13, 19). The reversal or the
"switching-on" of transferases involved in either the production of
glycoprotein chains that serve as substrates for sialyltransferase or

the production of specific sialyltransferases could lead to the "masking" of fetal antigens. However, at the present time, alterations in the glycosyltransferases have not been monitored during the embryogenesis of the hamster.

The levels of sialic acid detected in the membrane, microsomal, and soluble fractions of fetal tissue reflect the same trend of elevating concentrations with increasing age of fetus that was seen for total sialic acid. The uniform levels of sialic acid observed in the mitochondrial fraction may reflect the fact that mitochondria are already differentiated cellular organelles functioning in the germinal cells and the fertilized egg. The values for sialic acid in the fractionated tumor tissue were more variable and possibly reflect a difference in the alterations occurring with viral transformation and those occurring in embryogenesis.

The observed alterations in total sialic acid (Fig. 1) are markedly similar to those reported for cyclic AMP in hamster fetus during gestation (7). A fourfold increase in cyclic AMP in the developing fetus was noted between the 9th and 14th days of gestation. This similarity suggests that cyclic AMP may perform a role in regulating the deposition of sialic acid and, perhaps in an indirect manner, the regulation of cellular antigenicity.

In agreement with the changes reported here for the developing fetus, McQuiddy and Lilien (24) reported that a 50% increase in total sialic acid is evident in the 7- to 14-day period of embryonic development of the chick neural retina. They found that the concentration of sialic acid in the plasma membrane was low for cells of the 7th day, greatly increased with 10th day, and began to level off by the 14th day. These changes in surface sialic acid of embryonic retina cells, although not relating to a known embryonic antigen, do correspond to membrane changes in available binding sites for phytoagglutinins (22).

It is also possible that the total alterations in sialic acid levels we observed in the developing fetus do not reflect the biochemical explanation for the changes in fetal antigenicity; that is, localized decreases or increases in sialic acid could occur and these might not be reflected by the concentration found for the complete subcellular components or cells. Clearly in support of this type of localized alterations Warren et al. (30) demonstrated that a glycoprotein component found in higher concentrations with transformed cells can be converted to a component resembling that found in normal cells by enzymic removal of a sialic acid. Hence, an elevation in sialic acid for a specific cellular component of transformed cells might occur, whereas reductions are found with complete and fractionated homogenates of transformed cells (Table 3 and Ref. 19).

An investigation is presently being pursued into the direct involvement of sialic acid in the expression of fetal antigens. The reversal of the "masking" of fetal antigens will be attempted by enzymic removal of sialic acid from nonimmunogenic fetal cells and by testing of these cells in a transplantation immunity system.

SUMMARY

The immunogenicity of hamster fetal antigens cross-reactive with SV40-induced tumor neoantigen was documented by several methods and antigenicity terminated abruptly at the 11th day of gestation. Deposition of sialic acid was monitored for the developing hamster through fetal, neonatal, and suckling stages. Total bound sialic acid increased from the 10th through the 15th day of gestation. The concentrations in neonatal and suckling hamsters were not different from those of the 15-day-old fetus. Homogenates of fetal, neonatal, and suckling hamster tissue were fractionated by centrifugation. The levels of sialic acid in the membrane, microsomal, and soluble fraction reflected the same trend as observed for total sialic acid, whereas the mitochondrial fraction appeared to remain constant. Similar investigations of sialic acid were carried out for SV40-induced tumor tissue of hamsters. Alterations in concentrations for this tissue were consistent with those seen for fetal tissue. We propose that changes in the concentrations of bound sialic acid are related to the "masking-unmasking" of immunogenic fetal antigens.

ACKNOWLEDGMENTS

The research project was supported by the National Cancer Institute, the National Institute of General Medical Sciences, the National Institute of Allergy and Infectious Diseases, the United States Atomic Energy Commission, and in part, by AEC Contract AT (40-1) 3646.

The Oak Ridge National Laboratory is operated by Union Carbide Corporation Nuclear Division for the United States Atomic Energy Commission.

REFERENCES

1. K. R. Ambrose, N. G. Anderson, and J. H. Coggin, Jr., Cytostatic antibody and SV40 tumor immunity in hamsters, Nature, 233, 321 (1971).

2. N. G. Anderson and J. H. Coggin, Jr. (eds.), Embryonic and Fetal Antigens in Cancer, Vol. 1, U. S. Department of Commerce, Springfield, Virginia, 1971, pp. 1-400.

3. N. G. Anderson and J. H. Coggin, Jr. (eds.), Embryonic and Fetal Antigens in Cancer, Vol. 2, U. S. Department of Commerce, Springfield, Virginia, 1972, pp. 1-369.

4. C. C. Boyer, "Embryology, " in The Golden Hamster: Its Biology and Use in Medical Research (R. A. Hoffman, P. F. Robinson, and H. Magalhaes, eds.), Iowa State Univ. Press, Ames, 1968, p. 91.

5. R. J. Brawn, "Evidence for Association of Embryonal Antigen (s) with Several 3-Methylcholanthrene-Induced Murine Sarcomas, " in Embryonic and Fetal Antigens in Cancer, Vol. 1 (N. G. Anderson and J. H. Coggin, Jr., eds.), U. S. Department of Commerce, Springfield, Virginia, 1971, pp. 143-150.

6. M. M. Burger, A difference in the architecture of the surface of normal and virally transformed cells, Proc. Nat. Acad. Sci., 62, 994 (1969).

7. J. H. Coggin, Jr., "Fetal Antigens in Cancer, " Proceedings Fourth International Conference on Lymphatic Tissue and Germinal Centers in Immune Response, Plenum, New York, 1972.

8. J. H. Coggin, Jr., K. R. Ambrose, and N. G. Anderson, Fetal antigen capable of inducing transplantation immunity against SV40 hamster tumor cells, J. Immun., 105(2), 524 (1970).

9. J. H. Coggin, Jr., K. R. Ambrose, B. B. Bellomy, and N. G. Anderson, Tumor immunity in hamsters immunized with fetal tissues, J. Immunol., 107(2), 526 (1971).

10. J. H. Coggin, Jr., V. M. Larson, and M. R. Hilleman, Prevention of SV40 virus tumorigenesis by irradiation, disrupted and ido-deoxyuridine treated tumor cell antigens, Proc. Soc. Exptl. Biol. Med., 124, 774 (1967).

11. F. A. Cumar, R. O. Brady, E. H. Kolodny, V. W. McFarland, and P. T. Mora, Enzymatic block in the synthesis of gangliosides in DNA virus-transformed tumorigenic mouse lines, Proc. Nat. Acad. Sci., 67, 757 (1970).

12. G. A. Currie, W. Van Doorninick, and K. D. Bagshawe, Effect of neuraminidase on the immunogenicity of early mouse trophoblast, Nature, 219, 191 (1968).

13. H. Den, A. M. Schultz, M. Basu, and S. Roseman, Glycosyl-transferase activities in normal and polyoma transfered BHK cells, J. Biol. Chem., 246, 2721 (1971).

14. P. Dierlam, N. G. Anderson, and J. H. Coggin, Jr., "Immunization against Tumors with Fetal Antigens: Detection on Immunity
by Colony Inhibition Test and by Adoptive Transfer," in Embryonic
and Fetal Antigens in Cancer, Vol. 1 (N. G. Anderson and J. H.
Coggin, Jr., eds.), U. S. Department of Commerce, Springfield,
Virginia, 1971, pp. 203-214.

15. A. J. Girardi and M. R. Hilleman, Host-virus relationship in
hamsters inoculated with SV40 virus during the neonatal period,
Proc. Soc. Exptl. Biol. Med., 116, 723 (1964).

16. A. J. Girardi and P. Reppucci, "The Relationship of Hamster
Fetal Antigens to SV40 Tumor Specific Transplantation Antigens,"
in Embryonic and Fetal Antigens in Cancer, Vol. 2 (N. G. Anderson and J. H. Coggin, Jr., eds.), U. S. Department of Commerce,
Springfield, Virginia, 1972, pp. 167-170.

17. P. Gold and S. O. Freedman, Specific carcinoembryonic antigens
of the human digestive system, J. Exptl. Med., 122, 467 (1965).

18. H. Goldner, A. J. Girardi, V. M. Larson, and M. R. Hilleman,
Interruption of SV40 virus tumorigenesis using irradiated homologous tumor antigen, Proc. Soc. Exptl. Biol. Med., 117, 851
(1964).

19. W. J. Grimes, Sialic acid transferase and sialic acid levels in
normal and transformed cells, Biochemistry, 9, 5083 (1970).

20. S. Hakomori and W. Murakami, Glycolipids of hamster fibroblasts and derived malignant-transformed cell lines, Proc. Nat.
Acad. Sci., 59, 254 (1968).

21. R. B. Kemp, Effect of the removal of cell surface sialic acids on
cell aggregation in vitro, Nature, 218, 1255 (1968).

22. S. J. Kleinschuster and A. A. Moscona, Interaction of embryonic
and fetal neural retina cells with carbohydrate-binding phytoagglutinins: cell surface changes with differentiation, Exptl.
Cell Res., 70, 397 (1972).

23. O. H. Lowry, N. J. Rosenbrough, A. L. Farr, and R. J. Randall,
Protein measurements with the folin phenol reagent, J. Biol.
Chem., 193, 265 (1951).

24. P. McQuiddy and J. Lilien, Sialic acid and cell aggregation,
J. Cell Sci., 9, 823 (1971).

25. N. Ohta, A. B. Pardee, B. R. McAuslan, and M. M. Burger, Sialic
acid content and controls of normal and malignant cells, Biochim.
Biophys. Acta, 158, 98 (1968).

26. J. G. Perdue, R. Kletzien, and U. L. Wray, The carbohydrate
composition of membranes isolated from oncogenic RNA virus-
converted chick embryo fibroblasts, Biochim. Biophys. Acta,
266, 505 (1972).

27. V. R. Potter, Recent trends in cancer biochemistry: The importance
of studies on fetal tissue, Can. Cancer Conf., 8, 9 (1969).

28. D. F. Smith and E. F. Walborg, Jr., Isolation and chemical charac-
    terization of cell surface sialoglycopeptide fraction during
    progression of rat ascites hepatoma AS-30D, Cancer Res., 32,
    543 (1972).
29. L. Warren, The thiobarbituric acid assay for sialic acid, J. Biol.
    Chem., 234, 1971 (1959).
30. L. Warren, J. P. Fuhrer, and C. A. Buck, Surface glycoproteins
    of normal and transformed cells: A difference determined by
    sialic acid and a growth dependent sialyltransferase, Proc. Nat.
    Acad. Sci., 69, 1838 (1972).
31. H. C. Wu, E. Meezan, P. H. Black, and P. W. Robbins, Compara-
    tive studies on the carbohydrate containing membrane components
    of normal and virus-transformed mouse fibroblast. I. Glycosamine-
    labeling patterns in 3T3, spontaneously transformed 3T3, and
    SV40-transformed 3T3 cells, Biochemistry, 8, 2509 (1969).

Chapter 38

ROLE OF IMMUNITY IN ONCOGENESIS

Richmond T. Prehn

The Institute for Cancer Research
Philadelphia, Pennsylvania
and
Department of Pathology
University of Pennsylvania
Philadelphia, Pennsylvania

It has become traditional to regard the immune response as a purely defensive mechanism that operates most effectively very early in the evolution of a tumor. However, considerable recent evidence suggests that immunity does not ordinarily suppress very early neoplasms, but may, on the contrary, stimulate their growth. The immune mechanism thus appears to have a dual role in oncogenesis, and it remains a question as to which role may actually predominate in any particular tumor system. Indeed, the presently available data are consistent with the hypothesis that an immune reaction may be a prerequisite for the proliferation in vivo of small foci of nascent tumor.

The recent evidence that gives rise to this immunostimulation hypothesis of tumorigenesis consists of the observations that specifically sensitized spleen or lymphoid cells when mixed in very small numbers with target tumor cells, stimulate the growth of the latter (1). The stimulation observed is relative to that produced by admixed normal lymphoid cells or to that produced by lymphoid cells nonspecifically sensitized. Both in vivo and in vitro, larger ratios of specifically sensitized lymphoid cells to target tumor cells produce the inhibition of tumor proliferation expected if the immune response is a defensive mechanism. Thus, the defensive role appears to break down and actually become tumor stimulatory when and only when the immunocytes are present in small numbers relative to the numbers of target tumor cells. At present, the mechanisms by which low ratios of sensitized spleen cells stimulate tumor growth are unknown. The reaction may be mediated by cell-to-cell interactions, by antibody, or by lymphotoxin or related substances. It is also possible that the spleen cell population may contain a mixture of two different subpopulations, one of which might be stimulatory and the other inhibitory to tumor growth. If these occurred in different proportions or had different thresholds of activity, the paradoxical effects of high and low ratios of spleen cells to target cells might be explained.

It has been known for many years that prior immunization can, in some mouse tumor systems, result in better growth of tumor inocula than occurs in nonimmunized recipients. Much evidence suggests that most and perhaps all of this classic "tumor enhancement" is due to the presence in the serum of the immunized animals of specific blocking substances — either antibody or antigen-antibody complexes — that are capable of interfering with the action of otherwise specifically cytotoxic lymphoid cells. The serum blocking factors may also interfere with further sensitization by the tumor cell challenge inocula. The net result is that the tumors may, because of the previously induced blocking factors, grow better than they would have done had they been inoculated into nonimmunized recipients. No actual stimulation of tumor growth is necessarily involved in this classic "enhancement" system — the tumors in the sensitized mice probably grow no better and perhaps worse than they would have grown had they been inoculated into mice completely incapable of any type of an immune response (2).

In contrast to the situation in classic "enhancement," the form of tumor facilitation produced by admixed sensitized lymphoid cells can be demonstrated in vivo in recipient mice that have been immunocrippled or it can be demonstrated in vitro where there is no host immunity to be blocked (1). It is therefore difficult, although perhaps not impossible, to ascribe this form of tumor facilitation to any type of classic blocking mechanism. Rather, it seems much easier to invoke a direct stimulatory effect of the immunocytes upon the target tumor cells.

Although the evidence as already cited shows that a weak immune reaction, as represented by a low ratio of admixed lymphoid cells to target tumor cells, can facilitate tumor growth, it has not yet been established that such a mechanism is actually operative at any stage of tumor development. Conceivably, it could be operative at two different times. Firstly, the immune response might be weak relative to the number of tumor cells, after the tumor reaches a large size and the immune response becomes exhausted or damaged by chemotherapy. Secondly, very early in the course of tumor development, when sensitization first occurs, the antigenic stimulus, provided by a small number of tumor cells, may be weak and the consequent reaction may develop slowly. Thus, it is possible that immunostimulation may be important at more than one point in the life history of a tumor. In this chapter I am largely concerned with the second situation, since it could determine whether a tumor ever reaches a clinically detectable size.

Theoretically, immunostimulation very early in the course of tumor development may be important because there is a possibility that, owing to nonimmunologic homeostatic controls, the nascent tumor, in the absence of such immunologic stimulation, might not be able to grow. Immunostimulation may therefore determine whether the nascent tumor can actually develop. It can be speculated that the deciding factors in determining whether stimulation occurs are how large the tumor burden becomes prior to sensitization and how efficiently immunization occurs when once begun. Unfortunately, there are little available data on this point in most systems of oncogenesis. However, some data are available on the mouse mammary tumor system. This system also dramatically demonstrates a form of nonimmunologic surveillance that can operate to hold nascent mammary tumors in check.

The basic information concerning the mammary tumor system in the mouse has been developed by the work of many investigators over the past half century. However, the technique of gland transplantation into so-called "cleared fat pads" was first exploited by DeOme and his associates. In my laboratory this technique has been applied to immunologic studies by Slemmer (3). Space does not permit an account of the details and only the conclusions along with an extremely superficial explanation of the methodology can be given here.

Mammary tumors can be induced in the mouse by either chemical oncogens or by the mammary tumor virus interacting with genetically determined host factors and the hormonal milieu. The tumors characteristically go through several distinct stages of development, appearing first as small, discrete, focal areas of hyperplasia, the so-called "hyperplastic nodule." These can be considered benign tumors. They grow to a size of several millimeters but then usually become stationary for long periods of time and often permanently. At this stage, it can be shown by appropriate transplantation experiments that their further growth is restricted by the presence of surrounding normal mammary epithelium. Thus, at this stage of tumor development a non-immunologic mechanism is responsible for restricting tumor growth. It can be shown that, although the tumor cells are potentially immunogenic, the hyperplastic nodule does not

immunize the host animal. In fact, the tumor apparently immunizes
poorly, if at all, as long as it is confined within the anatomic limits
of the mammary fat pad. If a portion of the particular tumor is inoculated outside the fat pad, the tumor in the fat pad is destroyed by a
specific immune response (3). The fat pad is thus an immunologically
privileged site owing to a defect in the afferent limb of the immune
response mechanism. In this system, the tumor can attain considerable size while engendering little or no immune reaction. It would
therefore appear that the early mouse mammary tumor is a good
candidate for immunostimulation to help it overcome the nonimmunologic growth controls found in the mammary gland. However, whether
such immunostimulation actually occurs in this system remains to be
determined and this question is only now being investigated.

Similar possibilities for immunostimulation of nascent tumors
may exist in a number of epithelial tumor systems. In fact, any
epithelial tumor in situ, i.e., before the basement membrane is
penetrated, may exist in an immunologically privileged site and
immunize poorly. This possibility is demonstrated in the case of
guinea pig skin by the work of Billingham and his associates.
Allografted melanophores were found to persist indefinitely and not
to immunize the host when the graft was carefully placed in the epi-
dermis (4). Intraepithelial tumors, by analogy, might also be
expected to immunize poorly and therefore be subject to immunostimulation.

These considerations make the interpretation of the lymphoid
infiltration so often seen in very early neoplasia difficult. The
immune reaction that the lymphoid infiltration represents could be
either stimulatory or inhibitory to the tumor depending upon quantitative relationships. According to the immunostimulation hypothesis,
this quantitative relationship probably starts in the stimulatory range
and then gradually shifts to inhibitory proportions, hopefully before
the tumor is too large. However, the hypothesis also suggests that
the tumor might never have had the opportunity to grow too large had
it not been stimulated by the weak early immune reaction.

The fact that the immune reaction can, under some circumstances,
stimulate tumor growth suggests that immunoselection, by stimulation, may be the reason that most tumors, but not all, have tumor-
associated transplantation-type antigens. It has been shown that
the effective titer of antigen on the cell surface is very variable even
in cloned tumor cell populations (5). Therefore, one can presume
that the tumor is capable, by selection, of adjusting its antigenicity
over a wide range to just that level that is optimum for tumor growth.
If this is the case, the prospects for decisive immunotherapy may be
dimmer than we had hoped might be the case. However, I remain

optimistic. Immunotherapy is already helping some cancer victims, despite the complexities involved. When the mechanisms of the interaction of the immune system with tumor are sufficiently understood, ways will be found to improve upon the exciting results already obtained.

ACKNOWLEDGMENT

This investigation was supported by Public Health Service Research Grant Nos. CA-08856, CA-06927, CA-05255, RR-05539 from the National Institutes of Health, and by an appropriation from the Commonwealth of Pennsylvania.

REFERENCES

1. R. T. Prehn, The immune reaction as a stimulator of tumor growth, Science, 176, 170 (1972).
2. I. Hellström, K. E. Hellström, C. A. Evans, G. H. Heppner, G. E. Pierce, and J. P. S. Yang, Serum-mediated protection of neoplastic cells from inhibition by lymphocytes immune to their tumor-specific antigens, Proc. Nat. Acad. Sci., 62, 362 (1969).
3. G. Slemmer, Host response to premalignant mammary tissues, Nat. Cancer Inst. Monogr., 35, in press.
4. R. E. Billingham and W. K. Silvers, Studies on the migratory behavior of melanocytes in guinea pig skin, J. Exptl. Med., 131, 101 (1970).
5. R. T. Prehn, Analysis of antigenic heterogeneity within individual 3-methylcholanthrene-induced mouse sarcomas, J. Nat. Cancer Inst., 45, 1039 (1970).

Chapter 39

CELL ANTIGEN CHANGES DURING CHEMICAL CARCINOGENESIS

R. W. Baldwin

Cancer Research Campaign Laboratories
University of Nottingham
Nottingham, England

Several distinct types of neoantigen may be expressed in chemically induced tumors. These included "tumor-specific" rejection antigens, essentially located within the plasma membrane, and re-expressed fetal antigens, detectable both at the cell surface and in the cytoplasm. In addition, malignant cells may contain normal proteins modified by interaction with chemical carcinogens. These antigens have been detected in the early stages of carcinogenesis, e. g., in rat liver cells during aminoazo dye carcinogenesis (2), but their persistance and relation to other neoantigens on transformed cells is still not resolved. While all of these neoantigens may not play a significant role in host immunosurveillance, they may be viewed as specific markers for studying transformation and metabolic events during carcinogenesis.

The immunology of chemically induced tumors has been recently reviewed (3, 4); therefore this communication is restricted to studies on the immunology of chemically induced rat tumors which have particular relevance to the study of chemical carcinogenesis.

TUMOR-SPECIFIC REJECTION ANTIGENS

Tumor-specific rejection antigens are those cell components involved in producing immune rejection reactions against tumor cells. These antigens were initially detected by the induction of immunity to transplanted tumor cells in syngeneic recipients, and, furthermore, similar immune rejection responses have been demonstrated in the autochthonous host. Antigenic analysis has been aided by the

691

development of in vitro assays so that, for example, immune responses
to tumor-rejection antigens on aminoazo dye-induced rat hepatomas
can be detected by the cytotoxicity of sensitized lymphocytes or
serum for tumor cells in culture using colony inhibition methods (8).
Antigens specific to individual hepatomas can also be detected by
membrane immunofluorescence reactions of tumor-immune sera with
target cells in suspension (6, 11). Although these antigens have the
same specificity as the tumor rejection antigens, it is conceivable
that they may not, in fact, be the same.

While tumor-associated rejection antigens have been detected on
tumors induced by a wide range of chemical carcinogens, including
polycyclic hydrocarbons, aromatic amines, aminoazo dyes, and
alkylinitrosamines, their expression is not a constant feature and
this variability remains unexplained (4). For example, tumor-rejection
antigens are constantly expressed on 4-dimethylaminoazo-benzene
(DAB) induced rat hepatomas, whereas hepatomas induced in the same
strain of rats by N-2-fluorenylacetamide (FAA) are generally lacking
in these antigens. Moreover the majority of FAA-induced mammary
carcinomas and ear duct carcinomas that have been tested also proved
to be nonimmunogenic (7, 9). Because of the limitations of the test
systems measuring rejection of transplanted tumor cells in syngeneic
rats and the associated in vitro assays of cellular and humoral immunity,
it is not possible to decide whether FAA-induced tumors are totally deficient in tumor-rejection antigens or whether they are expressed too
weakly to be detectable by available methods. Nevertheless the
immunogenicity of DAB-induced hepatomas contrasts with the nonimmunogenicity of FAA-induced hepatomas and this discrepancy remains to be explained in view of the similarities in their metabolic
activation and tissue interactions (22). The possibility that FAA-
induced tumors express tumor rejection antigens that are masked at
the cell surface by sialic acid residues is unlikely since treatment of
FAA-induced mammary carcinoma cells with Vibrio cholera neuraminidase
does not lead to the development of immunogenicity (31). Another possibility, initially posed by Prehn (25) is that immunogenicity of a tumor
is inversely related to its latent period of induction, the notion being
that slowly developing tumors may be immunoselected against during
this period. There is indeed such a correlation between latent induction periods and immunogenicities of the rat tumors studied because
DAB-induced hepatomas and 3-methylcholanthrene (MCA)-induced
sarcomas, the majority of which were immunogenic, had relatively
short latent induction periods (16 to 28 weeks). The nonimmunogenic
FAA-induced tumors, in contrast, arose much more slowly (24 to 68
weeks). The concept of immunoselection as a significant factor in
explaining the nonimmunogenicity of certain chemically induced tumors
is less acceptable for a number of reasons.

1. Variable antigen expression has been observed in tumors with similar latency periods, e.g., MCA-induced murine sarcomas (26).
2. Tumors having significant immunogenicities generally retain this property through many generations of transplantation in immunologically competent hosts.
3. Tumors induced under conditions where immunosurveillance is positively excluded also show antigenic variability. Mondal et al. (23, 24) have observed variability in the expression of tumor-rejection antigens on mouse prostate cells transformed in vitro by MCA, and Prehn and Basombrio (27) observed similar effects in MCA-treated cells maintained in vivo in the immunologically protective confines of diffusion chambers.

Immunosurveillance, therefore, would appear not to be a significant factor in accounting for variability of antigen expression and this event remains to be explained.

SPECIFICITY OF TUMOR REJECTION ANTIGENS

Undoubtedly the most significant feature of the tumor-rejection antigens associated with chemically induced tumors is their great diversity. This was initially explored by showing that immunization of syngeneic animals with one transplanted tumor did not confer resistance to other tumors induced by the same carcinogen. In vitro studies of the specificity of the cellular and humoral immune responses elicited by immunization against transplanted tumor cells have provided more comprehensive and reliable methods of antigen analysis. In this way, for example, membrane immunofluorescence assays of sera from rats immunized against individual MCA-induced sarcomas or DAB-induced hepatomas showed that each serum reacted with cells of the immunizing tumor (6, 11). In contrast, none of the sera reacted with cells of other tumors and moreover tumor-specific antibody could not be absorbed from serum with cells other than those of the immunizing tumor. The specificity of the antigens associated with these rat hepatomas and sarcomas was confirmed in comparable studies on cross-tests of the cytotoxicity of serum and lymph node cells from tumor-immune rats (8). These studies establish that the tumor-rejection antigens associated with DAB-induced hepatomas and MCA-induced sarcomas are highly specific components of individual tumors.

SIGNIFICANCE OF TUMOR REJECTION ANTIGENS

Tumor-specific rejection antigens may be viewed as arising from a direct or indirect interaction of carcinogen within the cell genome producing heritable mutation-like alterations. The alternative concept, initially proposed by Burnet (16), that neoplastic transformation merely makes evident, by clonal amplification, antigenic differences that were already present in the normal cell has been largely refuted. Studies by Embleton and Heidelberger (18) demonstrated that tumors arising following MCA treatment in vitro of a cloned cell line of mouse prostate cells had distinctive tumor rejection antigens. Likewise Prehn and Basombrio (27) showed that Balb/c 3T3 cells cloned in vitro and transformed by MCA in vivo in Millipore chambers led to the development of antigenically distinct tumors. If tumor antigens are viewed as being the products of newly expressed genetic information, antigenic diversity may reflect random changes induced by the carcinogen that can lead to neoplastic transformation. This hypothesis must also account for the general lack of immunogenicity of some tumors such as FAA-induced hepatomas and mammary carcinomas. As already discussed, this may reflect the inadequacies of the assay systems, the effect being quantitative rather than qualitative. This might be so, since in all of the studies so far reported, a proportion of the tumors were at least weakly immunogenic. If, however, it is accepted that some tumors are deficient in tumor rejection antigens, this implies that antigen expression and neoplastic transformation are not necessarily concomitant events. For example, the site of attack by the carcinogen in some cases may not specifically code, directly or indirectly, for cell surface proteins.

EMBRYONIC ANTIGEN EXPRESSION ON
CHEMICALLY INDUCED RAT TUMORS

Another class of neoantigens that has been detected on carcinogen-induced rat tumors are re-expressed embryonic components. These antigens are not known to be expressed in normal adult tissues, but are detectable on embryo cells, and may be viewed as time-displaced components.

One of the earliest demonstrations of tumor-associated embryonic antigen was the report by Abelev et al. (1) that o-aminoazotoluene-induced mouse hepatomas synthesize an α-fetoprotein that is normally present in newborn serum but not adult mouse serum. These antigens have also been detected in the serum of rats with hepatomas induced by aminoazo dyes (5, 20, 28) and diethylnitrosamine (19). These

α-fetoproteins are detectable in soluble extracts from hepatoma homogenates and are also present in the serum of tumor-bearing animals. As far as DAB-induced rat hepatomas are concerned, there-fore, they differ from the tumor-rejection antigens, which are inti-mately associated with the plasma membrane (10, 13, 14).

There is also evidence that DAB-induced hepatomas and MCA-induced sarcomas in the rat express other embryonic antigens that are more firmly associated with the cell surface. These antigens were initially detected by membrane immunofluorescence staining of target tumor cells in suspension with serum from multiparous rats (6, 11). It was subsequently shown that serum or lymph node cells from multiparous rats were cytotoxic for rat hepatoma and sarcoma cells in culture (12). The nature of these assays, i.e., lymphocyte cytotoxicity, complement-dependent serum cytotoxicity, and immuno-fluorescence tests measuring IgG immunoglobulin, indicates that immunologic events are being measured and also localizes the embryonic antigens at the cell surface. Moreover, these test sys-tems have been employed to detect embryonic antigens on normal embryonic cells but not adult cell counterparts of the two tumor systems analyzed (12). Thus, for example, membrane immuno-fluorescence assays using multiparous rat serum detect embryonic antigen on rat hepatomas and normal 14- to 17-day-old embryo cells, but not on freshly prepared or cultured adult rat liver cells (12).

One question raised by these studies is the possibility that the tumor-rejection antigens detected on chemically induced rat hepa-tomas and sarcomas may be embryonic components. This postulate has already been made in the case of SV-40-induced hamster tumors where immunization with fetal tissue can retard tumor growth or even tumor induction (17). That this is not so in the case of chemically induced rat tumors is indicated by several pieces of evidence.

1. Serum from multiparous rats reacts with more than one target tumor including both hepatomas and sarcomas (12). This cross reactivity of antibody in multiparous rat serum is more clearly demonstrated in absorption studies, since absorption with cells of one target tumor removes reactivity to both the absorbing and other rat tumors (12). In contrast, antibody elicited in syngeneic rats immunized to a transplanted tumor reacts only with cells of this tumor and it cannot be absorbed with cells of unrelated tumors (6, 11).

2. Tumor-specific and embryonic antigens can also be differenti-ated by the capacity of tumor-immune and multiparous rat sera to specifically block the cytotoxicity of senstized lympho-cytes for tumor cells in culture (32). In tests with hepatoma D23, for example, the cytotoxicity of hepatoma D23-immune

lymph node cells could be abrogated by pre-treating tumor cells with the tumor immune serum, whereas multiparous rat serum was inactive. Conversely, the cytotoxic action of lymph node cells from multiparous rats was blocked by serum from these animals.

These studies indicate fairly clearly that the embryonic antigens expressed on chemically induced rat tumors differ from the highly distinctive "tumor-specific" antigens. Nevertheless the reappearance of embryonic antigens on tumor cells indicates a derepression of genes producing an antigen normally found only during embryogenesis. The frequency of embryonic antigen expression in chemically induced tumors has yet to be evaluated, so that it cannot yet be stated that this event is a necessary concomitant of neoplastic transformation. This point has considerable relevance to the possibility of utilizing embryonic antigen typing for the analysis of cells transformed in vitro by chemical carcinogens. In this respect, preliminary studies indicate that lymph node cells from multiparous rats are not cytotoxic for cells of a line established from normal adult rat liver. These lymphocytes, however, react with cell lines isolated following treatment with N-methyl-N-nitrosamine and 3'-methyl-DAB (33).

CONCLUSIONS

The objective of this contribution was to outline the types of neoantigen known to be associated with chemically induced rat tumors, particularly aminoazo dye-induced hepatomas and MCA-induced sarcomas. It is pertinent to consider how these neoantigens may be utilized as cell markers in studies on carcinogenesis, particularly with in vitro transformed cells. Conversely in vitro transformed cells may be utilized for more definitive studies of neoantigen expression.

The individually specific rejection antigens are the most distinctive class of neoantigen associated with chemically induced tumors, and from the studies of Heidelberger and colleagues (18, 23, 24), it is clear that they can be used to characterize in vitro transformed cells. Detection of these antigens, may, therefore, provide an important parameter for evaluating transformation. Characterization of these antigens in biochemical terms is now feasible (10, 13), and recent developments in radioimmunoassay techniques will make possible precise analysis of the amount of antigen expressed on transformed cells. In this way, therefore, tumor-specific antigens will provide specific and quantitative markers for studies on the extent of cellular derangement induced by a particular carcinogen.

Furthermore, in vitro systems, where immunoselection by the host is positively excluded, will allow analysis of the carcinogen inter- actions within the cell that lead to neoantigen expression. In this way, it should be possible to ascertain whether neoantigen expres- sion is a concomitant of neoplastic transformation. Also, the degree of diversity of antigen expression can be more adequately defined, and by chemically characterizing these antigens, it should be pos- sible to ascertain whether the multiplicity of neoantigens reflects a similar variability of cell membrane proteins on neoplastic cells or whether this represents specific variations within a small class of proteins.

Because of their diversity, tumor-specific antigens are not readily applicable for analyzing early events in chemical carcino- genesis, but this may be more feasible by studying embryonic antigen expression. It has not yet been established satisfactorily that re-expression of embryonic antigen is a concomitant of neo- plastic transformation, since, so far, the types of tumor studied are limited. Certain virus-induced tumors such as SV-40- and polyoma- induced tumors (17, 29) express embryonic antigens. Chemically induced tumors studied so far include DAB-induced hepatomas, MCA- induced sarcomas, and FAA-induced mammary carcinomas (15, 12). Tumors induced with a broader spectrum of chemical carcinogens need to be analyzed, including in vitro transformed cells where neo- plastic characteristics have been clearly established. Also, it is necessary to ascertain that embryonic antigen is not synthesized as a result of chemically induced acute or chronic toxicity. This require- ment is emphasized by studies (20, 21, 30) showing that α-fetoprotein is present in the serum of rats during the early stages of hepatocar- cinogenesis well before overt tumors are detectable.

The ultimate objective of these studies is to develop immunologic procedures for defining changes in cell surface architecture following transformation by chemical carcinogens. The use of specific immuno- histologic labels such as peroxidase- or ferritin-labeled antibody should provide methods for ultrastructure studies, of tumor antigen localization, while developments in the biochemistry of tumor anti- gens will eventually lead to the precise characterization of these tumor components.

REFERENCES

1. G. I. Abelev, S. D. Perova, N. I. Khramkova, Z. A. Postnikova, and I. S. Irlin, Transplantation, 1, 174 (1963).
2. R. W. Baldwin, Brit. J. Cancer, 18, 285 (1964).
3. R. W. Baldwin, Europ. J. Clin. Biol. Res., 15, 593 (1970).
4. R. W. Baldwin, Advan. Cancer Res., 18, 1 (1973).
5. R. W. Baldwin and C. R. Barker Brit. J. Cancer, 21, 338 (1967).
6. R. W. Baldwin, C. R. Barker, M. J. Embleton, D. Glaves, M. Moore, and M. V. Pimm, Ann. N. Y. Acad. Sci., 177, 268 (1971).
7. R. W. Baldwin and M. J. Embleton, Intern. J. Cancer, 4, 47 (1969).
8. R. W. Baldwin and M. J. Embleton, Intern. J. Cancer, 7, 17 (1971).
9. R. W. Baldwin and M. J. Embleton, Israel J. Med. Sci., 7, 144 (1971).
10. R. W. Baldwin and D. Glaves, Clin. Exptl. Immunol., 11, 51 (1972).
11. R. W. Baldwin, D. Glaves, and M. V. Pimm, in Progress in Immunology (B. Amos, ed.), Academic, New York, 1971, pp. 907-920.
12. R. W. Baldwin, D. Glaves, and B. M. Vose, Intern. J. Cancer, 10, 233 (1972).
13. R. W. Baldwin, J. R. Harris, and M. R. Price, Intern. J. Cancer 11, 385 (1973).
14. R. W. Baldwin and M. Moore, Intern. J. Cancer, 4, 753 (1969).
15. R. J. Brawn, Intern. J. Cancer, 6, 245 (1970).
16. F. M. Burnet, Nature, 226, 123 (1970).
17. J. H. Coggin, K. R. Ambrose, B. B. Bellomy, and N. G. Anderson, J. Immunol., 107, 526 (1971).
18. M. J. Embleton and C. Heidelberger, Intern. J. Cancer, 9, 8 (1972).
19. M. Garisoain and J. Arcos, Acta Oncol., 9, 40 (1970).
20. T. Kitagawa, T. Vokochi, and H. Sugano, Intern. J. Cancer, 10, 368 (1972).
21. R. Kroes, G. M. Williams, and J. H. Weisburger, Cancer Res., 32, 1526 (1972).
22. E. C. Miller and J. A. Miller, Ann. N. Y. Acad. Sci., 163, 731 (1969).
23. S. Mondal, M. J. Embleton, H. Marquardt, and C. Heidelberger, Intern. J. Cancer, 8, 410 (1971).
24. S. Mondal, P. T. Iype, L. M. Griesbach, and C. Heidelberger, Cancer Res., 30, 1593 (1970).
25. R. T. Prehn, in Cross-Reacting Antigens and Neoantigens (J. J. Trentin, ed.), Williams and Wilkins, Baltimore, 1967, pp. 105-117.

26. R. T. Prehn, J. Nat. Cancer Inst., 45, 1039 (1970).
27. R. T. Prehn and M. A. Basombrio, Intern. J. Cancer, 10, 1 (1972).
28. M. Stanislawski-Birencwajg, J. Uriel, and P. Grabar, Cancer Res., 27, 1990 (1967).
29. C. C. Ting, D. H. Lavrin, G. Shiu, and R. B. Herberman, Proc. Nat. Acad. Sci., 69, 1664 (1972).
30. H. Watabe, Cancer Res., 31, 1192 (1971).
31. R. W. Baldwin and M. V. Pimm, unpublished results.
32. R. W. Baldwin and B. M. Vose, Brit. J. Cancer, 29 (1974).
33. P. T. Iype, R. W. Baldwin, and D. Glaves, to be published.

Chapter 40

IMMUNOTHERAPY OF TRANSPLANTABLE, DIETHYLNITROSAMINE-INDUCED HEPATOMAS IN SYNGENEIC GUINEA PIGS

Herbert J. Rapp

Biology Branch
National Cancer Institute
Bethesda, Maryland

There are at least two ways in which immunologists might contribute to the control of human cancer. The preferred method would be to vaccinate healthy individuals with appropriate vaccines to prevent progression of the disease to a pathologic state. The second method would be to treat the disease immunologically as soon as possible after diagnosis. While prevention of cancer immunologically would be preferable to treating it, there are now no vaccines that are effective against any of the various forms of human cancer. The major barrier to the development of cancer vaccines is that no one has yet identified infectious agents that cause human cancer. Even if such agents were available, it would take many years (perhaps several decades) to prepare vaccines and test them for safety and effectiveness.

Prevention of cancer by any means would be preferable to treatment. If the development of the major forms of cancer requires contact with environmental factors and if these factors could be eliminated or their physiologic effects suppressed, therapists would not have to concern themselves with the problem of how to reduce the morbidity and mortality of the disease. Unfortunately there are no instances in which the identification of environmental carcinogens has led to a reduction in the incidence of a major form of human cancer. For example, it is well established that there is a relationship between chronic cigarette smoking and lung cancer, and yet the consumption of tobacco continues to increase. Education may someday lead to significant reduction in cigarette smoking, but there is no assurance that this will come about. The approach to cancer control by prevention offers the best solution for the future, while

701

treatment, although not as satisfactory as prevention, has the virtue that it is applicable now.

The idea that the immune system might serve as a basis for cancer treatment goes back more than 200 years. From that time to the present physicians have observed and recorded spontaneous regressions of a variety of neoplastic diseases in humans. These spontaneous regressions were often associated with concurrent acute bacterial infections and it was suggested that the immune response to infection was in some way responsible for tumor regression. The leading proponent of this theory, W. B. Coley, observed that best results were obtained when the infection occurred at the tumor site or when a toxic product of bacterial metabolism was applied directly to the tumor (1). This principle of Coley's has been belatedly confirmed in our work with guinea pig hepatomas and is the basis for the remarkable and successful treatment of human multiple basal cell carcinoma developed by Klein (2). Klein induces an inflammatory response at each of the tumor sites by application of a contact allergen such as dinitrochlorobenzene. After several applications of the allergen, the tumors regress and new skin grows over the treated sites.

Similarly we have found that the inflammatory response induced by a single injection of living Mycobacterium bovis (strain BCG) into an established, intradermal, guinea pig hepatoma is followed by regression of the established tumor, elimination of tumor cells that have spread to the draining lymph node, and complete and permanent cure of most of the treated animals.

DEVELOPMENT OF TRANSPLANTABLE GUINEA PIG HEPATOMAS

These studies began 10 years ago and were based on strong evidence that a major mechanism of tumor suppression was mediated by sensitized lymphocytes capable of recognition of specific antigens present on tumor cells but not detectable on normal cells (3). Most tumor immunologists use mice in their investigations, but these animals are not as convenient as guinea pigs for studies of so-called cell-mediated immunity. This difficulty with mice is the main reason we chose guinea pigs for our studies, which were designed to find optimal conditions for the elimination of established tumors by immunologic methods. Guinea pigs, like humans, and unlike the usually available laboratory animals, are capable of developing vigorous and prolonged delayed cutaneous hypersensitivity characterized by the delayed appearance of erythema and induration following intradermal challenge with minute quantities of antigen. Our

first goal was to determine whether tumor specific immunity could be
demonstrated and measured by the delayed cutaneous hypersensitivity
(DCH) reaction. The tumors used to achieve this goal were obtained
in the following way: Inbred guinea pigs (strain 2) were given the
water-soluble carcinogen diethylnitrosamine in their drinking water
daily. Eventually all guinea pigs receiving this agent developed
highly metastatic liver cancers. Transplantable lines of tumors were
established from individual primary nodules in their liver (4). These
tumor lines were maintained in the ascites form by adapting them to
grow in the peritoneal cavity. Most of our work has been done with
three of these lines, designated line 1, line 7, and line 10. Line 1 is
a well-differentiated adenosarcoma, line 7 is a carcinosarcoma, and
line 10 is a hepatocellular carcinoma. Each of these lines is characterized by the fact that intraperitoneal or intramuscular injection of
tumor cells produces fatal, metastatic disease; death usually follows
the development of pleural effusions. They differ, however, in how
they grow in the skin. Intradermal injection of 10^6 line 1 tumor cells
into syngeneic guinea pigs produces a papule that increases in size
for about ten days and then ulcerates and eventually regresses completely. Animals in whose skin a line 1 tumor has grown and regressed
are immune to systemic challenge with cells from this tumor line.
Intradermal injection of 10^6 line 7 tumor cells into syngeneic guinea
pigs produces a progressively growing papule but cells of this line
spread relatively slowly from the skin. These animals, therefore, can
be immunized to systemic tumor challenge simply by surgical excision
of the papule before the development of metastases. Intradermal injection of line 10 tumor cells also produces a progressively growing
papule but metastasis occurs so rapidly that it has not been possible
to immunize animals against this tumor by conventional methods.
Immunization to line 10 tumor has been achieved by using BCG. The
immunization procedure is given later in this report.

HOST RESPONSE TO TUMOR DEMONSTRATED BY THE
DELAYED CUTANEOUS HYPERSENSITIVITY REACTION

Ascites cells of the line 1 tumor were injected intradermally into
normal strain 2 guinea pigs. In a few days growing tumor papules
appeared at the site of injection; the papules increased in size for
several days and then began to regress. After the skin tumors regressed,
the animals were challenged intradermally with living line 1 tumor
cells. The following day there were typical DCH reactions at the
challenge sites (5). In unimmunized animals, the intradermal challenge
produced no DCH reactions and 7 days later there were tumor papules
growing at the injection sites. At this time there was almost complete

inhibition of tumor growth in the immunized animals. The observation
that animals immunized to line 1 tumor developed systemic tumor
immunity suggested a method to study the efficacy of cancer immunotherapy.

MODELS FOR CANCER IMMUNOTHERAPY

An ideal cancer immunotherapy model should fulfill three requirements: (a) tumor challenge must precede therapy, (b) an established
tumor (palpable and/or visible) must be present before therapy is
started, and (c) metastases must be present before therapy is started.
The first model to be described fulfills the first but not the second and
third of these requirements; the second model fulfills all three requirements. In the first model, unimmunized strain 2 guinea pigs received
intramuscular injections of living line 1 tumor cells at a dose that
caused death of untreated animals in 60 to 90 days. On day 5 after
challenge, treated animals received the first of three intradermal injections of living line 1 tumor cells. The second and third injections
were given on days 12 and 19, respectively. The first immunizing
dose produced no delayed skin reaction, and the papule increased in
size at the same rate as in unimmunized animals without the intramuscular challenge. The second and third immunizing doses produced
delayed skin reactions and there was no growth of tumor in the skin at
the site of injection. All 12 unimmunized animals were dead by 90
days, while five of 12 immunized animals survived for more than a
year and four remained tumor free for the rest of their lives (6). Although this experiment did not fulfill the requirements for an ideal
immunotherapy model, it did demonstrate that it was possible to interfere with tumor growth by an immunologic procedure instituted after
challenge with a lethal dose of tumor cells.

EXPERIMENTAL BASIS FOR CURRENT APPROACH
TO CANCER IMMUNOTHERAPY

Animals immunized to line 1 tumors were able to reject line 1 but
not line 7 transplants, and animals immunized to line 7 tumors were
able to reject line 7 but not line 1 transplants (7). The following experiment took advantage of these facts and provided the basis for our
current approach to cancer immunotherapy: Animals immunized to line
1 tumor were challenged on the same day at three separate sites. One
site received living line 1 tumor cells, another living line 7 tumor
cells, and a third a mixture of living line 1 and line 7 tumor cells. On

the following day there were delayed skin reactions at the sites containing line 1 alone and the mixture of line 1 and 7 but not at the site containing line 7 alone. During the next few days a growing tumor papule developed at the site containing line 7 cells alone but there were no tumor papules at either the site containing line 1 alone or at the site containing the mixture of line 1 and line 7. The suppression of line 7 growth at a site in which an inflammatory response immunologically unrelated to line 7 was taking place suggested that tumor suppression in vivo might require components of the immune system that are not immunologically specific (8). A major histologic feature of delayed skin reactions is the infiltration of mononuclear cells (macrophages or histiocytes). These cells, therefore, were tested for their ability to suppress tumor growth. Cells present in the peritoneal cavity of unimmunized strain 2 guinea pigs 3 days after intraperitoneal injection of mineral oil were separated and the macrophages injected into the skin of the same animal from which the cells were taken. There was erythema at the skin site 6 hr after the injection. The growth of line 7 tumor cells injected at the inflamed site was suppressed (9). Migration inhibition factor (MIF) was tested for its ability to suppress tumor growth. MIF was prepared in vitro with PPD, a purified protein derivative of tubercle bacilli, and MIF activity was assayed by the measurement of inhibition of the migration of macrophages from capillary tubes. A purified and concentrated fraction containing MIF was injected into the skin of normal guinea pigs. Within 3 hr there was a strong inflammatory reaction at the site of injection. Tumor cells injected into such sites did not multiply (10). Inflammatory responses induced by other agents were tested for their inhibitory effect on tumor growth. Tumor growth was suppressed at sites of inflammation induced by turpentine, by India ink, and by delayed skin reactions in response to antigens unrelated to the tumor. While it was clear that immunologically nonspecific components of the immune system exerted an inhibitory effect on tumor growth, it was evident from the results of other experiments that this effect was not potent enough to cause regression of an established tumor.

A search was made for agents that produce stronger inflammatory responses than those already tested. One of the agents, BCG, was tested and, as stated previously, was found to be capable of inducing regression of an established tumor as well as early metastases. These studies were carried out with line 10 tumors that by ordinary methods appeared to be nonimmunogenic. A mixture of living line 10 tumor cells and living BCG injected into the skin of strain 2 guinea pigs, however, produced no tumor papule and rendered the animals systematically immune to further challenge with line 10 tumor cells (11).

Experiments were performed to determine whether BCG-induced tumor suppression was due to a direct cytotoxic effect or whether a host response was required. The following evidence derived from in vitro and in vivo experiments indicates that BCG is not directly cyto-toxic to tumor cells and tumor suppression by BCG in vivo requires a host response: Tumor cells, in vitro, incorporated tritiated thymidine to the same extent as tumor cells in the absence of BCG. Tumor cell viability was unaffected in the presence of BCG by the criterion of trypan blue dye exclusion. In vivo evidence that tumor cells are not directly affected by BCG was obtained by taking advantage of the observation that intravenous injection of certain antigens induces a state of immunosuppression so that the recipient has a reduced capacity to develop a cell-mediated response to the antigen. Accordingly BCG was administered intravenously and a mixture of BCG and tumor cells was inoculated intradermally. Under these conditions tumor cells grew in the presence of BCG.

ELIMINATION OF ESTABLISHED TUMORS AND METASTASES BY INTRALESIONAL INJECTION OF BCG

These studies have provided a model suitable for determining optimal conditions for cancer immunotherapy. Normal strain 2 guinea pigs received intradermal injections of one million line 10 tumor cells. On day 7 after challenge each site contained a tumor about 1 cm in diameter, weighing about 100 mg. In previous experiments it was found that on day 7 after challenge tumor cells were present in the draining lymph node as a result of metastatic spread from the intra-dermal tumor. On day 7, guinea pigs with tumors were treated in one of three ways. The tumors in one group of animals were treated by the intralesional injection of diluent, tumors were excised from a second group, and the third group received injections of living BCG into their tumors. The tumors in the animals that received diluent intralesionally grew progressively, and all animals in this group eventually died fol-lowing widespread metastases. The animals whose skin tumors were excised also died following development of extensive metastases. More than half of the animals that received living BCG intralesionally were completely and permanently cured. Those animals in the treat-ment group that eventually developed metastases all lived a signifi-cantly longer time than tumor-bearing animals that did not receive BCG. If treatment was withheld until day 12, only about 20% of the animals were cured. On day 12 after challenge the tumors weighed about 500 mg (12). Histologic examination of draining lymph nodes several days after intralesional injection of BCG revealed the presence of a larger number of histiocytes and a few tumor cells that appeared

to be degenerating (13). Draining lymph nodes of cured animals
eventually returned to normal appearance.

HYPOTHESIS FOR THE MECHANISM OF TUMOR
REGRESSION INDUCED BY BCG

Following injection of BCG into the tumor there are immunologic
responses to BCG antigens. One of the responses is characterized by
the appearance of lymphocytes that have acquired the immunologically
specific ability to recognize and react with BCG antigens. One of the
consequences of the interaction between these sensitized lymphocytes
and BCG antigens is the release of a soluble product by the lymphocytes with the capacity to immobilize macrophages or histiocytes. If
BCG is injected into the tumor, the immobilized macrophages must, at
least by chance, encounter tumor cells. Although BCG was not injected into lymph nodes, histologic examination of the node revealed the
presence of acid-fast bacilli. This means that the BCG-lymphocyte
interaction with MIF release that takes place in the tumor transplant
can also take place in the lymph node. In some unknown fashion, and
apparently not requiring phagocytosis or specific recognition of tumor
antigens, the histiocytes kill the tumor cells and perhaps a few host
cells. One may speculate that the killed tumor cells are processed by
the immune system resulting in the appearance of lymphocytes specifically sensitized to tumor antigens. These specifically sensitized
lymphocytes can react directly with tumor antigen and either kill the
cells directly or, by releasing MIF, cause further influx of histiocytes.
It is possible, therefore, that histiocytes serve at least two purposes:
(a) the immunologically nonspecific destruction of tumor cells, and
(b) the mediation of a specific immune response leading to the appearance of lymphocytes specifically sensitized to tumor antigens.

SPECULATION ABOUT THE IMMUNOTHERAPY OF HUMAN CANCER

The results obtained so far with the guinea pig immunotherapy
model have not yet been applied to human cancer. Current use of BCG
in the treatment of human cancer is based on the premise that immunotherapy must be an adjunct to conventional modes of cancer treatment,
i.e., surgery, X irradiation, and chemotherapy. Results from the
guinea pig model studies indicate that if this premise continues to be
the basis for cancer immunotherapy, this may prevent the establishment of optimal conditions for the treatment of human cancer with BCG.
The two most important points that emerge from the guinea pig studies

are that BCG must come into direct contact with the cells of the primary
tumor and that BCG immunotherapy must be started as early as possible
in the disease process at a time when metastases are incipient and
not palpable. While this model is far from ideal in terms of the kinds
of human cancer it can be applied to, it is the only one that deals
with metastatic cancer. If clinicians wish to treat cancer patients
with BCG, then some guidelines may be derived from the guinea pig
model. For example, a patient with lung cancer and early metastases
detectable only by microscopy could be given BCG intravenously, by
inhalation, or by direct injection at bronchoscopy, whichever route
delivers the largest number of organisms directly to the primary tumor
site. Colon cancer in elderly patients could be treated by oral administration of BCG or direct injection into the primary tumor during sig-
moidoscopy. Deposition of BCG directly into any primary tumor site
should be possible, but it should not be done at an advanced stage of
the disease especially after the surgeon, radiologist, and chemo-
therapist have completed their treatments and as a result have upset
the delicate balance of the immune system. BCG promises to be a
powerful tool in the treatment of human cancer, but unless and until
current attitudes change we are only going to acquire more anecdotal
evidence of the value of BCG in advanced of terminal cancer rather
than the kind of evidence needed to make it a standard treatment.
There is almost no doubt that occasionally spectacular results have
been obtained with BCG and other infectious agents or products of
infectious agents in the treatment of advanced human cancer. The
promise of this type of cancer immunotherapy, however, will not be
realized until it is tried at a time when the patient's immune system
is intact and not compromised by widespread metastases or by the
immunosuppressive effects of current modes of therapy. The guinea
pig model has provided a tool to study cancer immunotherapy in a rational manner; it is now up to the clinician to find ways of applying
this knowledge to the human cancer problem.

REFERENCES

1. H. C. Nauts, The apparently beneficial effects of bacterial infections on host resistance to cancer: End results in 435 cases,
   Monograph No. 8, Vol. I, New York Cancer Research Inst., New
   York, 1969.
2. E. Klein, Hypersensitivity reactions at tumor sites, Cancer Res.,
   29, 2351 (1969).

3. L. J. Old, E. A. Boyse, D. A. Clarke, and E. A. Carswell, Antigenic properties of chemically induced tumors, Ann. N. Y. Acad. Sci., 101, 80 (1962).
4. H. J. Rapp, W. H. Churchill, Jr., B. S. Kronman, R. T. Rolley, W. G. Hammond, and T. Borsos, Antigenicity of a new diethyl-nitrosamine-induced transplantable guinea pig hepatoma: Pathology and formation of ascites variant, J. Nat. Cancer Inst., 41, 1 (1968).
5. W. H. Churchill, H. J. Rapp, B. S. Kronman, and T. Borsos, Detection of antigens of a new diethylnitrosamine-induced transplantable hepatoma by delayed hypersensitivity, J. Nat. Cancer Inst., 41, 13 (1968).
6. B. Kronman, H. T. Wepsic, W. H. Churchill, Jr., B. Zbar, T. Borsos, and H. J. Rapp, Immunotherapy of cancer: An experimental model in syngeneic guinea pigs, Science, 168, 257 (1970).
7. B. Zbar, H. T. Wepsic, H. J. Rapp, T. Borsos, B. S. Kronman, and W. H. Churchill, Jr., Antigenic specificity of hepatomas induced in strain-2 guinea pigs by diethylnitrosamine, J. Nat. Cancer Inst., 43, 833 (1969).
8. B. Zbar, H. T. Wepsic, T. Borsos, and H. J. Rapp, Tumor-graft rejection in syngeneic guinea pigs: Evidence for a two-step mechanism, J. Nat. Cancer Inst., 44, 473 (1970).
9. B. Zbar, I. D. Bernstein, and H. J. Rapp, Suppression of tumor growth by peritoneal exudate macrophages from unimmunized strain 2 guinea pigs, Proc. Amer. Assoc. Cancer Res., 11, 87 (1970).
10. I. D. Bernstein, D. E. Thor, B. Zbar, and H. J. Rapp, Tumor immunity: Tumor suppression in vivo initiated by soluble products of specifically stimulated lymphocytes, Science, 172, 729 (1971).
11. B. Zbar, I. D. Bernstein, and H. J. Rapp, Suppression of tumor growth at the site of infection with living Bacillus Calmette-Guerin, J. Nat. Cancer Inst., 46, 831 (1971).
12. B. Zbar, I. D. Bernstein, G. L. Bartlett, M. G. Hanna, Jr., and H. J. Rapp, Immunotherapy of cancer: Regression of intradermal tumors and prevention of growth of lymph node metastases after intralesional injection of living Mycobacterium bovis, J. Nat. Cancer Inst., 49, 119 (1972).
13. M. G. Hanna, B. Zbar, and H. J. Rapp, Histopathology of tumor regression following intralesional injection of Mycobacterium bovis (BCG). II. Comparative effects of vaccinia virus, oxazolone and turpentine, J. Nat. Cancer Inst., 48, 1697 (1972).

VIII

SUMMARY AND PREDICTION

Chapter 41

SUMMARY OF THE CHEMICAL ASPECTS OF CARCINOGENESIS

Bernard Pullman

Institut de Biologie Physico-Chimique
Fondation Edmond de Rothschild
Paris, France

The cancer problem is a world problem and it was therefore particularly appropriate that this Symposium on "Model Studies in Chemical
Carcinogenesis" should be named the World Symposium. I would not,
however, be frank if I wouldn't admit the pleasure and emotion which
I felt and which, I am sure, was shared by all my French colleagues
here, at the recognition given at the opening of this meeting to the
outstanding contribution to this problem by Professor Lacassagne. He
devoted his life to research on the origin and mechanism of chemical
carcinogenesis and Professor Arcos has given us a stirring account of
his remarkable personal discoveries in this field and of the stimulating
and guiding effect which these discoveries and his personal influence
had on the works of many of us and in particular, naturally, on the
works of the other members of the French school. We were also happy
that the name of Dr. Buu-Hoi was associated in this tribute. He has
been the most direct and most devoted collaborator of Prof. Lacassagne
and a great scientist on his own, with nearly artistic qualities for the
imagination and synthesis of potential carcinogenic compounds. In the
name of all the French scientific community in deep sorrow over these
heavy losses, I would like to thank again the organizers of this meeting
and all those who have associated themselves with them for having
placed this symposium under the auspices of a tribute to two great
colleagues.

I have been asked to summarize the chemical aspects of the problems discussed during the last few days and to make predictions about
what I believe to be the next developments. My task has thus been
defined with respect to the present and the future. I feel, however,
that the best way for me to accomplish this, particularly the evaluation
of this meeting's achievements, is to place it against the background

713

of a recent past. For this purpose I have taken as reference a very similar meeting that, under the title of <u>Physico-chemical Mechanisms of Carcinogenesis,</u>* was held four years ago, in October 1968, in Jerusalem, under the auspices of the Israel Academy of Sciences and the Edmond de Rothschild Foundation of Paris and in which a number of the scientists present here today participated. There is, in my opinion, a striking continuity of thought, themes, arguments, and failures between these two meetings, the Jerusalem one and this one. But there are also differences, some essentially in the emphases placed on various themes, and others in new perspectives toward the future. Delineating these new emphases and perspectives seems to me the most useful way of accomplishing my task.

I believe that this viewpoint will become clearer if I quote a few words from the introductory lecture that I gave at the Jerusalem Symposium. My opening statement there was: "In view of the extremely rapid development of modern sciences, and in particular of molecular biology, it is somewhat disheartening to observe that our knowledge of the basic mechanism of chemical carcinogenesis is progressing extremely slowly. While a large amount of data is being gathered on the interaction of carcinogens with various cell components and in particular with the fundamental macromolecules, and while it is obvious that somewhere there must be the decisive step leading to the generation and appearance of tumors, the precise significance of these reactions for carcinogenesis is unclear."

This statement was followed by the specification of the five principal problems which I thought to be at the heart of the theme of the Jerusalem meeting, classified in what appeared to me <u>at that time</u> as the relative order of the interest that they were arousing. These problems were:

1. The nature of the principal receptor, the interaction with which leads directly to carcinogenesis. Schematically this problem can probably be stated: proteins or nucleic acids? — although significant interactions of carcinogens with other cellular components are also known.
2. If nucleic acids, which type — DNA, RNA's, double-stranded, dividing?
3. The nature of the interaction or reaction leading to carcinogenesis — physical or chemical?
4. The nature of the proximate carcinogen — initial molecule or a metabolite?
5. The relation of carcinogenesis to mutagenesis.

* E. D. Bergmann and B. Pullman (eds.), distributed by Academic Press, New York.

These "different" problems are, of course, intermingled and frequently have to be treated together. But they do seem to represent the essential questions that may be asked.

If I review in my mind the communications and discussions that we have heard here during the last few days, as far as the chemical aspects are concerned, I think that these five problems still are the central problems that we have debated and that we tried to solve. On the other hand, however, it appears that a definite shift has occurred as to the relative importance of some of these themes, as can be judged by the number of lectures that referred to them and the time spent on their discussion. Thus, although the problem of the nature of the principal receptor remains certainly a crucial one, it has not been particularly debated here (much less than in Jerusalem). Much more attention has been paid in this meeting, in its chemical part, to the problem of the nature of the proximate or ultimate carcinogen and to its fate in the organism. In fact, this question seems to dominate the work of a few of our most outstanding colleagues, particularly in connection with the aromatic hydrocarbons. For that reason I both discuss this problem at the beginning of my summary and devote perhaps most of my time to it. In fact, starting with this problem, which represents possibly the first step in the series of processes that lead to tumor formation, makes the discussion more chronological with respect to the whole series.

NATURE OF THE PROXIMATE CARCINOGEN

It is a continuous feature of the main problems in carcinogenesis that they always appear in the form of dilemmas, apparently simple dilemmas, but so difficult to solve. One of these has always been the question of the nature of the proximate or ultimate carcinogen, the dilemma being whether this is the initial molecule or a metabolite. While it was realized early, due to works of Lawley, Brookes, Ross, etc., that carcinogens such as certain alkylating agents are probably active per se, and due to the works of Miller, Heidelberger, Weisburger et al., that carcinogens such as the azo-dyes or 2-acetylaminofluorene need a transformation into an active metabolite, the question of whether the aromatic hydrocarbons are carcinogenic per se or through the intermediate of a metabolic derivative was for a long time an open one. One has the definite impression that the older belief that they may be carcinogens per se (a belief which, if I may remind us, was shared by Prof. Miller, who, however, has given us here the most complete and persuasive presentation of the necessity of metabolic activation for the majority of carcinogenic substances including the aromatic ones) is presently yielding ground to the opinion that they must undergo a metabolic transformation before becoming reactive enough to interact strongly with a possible biologic receptor. In recent publications, the only adherents of the per se idea seem to be Dr. Arcos and Dr. Argus (in their large 1968 review in Advances in Cancer Research, Vol. 11). Perhaps they have changed their opinion since.

In this meeting a series of speakers, including in particular Dr. Sims, Dr. Heidelberger, Dr. Miller, Dr. Nagata, Dr. Brookes, Dr. Jerina, Dr. Ts'o and others have given us abundant evidence of the importance of metabolic transformations of polycyclic hydrocarbons for the manifestation of their carcinogenic activity. We do not repeat these arguments again.

If we agree to solve this dilemma in favor of the metabolite (if we do so, this will be the first, but I am afraid the only, dilemma that we shall be able to solve), another dilemma immediately appears and it concerns the nature of the proximate carcinogen. Among those that have been proposed, the most serious candidates seem to be: the K-region epoxide, the cation radical, and the free radical(s). Moreover, it is apparent from the discussion that a dilemma, which could be an important one, immediately attaches itself to this first one, namely, should we consider the same type of proximate carcinogen for the unsubstituted and substituted polycyclic hydrocarbons or do we need to consider two different such proximate carcinogens for the two groups?

Let us try to look more closely at these different questions.

Cation Radical

The fact that cation radicals of polycyclic hydrocarbons may be formed with relative ease is well established. The simplest of such compounds are those that derive from the hydrocarbons by the abstraction of an electron. Dr. Wilk, Dr. Fried, and Dr. Ts'o have beautifully demonstrated their formation from a large number of polycyclic hydrocarbons and their potential for being involved in interactions with biologic substrates or molecules representing such substrates (pyrimidine, purine, pteridine). Such cations would also fit Dr. Miller's general proposition, which he presented here with his usual brio, about the electrophilic nature of the proximate carcinogens derivable from most types of carcinogenic molecules. Dr. Nagata, who once voiced objections against the role of a radical cation in carcinogenesis (objections based on the absence of an acceleration of carcinogenicity of benzpyrene by injection of iodine shortly after the application of the carcinogen) did not manifest his objections here. So I suppose that he does not insist on this objection any more.

In spite of these favorable opinions, I must confess that I have reservations about the direct importance of these radical cations (especially those obtained simply by electron abstraction, one-electron oxidation) in carcinogenesis by polycyclic hydrocarbons. My doubts are due to difficulties in correlating any characteristic of structure of such radicals with their activity. I discussed this problem in detail at the Jerusalem Symposium, where I demonstrated the disputable nature of proposals that tended to develop a relationship among several properties of such cation radicals (the ease of their formation, their stability, etc.) and carcinogenic activity, in particular in the field of aromatic hydrocarbons. Thus, contrary to a number of statements, no general relationship whatsoever exists between the ionization potential of such molecules and their carcinogenic activity. No correlation exists between carcinogenicity and the stability of such radicals of polycyclic hydrocarbons. No correlation exists between the magnitude of the positive charge at their most positive center and carcinogenic potency, etc. We therefore don't expect the cation radicals of carcinogenic polycyclic hydrocarbons to be selectively different in any known property from the cation radicals of noncarcinogenic polycyclic hydrocarbons.

Nothing was brought forward in this meeting that induces me to change my opinion on this point. On the contrary. Thus some of the findings described by Dr. Wilk, who had the merit of investigating a large number of compounds, strengthen my scepticism as to the direct importance of such cation radicals for carcinogenic processes. When one looks carefully at Dr. Wilk's results on the interaction of cation radicals of polycyclic hydrocarbons with their partners it is seen that the interactions between such cation radicals and, say, purine and pyrimidine, are not selective with respect to carcinogenic activity of the parent molecules. It is true that the cation radicals derived from the very potent 7, 12-dimethylbenzanthracene (DMBA), methylcholanthrene, and benz(a)pyrene interact strongly with purine but so do the cation radicals derived from the noncarcinogenic anthanthrene and perylene. On the other hand, the cation radical derived from the carcinogenic dibenz(a, h)anthracene shows no reaction. Moreover the reaction takes place only with unsubstituted purine but not with the biologic purines: adenine or guanine.

This model study, most interesting in itself, does not seem therefore to mimic sufficiently the problem that we are investigating to constitute a persuasive representation of it. In fact my personal conclusion from it would be a strong feeling that this type of interaction is not decisive by itself for carcinogenesis.

May I also recall the fact that, as shown by a number of investigators, such cation radicals of polycyclic hydrocarbons also add to,

nucleic acid bases through photochemical activation: thus benz(a)-
pyrene has been shown to become bound in this way through its position 6 to position 5 of cytosine or thymine, a reaction which led
some authors (Cavalieri and Calvin) to quick but very loose conclusions
about the significance of this model interaction in carcinogenesis.
When Blackburn et al. in England extended the study to other carcinogenic hydrocarbons, they found that the binding decreases in the series:

   anthracene > benz(a)pyrene > dibenz(a, h)anthracene >

   benz(e)pyrene > methylcholanthrene > dibenz(a, c)anthracene

showing no relationship between bonding and carcinogenic potency.

Other Types of Radicals

The most outstanding radical is the 6-oxy- radical of benzpyrene,
which has two potent defendants in Dr. Nagata and Dr. Ts'o. According to Dr. Nagata it is formed enzymically on interaction of benzpyrene with liver or skin homogenates, through the intermediate of
6-hydroxybenzpyrene. The radical binds covalently to DNA (which
benzpyrene does not do), particularly to guanine. Dr. Nagata considers the possibility that the radical is reactive through its K-region.

Dr. Ts'o generates the radical upon the transformation of the physical binding of benzpyrene with DNA into chemical binding through the
action of I_2. He confirms its reactivity with the nucleic acid bases,
in particular the purines. He considers the possibility that it is
reactive through rearrangement into a radical cation. (This oxy radical
cation is different from the one considered in the preceding section
and has not been investigated theoretically.) He is persuasive; his
findings represent a most serious detailed investigation of the possible
reactions of such a radical and trace a link between this intermediate
and the series of quinones that are obtained as metabolic products. It
is an impressive piece of work, of great value to the understanding of
the chemistry of benzpyrene. Moreover, his reaction schemes are also
substantiated by studies on the electrochemical oxidation pathway of
benzpyrene.

This is obviously the beginning of an important new line of investigation; those of us who know Dr. Ts'o's energy are pretty certain that
it will progress quickly. Although there seems to be great justification
for centering one's studies on benzpyrene, the question must, however,
be raised as to the more general significance of these results. We
would very much like to know whether such oxy-radicals are also
formed with other carcinogens and what is the situation of the aromatic
noncarcinogens in this respect. An important point in this field, if it
is going to be enlarged, perhaps may be the possible tautomerism of

hydroxyaromatics. When I hear about a reaction of a carcinogenic polycyclic hydrocarbon that is claimed to be possibly involved in its activity, I immediately think of how a noncarcinogen would behave in such a reaction, so that when people speak of benzpyrene, I try to think of pentacene. From the point of view of hydroxylation, hydroxy-pentacene is known to exist essentially in the tautomeric keto form. This could perhaps be a significant distinctive pattern to check up on.

K-Region Epoxides

This old idea of Boyland's, which he has advocated for a long time, has gained importance and support during the last years. We have, gathered here, all the principal protagonists of this idea: Dr. Newman, who was the first to have synthesized a K-region epoxide of a poly-cyclic hydrocarbon; Dr. Jerina, who was the first to have shown its existence as a metabolic product of polycyclic hydrocarbons; Dr. Sims, who has done outstanding work in synthesizing most of the presently available such epoxides and in studying their properties; and Dr. Heidelberger, who has significantly contributed to some of the synthe-sis and investigations.

By now, the K-region epoxides of polycyclic hydrocarbons have been abundantly studied, and strong arguments have been put forward in favor of their significance for the generation of tumors. May I recall a few essential such arguments?

1. K-Region epoxides derived from polycyclic hydrocarbons react chemically with nucleic acids and histones, while the parent hydrocarbons and corresponding dihydroliols do not (Sims).
2. Epoxides are intermediates in microsomal oxidation of poly-cyclic hydrocarbons to hydroxylated derivatives (Jerina, Sims, Heidelberger).
3. K-Region epoxides of carcinogenic polycyclic hydrocarbons (benzanthracene, dibenz(a, h)anthracene, methylcholanthrene) are more active in inducing malignant transformations in vitro of hamster embryo and mouse prostate cells than the parent hydrocarbons, the corresponding diols and phenols. The 8-9 epoxide of benzanthracene (a non-K-region epoxide) is much less active than the K-region epoxide in transforming mouse cells. In mouse prostate cells, K-region epoxides of the non-carcinogenic phenanthrene and chrysene did not transform cells (Heidelberger, Sims).
4. The existence of a correlation between epoxide mutagenicity in bacteriophage and the carcinogenicity of the parent hydro-carbon (Heidelberger).

These are strong arguments in favor of a role of K-region epoxide in carcinogenesis. There are, however, also counterarguments.

1. The K-region epoxides are less potent carcinogens in mice than the parent hydrocarbons.

2. In the hamster kidney cell system, epoxide reactivity does not correlate with the carcinogenicity of the parent hydrocarbons. For example, the epoxide of the carcinogenic dibenz(a,h)-anthracene reacts less with DNA than the epoxide of the non-carcinogenic benzanthracene.

3. As opposed to previously quoted cases, the K-region epoxide of DMBA is less reactive in inducing malignant transformation in cell culture than DMBA itself.

Altogether, this is a beautiful piece of work and we have to congratulate all those who have contributed to it.

As to the relative value of the two types of argument for and against the role of K-region epoxides in carcinogenesis, I find it very difficult to decide. Happily a summarizer does not need to decide. What is essential is that this is certainly a line of research to be followed with utmost care and attention.

A summarizer does not need to decide either between the respective merits of the oxy radicals or the epoxides. The metabolic pathways leading to tumors may be numerous and both may be important. In any case, it is challenging to have two paths to investigate.

Let us now turn to the problem of the substituted, in particular methylated, derivatives of polycyclic hydrocarbons.

In the first place let me underline that there really are arguments that cause us to consider at least the possibility of different intermediates for the methylated and parent hydrocarbons. Among such arguments we may quote in particular:

1. As opposed to the activity of polycyclic hydrocarbons, the K-region epoxides of 7-methylbanzanthracene and of DMBA are inactive or less active in producing malignant transformation in mouse prostate cells than the parent compounds (Heidelberger).

2. In distinction to what happens in the parent compound, the induction of microsomal enzymes does not influence the yield of malignant transformation in mouse prostate cells treated with DMBA (Heidelberger).

3. 7,8-Benzoflavone, inhibitor of aryl hydrocarbon hydroxylase, influences the carcinogenic potency of benz(a)pyrene and of DMBA differently (Gelboin).

These are good arguments. They raise the troublesome problem of possibly having a different active center for interactions with the receptor in the substituted, particularly methylated, derivatives and in the parent hydrocarbons. The situation led some authors, the most prominent among whom is Dr. Brookes, to consider that a possible mechanism of metabolic activation of methyl substituted polycyclic hydrocarbons involves the methyl group as the critical site of metabolic attack and not the ring system.

Dr. Brookes' original idea was that this could be a cation radical of the form $AR-C^+H_2$, an idea that caused him to study 7-bromomethyl-benzanthracene (7-BrMeBA) and related molecules as model compounds.

The first results were already ambiguous. Thus, while 7-BrMeBA and 7-bromomethyl-12-methylbenzanthracene (7-BrMe-12-MeBA) bind covalently to DNA in the test tube and to the DNA of transformable cells in culture and while 7-BrMe-12-MeBA is a carcinogen as potent as DMBA, 7-BrMeBA is much less carcinogenic than 7-MeBA. Also, both 7-BrMeBA and 7-BrMe-12-MeBA are inactive or less active in producing malignant transformations in mouse prostate cells than the parent compounds 7-MeBA and 7,12-DMBA (Heidelberger). In this meeting, Dr. Brookes has shown by a careful study that essentially different binding products are obtained upon reaction of DNA with 7-MeBA, 7-BrMBA, and the K-region epoxide of 7-MeBA; thus it seems to me that the prevailing opinion would now be that bromomethyl derivatives are not appropriate models for studies of carcinogenesis by methyl derivatives, although, of course, they are interesting by themselves. I personally feel happy about this conclusion, as I never felt that they were good models.

The problem of a different reactive site for the unsubstituted and substituted derivatives, although unsolved, thus becomes less acute. In fact, Dr. Newman considers that the methyl substituent at position 7 of BA not only does not constitute a new reactive site but protects the molecule from an attack on the otherwise reactive 7 carbon. In his opinion the active site whose metabolism leads to carcinogenesis is at C-5 of BA, one of the carbons of the K region.

This conclusion is a result of a detailed investigation of a large series of fluoro derivatives of methylated benzanthracenes. I do not know whether Dr. Newman realizes how very close his proposals are to our K-L region theory of carcinogenesis. The essential difference between his proposal and ours is that he thinks in terms of carbon atoms (the C-7 and C-5 positions) while we think in terms of regions. In our conception, in order to be carcinogenic a molecule must have a reactive K-region and an unreactive L-region. In his proposal it must have a reactive C-5 carbon and an unreactive C-7 carbon. We put more accent on addition reactions, he on substitutions. We have given our reasons elsewhere for attributing more importance to additions than to substitutions in the processes leading to carcinogenesis and I do not repeat them here. In view of the new types of reactions that now appear possible, the divergence between us is perhaps less than it seems to be at first sight; this is another line of investigation that may be useful to explore.

I believe that this summarizes our discussions about the possible active, metabolically formed, proximate carcinogenic derivatives of polycyclic hydrocarbons. Although the problem is far from being solved, definite proposals are available, and serious work is progressing about the principal proposals. I believe that important results may be expected in this field shortly.

PROBLEM OF THE INTERACTION BETWEEN THE CARCINOGEN AND THE CELLULAR RECEPTOR

The problem has two facets. The first facet concerns the nature of the principal receptor, and this question generally reduces to: nucleic acids or proteins? The second facet concerns the mechanism of the interaction, particularly the predominance of the physical or chemical interaction.

As far as the nature of the receptor (the interaction with which is decisive for carcinogenesis) is concerned, surprisingly this subject was scarcely raised and still less discussed at this meeting. It was among the most disputed problems at the Jerusalem Symposium.

I don't think that this change in emphasis could be due to the fact that we find it less important now. This is certainly not the case. The reason resides simply in the fact that no progress is being made in this important field.

Nevertheless nearly all speakers (with the exception of Dr. Bonner) have considered, more or less explicitly, the interaction with the nucleic acids, which apparently has their preference. But nobody seems to be in a belligerent mood about this problem. When Dr. Sachs publicly affirmed his preference for DNA, I expected that Dr. Weinstein would rise and claim his preference for tRNA and that then Dr. Brookes would rise and support Dr. Sachs. I was also hoping that Dr. Heidelberger and Dr. Bendich would dispute each other about their preference for replicative or nonreplicative DNA. Nothing of this happened. Something is aging in this subject.

Whatever it may be, in view of the evident emphasis laid on the nucleic acids, I would like to recall that for a long period, extending grosso modo from 1950 to 1960, it was the interaction of the carcinogens with proteins that was essentially considered by most scientists to be of possible primordial importance for carcinogenesis. This situation was due to the extremely fruitful results obtained through the pioneering studies of the Millers, Heidelberger, and Sorof, in particular. Results such as the demonstration of the formation of a strong chemical bond between azo dyes or aromatic hydrocarbons and proteins; the correlation of the facile complex formation with the existence of carcinogenic activity (as indicated, e.g., by the selectivity of its formation in the species or tissues in which the tumors develop, the inhibition of its formation by factors inhibiting tumor formation, etc.) and with its potency; the significant observation that the binding of the carcinogens seems to involve preferentially a specific electrophoretic fraction of the protein (the h protein) that is absent from the tumors, while the exceptional binding of noncarcinogens involved a different fraction, etc., were considered as very persuasive. Nowadays most authors seem to be in favor of nucleic acids. What about the old arguments and correlations? They are still there. Sooner or later we will have to face this problem again. We do not necessarily have to choose between proteins or nucleic acids. The two may be equally important, but the problem has to be solved.

If the problem "nucleic acids versus proteins" is aging, the problem of "physical versus chemical binding" is ripening.

This is one of the happy subjects, by which I mean one in which we all seem to be going toward an agreement. The agreement is the primordial importance of the chemical interaction. I have been defending for many years this viewpoint for the simple reason that it is easily shown by theoretical treatments that physical interactions can bear no specificity with respect to the carcinogenic properties of hydrocarbons.

We are indebted to our host Dr. Ts'o and his collaborators, for having made the most efficient demonstration of the predominant importance of the chemical interaction by showing how the nonselective physical interaction of polycyclic hydrocarbons, carcinogenic and noncarcinogenic, with a biopolymer (DNA) can be transformed, by suitable reagents, into a selective chemical interaction with the carcinogen alone.

These studies are becoming classics in this field and are too well known to be summed up again. May I just remind you of the beautiful demonstration that while benz(e)pyrene is bound physically to DNA to the same extent as benz(a)pyrene, the chemical linkage, formed in aqueous solution, in a buffer ethanol solvent system using iodine and peroxide as activating agents, is obtained selectively with the carcinogen only. The feasibility of such a selective transformation opens new vistas for research and we are waiting impatiently for the extension of such studies to other molecules.

Dr. Ts'o believes that the active species for the production of the chemical binding is, at least in the case of benzpyrene, an oxy-radical, derived from 6-hydroxybenzpyrene, or a cation radical formed from it by an internal tautomerization, a problem that we have already dealt with.

He has also demonstrated that the chemical binding occurs preferentially with guanine. From the viewpoint of the site of attack, he thus joins an appreciable number of authors who locate it at the nucleic acid bases and who, moreover, among these bases, consider guanine as the most eager acceptor.

This dominant position of guanine as the possible target for carcinogenic agents is worth stressing. It becomes, I think, a working hypothesis for many investigators. Theory and experiment could surely collaborate in this field in a most profitable way by trying to understand better the principal reaction possibilities of this base and, therefore, the principal consequences of such reactions. Madame Pullman has shown you how the evaluation by quantum-mechanical methods of the electrostatic potential generated by guanine in the environmental space enables us to interpret or to predict the principal sites of nucleophilic attack on this base, a similar treatment being, of course, also possible for the other bases. Professor Weinstein has shown that one of the principal results of the fixation of acetylamino-fluorene on C-8 of guanine is to produce a conformation change in the base with respect to its sugar: from anti, this conformation becomes syn. Similarly one may also study the electronic consequences of this and other types of attack by calculating the electronic structure of such an N-7 alkylated guanine or guanine substituted at C-8 with AAF and comparing the structure of the product with that of the initial base. To some extent, this type of work was already presented by us at the Jerusalem meeting. The conjunction of theoretical and experimental methods seems extremely promising in this field.

CONCLUSIONS

Before concluding I would like to make two more short comments. One about the exceedingly important developments that seem to be occurring in the field of aryl hydrocarbon hydroxylase and that have been so elegantly presented at this symposium by Dr. Gelboin, Dr. Wiebel, and Dr. Nebert. Although concerned to a large extent with the biological aspects of our discussions, they have such a direct meaning for the different subjects that I discussed here that I have to underline the hope that the exploration of the activity of this enzyme system will raise our understanding of the metabolic processes involving hydrocarbons, whether activations or detoxications. This is a relatively new development but from which much is expected.

The second remark concerns the problem of carcinogenesis versus mutagenesis. This is a field that until a year ago was full of contradictions. I have three slides of quotations, which I don't have time to show, from most eminent scientists, showing the most bewildering jungle of contradictory opinions.

This period of liberty is terminated.

To some extent a breakthrough is occurring in this problem. This is due to the demonstration of the importance of the metabolic activation of potential mutagens in order to manifest their mutagenic activity (just as it is in carcinogenesis). Strangely this had escaped attention before. A number of people present at this meeting play a leading role in this transformation. Prominent among them are Dr. Heidelberger and Dr. Sims. This is certainly going to be one of the major subjects of our next symposium on carcinogenesis.

Time is late and I feel that I have to sum up this summing up. Should I have to state in a few words what we have and what we have not achieved here in connection with the different aspects of the problem indicated at the beginning of my summary, I think that I would be close to the truth by saying that we have made possibly appreciable progress in the field of the metabolic activation of the potential carcinogens into the proximate or ultimate ones. In this respect I have the impression that the researches on the K-region epoxide of polycyclic hydrocarbons are particularly promising although we perhaps may have some surprises with the problem of the substituted versus unsubstituted molecules. Another promising line in this direction, in particular in the benzpyrene series, could be the 6-oxy-radical.

Connected with this potential success are the remarkable results on aryl hydrocarbon hydroxylase, which indicate that we may possibly have put our finger on one of the essential, if not the essential, metabolizing agents for polycyclic hydrocarbons. The balance of the reactions that this enzyme system catalyzes seems, however, a very delicate one, and more progress is needed before we can substantiate its exact role in carcinogenesis.

Also substantial may be the progress that has been made in the unravelling of the relation between carcinogenesis and mutagenesis, with the important conceptional consequences that such a discovery may have. This is an old field that opens a new way to our research.

On the other hand, no appreciable progress seems to have been achieved since 1968 in the other two very important aspects of the problem: <u>the exact nature of the reaction</u> important or decisive for carcinogenesis, and <u>the principal important receptor.</u>

These two partial failures are possibly linked together. The carcinogenic agents participate in a great multitude of reactions and it has always been my feeling, based on the limited number of active compounds as compared with the great mass of inactive ones, that it is not their common reactions that are involved in the steps leading to malignancy. It is the uncommon ones that may be essential, but they are of course more difficult to identify.

This situation raises to some extent the problem of the significance and utility of model studies in carcinogenesis. When I look upon the great amount of results presented at this meeting, I feel that the balance is in favor of such studies. In this highly complicated problem, model studies are in fact a necessity. But it is obvious, of course, that models must be dealt with with utmost care and, particularly, that a very rigorous thinking must accompany every path of the exploration. Model studies tell us generally what may happen, what could have happened in circumstances similar to the ones that characterize our problem; they generally don't tell directly what actually happens in the system that the model represents. Critical thinking is thus particularly necessary for the establishment of the significance of the results obtained with a model system. All model systems are not necessarily appropriate because they do not mimic the real system to the same extent. An important thing to realize is, I believe, that negative results obtained with a given model system may be as significant as positive results and that one should not hesitate to deduce such negative conclusions. It is better to do so and change or modify the model system than to try to force reality into an unfitting scheme. Provided that one keeps in mind this <u>fundamental truth,</u> the utilization of model compounds and reactions can only be beneficial. They give the necessary stimulus to progress. I would like to relate a story to you, told to me by my friend Albert Szent-Gyorgyi and that seems quite relevant to the situation. A detachment of Hungarian troops was camped in the Alps during the First World War. Their commander, a young lieutenant, decided to send out a small group of men on a scouting mission. Shortly after the group left it began to snow, and it snowed steadily for four days. The scouting squad did not return, and the young officer had no doubt that he had sent his men to their death. Suddenly, on the fifth day, the scouting squad returned. There was great relief in the camp, and the young commander questioned his men: "How did you survive, how did you find your way back?" The sergeant who had led the group replied: "We were lost in the snow and we have given up hope. Then one of the men found a map in his pocket. With its help we knew we could find our way back.

We waited for the snow to stop and then as soon as we could travel we returned here." The young commander asked to see the map. It was a map not of the Alps but of the Pyrenees! Nevertheless it did its job.

So, we hope, will do our model studies.

Ladies and gentlemen, every good meeting on carcinogenesis raises more problems than it settles. From that point of view this one is a very good meeting. I believe that our meetings will continue like this to be better and better, with more and more problems, until the best of them all, the one in which the Answer will be given.

Chapter 42

BIOLOGICAL ASPECTS OF CHEMICAL CARCINOGENESIS:
SUMMARY AND PREDICTIONS

Umberto Saffiotti, M. D.

Associate Director for Carcinogenesis
Division of Cancer Cause & Prevention
National Cancer Institute
Bethesda, Maryland

BIOLOGICAL EVALUATION OF CHEMICAL ACTIVITY

The chemical aspects of the discussions on model studies in chemical carcinogenesis are clearly and succinctly summarized by Dr. Pullman in Chapter 41 (1). The task of this chapter is to summarize and discuss the biological aspects. We had to find the elusive dividing line between the chemical and the biological aspects in the complex interactions that occur in chemical carcinogenesis, although obviously we are dealing with a process in which the interplay of the two fields is intrinsic and essential.

The manner in which the chemical aspects of carcinogenesis are evaluated in biological terms has sometimes caused me some concern. One of the major problems in attempting to assess the pathways for chemical activation of carcinogens and in identifying ultimate carcinogens consists of relating chemical structure to the long-term biological effect that characterizes a given chemical as a carcinogen, i. e., the induction of tumors. Let me use, as an example, the compound dibenz-[a, c]anthracene, a five-ring aromatic hydrocarbon without K region. It was first bioassayed by repeated skin applications in mice during the initial studies on the carcinogenicity of polynuclear hydrocarbons in the early 1930s (2). In a first series of skin tests, an impure preparation was tested in a total of 60 mice, of which only 17 survived at one year; the only two mice which survived over 600 days developed skin carcinomas. A purer preparation was tested in 10 mice, of which two survived over 600 days and one developed a skin carcinoma. In a subsequent test using a pure sample, only 20 mice were used, only two survived at one year, the last mouse dying at 487 days, and no tumors were found. The authors went on to state: "we cannot say that no tumors would have been obtained had the mice lived exceptionally long, as in the earlier series with the impure material." However, in their discussion, the compound was considered noncarcinogenic and this classification was accepted, without further tests, by other authors. The compound was tested again in a similar way in a group of 15 mice by Heidelberger et al. (3) in the early 1960s and, since again no tumors were observed, the authors confirmed its lack of carcinogenicity: on this basis, the compound was later used as a "negative control."[*] Van Duuren et al. (4) then tested it, but just for initiating activity on mouse skin. They found it positive and therefore called it a noncarcinogenic initiator. We tested it (5) for full carcinogenic activity on mouse skin and found it quite active as a full carcinogen, although with a long latent period (eight carcinomas out of 30 initial mice, average latent period of 60 weeks). DiPaolo et al. have shown (6) and he has reported here (7), that this carcinogen induces neoplastic transformation in vitro. The important point that I want to stress by this example is that our knowledge of the carcinogenicity of a given chemical structure is a reflection of the biologic systems by which we determine carcinogenicity. A critical evaluation of these bioassay systems and of their sensitivity is needed in defining the biologic activity (or lack of activity) of a given chemical.

In the last few years, I have had the opportunity to review the present status of our information on chemicals that have been tested for carcinogenic activity, in order to determine which ones have been found carcinogenic. The answer is not an easy one since it requires a critical evaluation of both the adequacy of the experimental design used in bioassays and the significance of the results. The International Agency for Research on Cancer (IARC) in Lyon, France, has undertaken the task of preparing detailed reviews of the present information on the carcinogenicity of various chemicals. The reviewers, convened as working groups, are experts from several countries. The Carcinogenesis Program of the National Cancer Institute (NCI) has supported this activity and has contributed its data base to it. The results are published by the IARC as a series of monographs (8). The evaluation of carcinogenicity is a complex matter and I would like to stress that its major deficiency is in the paucity of good bioassay studies with adequate pathology. A survey of the literature data on all compounds that have been tested for carcinogenic activity was started by Hartwell (9), continued by Shubik and Hartwell (10), and now brought up to date by the NCI's Carcino-

---

[*] The compound was tested by subcutaneous injection in 4 groups of mice with negative results (A. Lacassagna, N. P. Buu-Hoi and F. Zajdela, Europ. J. Cancer, 4, 123 [1968]).

genesis Program (11). Up to 1972, only about 5000 different chemical compounds (and 500 mixtures) have been reported as having been tested in chronic animal bioassays. Many of these tests appeared in the old literature; many of them employed biological systems that we could not accept as adequate. Among those 5000 chemicals that are reported as having been tested, almost 1000 were reported as carcinogenic. The reason for this very high ratio, as it is easily realized, is that most of the compounds tested were selected by investigators who were interested in carcinogenesis studies and who chose compounds likely to be positive, including a large number of polynuclear hydrocarbons, azo-dyes, nitrosamines, etc. Therefore, the list of tested chemicals is by no means a random sample of environmental chemicals. Of the nearly 1000 compounds that have been reported as carcinogenic in the literature, many are not at all conclusively demonstrated to be so. I think that after the completion of the review process described above with critical monographs for each substance, maybe only a few hundred chemicals will stand up as being well-documented carcinogens. The 5000 chemicals so far tested really represent a small sample of the tens of thousands, maybe even hundreds of thousands, of chemicals that have extensive environmental contact with man, and that ought to be screened for potential carcinogenicity. There is a need for selecting new model systems for evaluating carcinogenic effects, particularly systems that do not require long-term tumor induction in large animal populations as their endpoint. However, these new test systems will need to be validated by comparing their results with those obtained by the conventional induction of tumors in large, well-controlled, long-term animal experiments. This is one of the reasons that compels us to continue bioassay programs in large and well-controlled animal populations, such as the one we have at the NCI for carcinogenesis testing of environmental chemicals.

As we progress in the development of bioassay procedures (both long-term and short-term), we will need to test not only individual compounds of environmental importance, but also families of compounds correlated by their chemical structure. In fact, without data on the correlations between structure and activity of large families of chemicals, we will not have the necessary basis to interpret chemical mechanisms of action of carcinogens.

A last word of caution along these lines. Quite often we still relate to different <u>potencies</u> of carcinogens as if these were intrinsic properties of the molecule. In some cases I believe that we can arrive at some valid generalization in this direction; but in many other cases, we only have limited biological data obtained, for example, in only one biological model. Now we know that changing the experimental model (e.g., the test species) often greatly changes the relative level of response to different carcinogens. We should not generalize from data obtained in one set of experimental conditions and state that compound x is more carcinogenic than compound y simply because we have seen a few more tumors in one experiment.

These remarks emphasize the need for a close correlation between the chemical side and the biological side of our field.

This symposium, like many recent meetings in our field, shows the comforting sight of chemists, physico-chemists, biochemists, pathologists, experimental biologists, immunologists, molecular biologists, geneticists, enzymologists, toxicologists, statisticians, and epidemiologists getting together to attack a problem by joining their forces, rather than doing their research in strictly segregated disciplinary fields. This symposium convened together an outstanding group of scientists from all these different disciplines; this has provided essential depth to the many facets of the discussion. I think that we can refer here to the great example that has been set for us by the two late colleagues whom we are honoring, Professor Lacassagne and Professor Buu-hoi. They gave us, with their co-workers, an outstanding example of scientific collaboration among scientists coming from very different backgrounds and they showed us how productive and critical such a collaboration can be. I think that it is important that we continue to be inspired and enlightened by the example they have set for us for the rest of our lives.

James A. Miller started the scientific program (12) with two re-marks that I found to be essential to the problem that we set out to discuss. The first one is that in spite of the great preponderance of mesenchymal cells in the human body, as well as in the mammalian species that we usually study, most human and experimental cancers are derived from epithelial cells and in most cases from lining epi-thelial cells. The other remark is that we need to develop new tools not only for the study of carcinogenesis in these epithelial cells, but to relate them to human events, so that we eventually become able to study carcinogenesis in the human by experimental methods. Until just a few years ago, we could not do it: we had no realistic approach to it. We now begin to see our way clear toward doing it — obviously by in vitro techniques of cell and organ culture. Acquiring the ability to study the carcinogenic process directly on human differentiated cells will be a major turning point in our field. The Carcinogenesis Program at NCI has directed new efforts in this direction. Hopefully, this will be a major topic of future symposia.

I shall now attempt to summarize the discussions of this sym-posium on the biologic aspects of carcinogenesis, around three phases of the process of carcinogenesis: (a) events occurring before the critical phenomena of transformation, (b) events occurring during and around the time of transformation, and (c) events occurring after transformation has been accomplished and cells still have to grow and establish themselves as a recognizable tumor.

EVENTS OCCURRING BEFORE TRANSFORMATION

The process of carcinogenesis starts, of course, when the chemical carcinogen (or pro-carcinogen) gains access to the body. Many of the initial interactions are essentially of chemical nature and have just been well reviewed by Pullman (1). It is important to remember that these interactions occur in a biological system and that there is always a biological counterpart responsible for them. Brookes (13) made an important contribution in this respect showing that different cells, particularly different isolated cells in vitro, have different capacities for metabolizing the same carcinogens. He also noted the fact that, in many situations, in vitro cultivation makes the cells lose their ability to accomplish certain metabolic steps — a very important point to keep in mind when we use in vitro tools in studies of carcinogen interactions. A major point has recurred in this context, namely, the need to develop selective model systems and then to be very critical about their use. In particular, there is a need to develop cell systems relating to differentiated cells, such as epithelial cells from various organs.

An important aspect of the events that precede transformation concerns the control of carcinogen activation through enzymatic systems. This rapidly growing field of studies has been widely discussed here and already reviewed in its chemical implications. We have to consider the fact that we are now beginning to define the biological conditions under which enzymatic activation varies. At least two major types of aryl hydrocarbon hydroxylases were described by Wiebel (14) and by Gelboin (15). The genetic control of these enzyme systems was clearly demonstrated by Nebert (16), who showed the genetic variance of aryl hydrocarbon hydroxylase induction in inbred strains of mice and their crosses. A major acquisition that has emerged in the last few years of research in this field is the recognition of the dual role of detoxification and activation of carcinogens performed by the same enzyme systems, as described by Gelboin (15). He reported the complexities of the problem of controlling the inducibility of these enzymes by means of inhibitors and enhancers and the marked differences in susceptibility of different cell types. One of the most important points to emerge from these studies is that there are initial results that show that these enzyme systems can be studied in human cells. Gelboin has reported his work with Whitlock which defines the activity of the enzyme system in human lymphocytes. Conney (17) has described his studies in human tissues using placenta and foreskin fibroblasts. An important point in Conney's presentation is his observation of wide individual variations in enzyme activity in different people: They show that we cannot generalize about the relative reactivity of man versus the mouse in the detoxification or activation of carcinogens. Before we can reach any generalization of practical value concerning the metabolic handling of carcinogens by humans, we must evaluate a great deal of specific data as to individual variabilities. However, I was encouraged by Conney's answer to my question on the stability of the levels of enzyme activity in the same individual, which indicated that this parameter appears to remain quite steady for long periods of time for the same individual. This approach could hopefully be used to identify the overall capability of an individual or of a population group to react to a carcinogen, as a measure of their susceptibility. These biochemical regulatory mechanisms, which control carcinogenesis, have been discussed in terms of protective biological systems. Gelboin has made the comment that perhaps they represent a kind of protective mechanism that is different but in a broad sense comparable with the protective mechanisms acting after the occurrence of transformation, particularly those of an immunological nature.

EVENTS OCCURRING AFTER TRANSFORMATION

I shall postpone the discussion of the central events of transformation and discuss now those that occur after neoplastic transformation has taken place, i.e., after the critical interaction of carcinogens with target cells and during the growth of transformed cells into a tumor. The problem of immunological control mechanisms in carcinogenesis is one that is now receiving much more attention than only a few years ago. Prehn (18), Coggin (19), Baldwin (20), and Rapp (21) illustrated the recent evolution of concepts on the immunological control of carcinogenesis and discussed extensively a variety of examples in this field. I am left with the feeling that it is still difficult to generalize the role and value of these mechanisms, and that these data need to be critically applied and interpreted in relation to each individual biological system of carcinogenesis we want to study. Prehn (18) discussed in brilliant terms his evaluation of present knowledge related to "immune surveillance, " emphasizing the ambivalence of some of its mechanisms. The expression of neo-antigens in chemically-induced tumors and the complexity of the immune reactions involved in carcinogenesis are reviewed by Baldwin (20). Cellular immunity systems, such as those described by Rapp (21) using BCG or its fractions and capable of remarkable effects in the killing of tumor cells, may well relate also to the immunologic control of the establishment and growth of tumors. When we discuss the biologic control and the inhibition of carcinogenesis, we really have to define what is the outer limit of the field of carcinogenesis. For example, the biologic phenomenon of metastases formation may still be considered part of carcinogenesis in a broad sense, since our need to define, interpret, and control the pathogenesis of tumors extends all the way to include their mode of spreading.

We know more now about the specificity of tumor antigens in a variety of tumor systems. An important step forward in this respect was reported by Heidelberger (22), who gave so many fundamental contributions to this symposium, when he reported the lack of cross reactivity of as many as 19 chemically transformed different clones, all derived from the same clone of origin. In this way, the biological individuality of a chemically transformed clone has been critically demonstrated in a well-defined cellular system.

Both the control mechanisms that occur before the target interaction of a carcinogen (particularly the enzyme systems that regulate the balance of carcinogen detoxification and activation) and those that control the spread of established cancer cells (particularly the immunologic systems) were discussed. In both cases, they were discussed essentially as protective mechanisms. I think that we have come to realize that these protective mechanisms may be double-edged swords that under certain conditions can turn against the good purposes for which we thought they had been developed. Prehn, in referring to "immune surveillance, " used the image of a sprinkler system that may start spraying oil on the fire instead of water. Similarly, the critical balance of detoxification versus activation in the activity of the enzyme control systems was stressed by Gelboin.

I have been considering this ambivalence of the main "protective" mechanisms against carcinogenesis in relation to their development during evolution. Cancer is a relatively late event in evolution and we see it mostly in the more developed species. In addition, cancer is an event that usually manifests itself late in individual life and in most cases well after the peak reproductive age. It has a relatively small effect on the average survival of a population and probably a negligible effect on the reproduction of the species as such. It is therefore not surprising that the main protective host mechanisms that work against the effects of environmental carcinogens would have developed as protection against other factors, namely detoxification of exogenous chemicals and immune response against abnormal antigens. When the foreign chemical is a carcinogen, the fact that its enzymatic attack may trigger its activation before detoxification is probably not registered in evolutionary terms because of the long latent period required for cancer expression. Similarly, "immune surveillance" mechanisms against cancer cells may result in increased growth of cancer cells, but this disadvantage to the host will not become a selective factor in evolution.

EVENTS OCCURRING AROUND THE TIME OF TRANSFORMATION

Let us now consider the central phase of carcinogenesis, or the events occurring during or around the process of transformation itself. This process has been the central theme of this symposium. The major characteristic of the present meeting, as compared with the symposium held four years ago in Jerusalem (23), is that we now have almost exclusively concentrated our discussions on in vitro cell systems. We are now studying the key events of carcinogenesis in a Petri dish. We are beginning to get away from the requirement of using the whole animal, with its implications as a black box system. This is a most important turning point. As I have indicated, we still need to continue our studies on whole animals in order to retain our terms of reference on the actual induction of tumors. However, the discovery of the enormous potential of the in vitro short-term models is a major step in our ability to assess the central events of the carcinogenic process. The models that have been developed for in vitro transformation by chemicals include a variety of cell systems from different species, such as mouse cell lines (Balb/c 3T3 cells, C3H $3T\frac{1}{2}$ cells, and C3H prostate fibroblasts), hamster embryo cell strains, guinea pig embryo cell strains, baby hamster kidney (BHK) cells, and finally cells that have already undergone epithelial differentiation, in particular rat liver parenchymal cells. A beautiful documentation on the latter was presented by Katsuta (24); similar studies were conducted by Weinstein (25, 26) and by Williams et al. at NCI (27). Yohn has recently reported his pilot experiments (28) in which the in vitro transformation of human cells by chemical carcinogens seems to be successful under appropriate hormonal control. We are beginning to move toward a goal that seemed extremely remote only a few years ago: We are learning to manipulate these in vitro systems, particularly by accounting for the mechanisms of enzymatic activation that were discussed earlier. A major contribution to this field came from DiPaolo (7) with his host-mediated assays (29) in which the carcinogen is administered during pregnancy to a parent animal, then the embryos are taken out, their cells are plated and then scored for transformation. This method combines the metabolic activation provided by the whole animal with the rapid detection of transformation obtained with embryo cells in vitro.

The development of the new in vitro methods is beginning to allow us to study the interactions of different types of carcinogenic effects directly on the target cells. In particular, we are beginning to acquire precise data on the interactions of radiation, chemicals, and viruses. The enhancement of chemically induced transformation by radiation with a critical time correlation has been reported by DiPaolo et al. (30). The manifestation of morphologic transformation in vitro is the main tool now being used to score the effects. It has been stressed that this is only a manifestation that occurs sometime after key events in the interaction of carcinogens with target macromolecules. The triggering event obviously occurs earlier than the appearance of morphologic transformation. The techniques of chromosome banding have made such progress that individual chromosomal changes can now be identified in the hamster system and followed up as markers from the in vitro transformed colonies to the tumors developing in the host when these colonies are reimplanted in vivo, as shown by DiPaolo in collaboration with Popescu (7, 31).

We did not have much discussion here about the use of organ cultures for in vitro studies of carcinogenesis, although, I believe, this is a field that offers much promise as a link in studying the comparison between isolated cells and cells in their tissue environment. Organ cultures will hopefully in the future be made to respond more directly to transformation mechanisms. Dao reported (32) that mammary nodules treated in vitro with DMBA and then reimplanted in vivo led to the development of carcinomas. He also documented their ability to provide a hormonal response in vitro with the synthesis of prolactin.

This point leads us to the next topic of growing importance: the study of hormonal effects in carcinogenesis and particularly the possibility of manipulating hormonal factors in vivo and in vitro, in model systems for carcinogenesis. An interesting approach, developed in Sato's laboratory, and reported here by Armelin (33), concerns the growth control of cells in culture by manipulating their hormonal milieu. They have also studied another important subject that may become a critical one in the future development of in vitro systems, i. e., the minimum maintenance level of serum factors that would allow cells to survive, but would not provide cell growth, so that one could add to this basal level several selective and well-defined factors to study their specific actions. Some of the implications of this type of approach, which were not discussed at this meeting, relate particularly to the recent work of Holley on the study of membrane uptake functions that may be responsible for the control of carcinogenesis (34).

The development of all the new methods for the study of carcinogenesis in vitro is of great importance in our effort to establish correlations between carcinogenic effects of chemicals and the state of activity of their target cells at the time of interaction. The role of DNA replication can be considered first. Heidelberger (22) has looked at the sequence of events in carcinogen metabolism in relation to the time of appearance of transformation and of cell toxicity. His data suggest that, in certain conditions of exposure to carcinogens in vitro, transformation may continue to increase in cells where toxicity no longer increases. On the other hand, he reported that transformation of mouse $3T\frac{1}{2}$ cells by DMBA reaches a maximum level after 6 hours; longer periods of exposure no longer increase transformation but they increase cell toxicity. Such a time gap between the manifestations of transformation and of toxicity suggests a response to different stages of metabolic activation. The most important point in this respect is the fact that transformation events occur before DNA replication, as is well demonstrated in two different systems: Heidelberger, using synchronized cells (22), demonstrates that transformation occurs long before DNA synthesis starts; Bader, in an entirely different system using Rous sarcoma virus (35), gave a remarkable demonstration that the expression of morphologic transformation and of its biochemical markers is entirely independent of DNA synthesis and occurs long before the target cells replicate. This is in keeping with the biochemical data that were obtained a few years ago in Bates' laboratory (36) at NCI, which showed carcinogen binding to nonreplicating DNA.

Some other major advances in cell biology were discussed for their potential usefulness in carcinogenesis research. One of the most important appears to be the model for cell hybridization through fusion. Cell fusion has been used by Gelboin to determine the effects of fusing cells having different levels of activity of the aryl hydrocarbon hydroxylases (15). Kao, from Puck's laboratory, described their extensive work (37) that has resulted in the development of hybrids of Chinese hamster cells with human cells: in these hybrids eventually only one human chromosome is retained because it provides a specific metabolic function absent from the hamster genome. Puck's laboratory is working to develop a whole battery of such hybrid cells, representing each human chromosome. Such hybrids could become an extremely useful tool in the study of specific changes in human chromosomes in the presence of carcinogens. These methods are already being used effectively in the study of mutagenic events. Other genetic methods can now be used to acquire more critical information on the role of the genome in carcinogenesis, such as the use of haploid cell lines, as described by Mezger-Freed (38), and of polyploid cell lines, as discussed by Harris (39).

This leads us conceptually to the last step in our review, which concerns the study of central molecular mechanisms of the interaction of carcinogens with target cell constituents. As noted before, this symposium concentrated almost exclusively on data relating to the interaction of carcinogens with the genetic material in the cells. Not much has been reported in terms of data about epigenetic mechanisms of interaction, although Bonner (40) provided a strong reminder of the role of proteins as targets. There has been, however, enough discussion of the possibility of epigenetic events that at least we can say that these have not escaped our attention.

The interaction of carcinogens with DNA was considered first for its remarkable similarity with the mechanism of mutagenesis. The systems used for mutagenesis studies are now given a great deal of attention as tools in the identification of carcinogens. Mutagenesis has now been adopted as a major component in our methodologies for the study of carcinogens. This is a recognition of the fact that in the last few years it became possible to articulate our biologic systems so that they can reproduce the necessary conditions of metabolic activation of chemicals. Advances in somatic cell genetics are being used to extend our collection of tools in carcinogenesis studies. The auxotrophic marker systems developed in Pick's laboratory (37) could be exploited further in the direction of carcinogenesis studies. The analysis of the direct interaction of carcinogens with DNA was discussed through a range of methodologies. They include theoretical approaches, such as the fine biophysical techniques developed in Ts'o's laboratory (41), and the computerized theoretical study of the interaction of a molecule of the carcinogen, 2-fluorenylacetamide, with a molecule of DNA, as was very impressively shown in Weinstein's discussion (26). Also included were the important direct observations of DNA damage and repair, reported by Setlow (42) and Roberts et al. (43). They point out the intimate connections between the mechanisms of carcinogenesis and of mutagenesis.

Van Lancker reported (44) that X-irradiation is without effect on the regulation of transcription, while it blocks the derepression, after partial hepatectomy, of DNA that is repressed in normal liver. The possibility of manipulating these systems could give us tools for a better appreciation of the specific events that control DNA repair in carcinogenesis. An important aspect of this mechanism is suggested by studies with the combination of viral and chemical carcinogens. Casto reported (45) on the use of the simian adenovirus SA-7 in combination with chemical carcinogens to study the insertion of a viral DNA genome into DNA of target cells undergoing repair. This is clearly indicated by the time relationship between chemical and viral exposure in hamster embryo cells: treatment with a chemical carcinogen prior to the addition of SA-7 enhances the frequency of viral

transformation, wnile carcinogen given after the virus inhibits transformation. These findings suggest that DNA damage by the carcinogen
provides an opportunity for the insertion of viral genome into DNA
during repair.

Another intriguing problem that was discussed concerns the passage
of DNA from one cell into another, or the passage of DNA into a cell
from the outside. Bendich described (46) the passage of DNA from
mouse erythrocyte cells into Chinese hamster cells in mixed culture,
with expression of mouse antigens in the Chinese hamster cells. He
also showed that DNA extracted from mouse erythrocyte cells can be
made to enter the Chinese hamster cells. And finally, he gave an
impressive demonstration of spermatozoa entering somatic cells.
Lastly, using T7 DNA introduced into hamster embryo cell cultures,
Leavitt et al. beautifully demonstrated (47) the spread of the
thymidine label to the majority of the growing cells. One step
further, consideration was given to extranuclear DNA, particularly
mitochrondrial DNA: At this time we do not have much information on
its possible role in carcinogenesis, and this area needs further study.

The last point to be considered has come out particularly from the
reports by Sachs (48) and Bader (49). It concerns the specific manifestations that occur soon after the transforming interactions have
taken place and it involves the phenomenon of reversion of transformed
cells to a normal phenotype. I think that the most important finding
is that the phenotype can change rapidly back and forth from a transformed state to an apparently normal one in a short time, under
special culture conditions such as temperature changes.

CONCLUSIONS

The discussions of this symposium have spanned the vast and
complex field of chemical carcinogenesis, going from the interaction
of an exogenous carcinogen with the whole organism to the molecular
events that control transformation and to those that regulate the growth
of the transformed cell. I think we are all aware that the field is now
rapidly developing. It is extremely encouraging to see a whole variety
of chemical, biologic, biochemical, and immunologic techniques,
coming from almost any of the major basic disciplines of science,
converge on the study of one of the key events in human pathology.
Our challenge is to close in on the applicability of these methods to
the prevention of human cancer.

Miller indicated at the beginning of this symposium (12) the need to concentrate our studies on the epithelial cells and on the possibility of using human cells. In the course of our discussions, perhaps we have not given enough attention to these end-points. I think this is really one of the clear goals of this whole field for the near future: how to make use of the existing tools to try and relate our knowledge of carcinogenesis to the effects on differentiated cells in the main target organs of cancer induction in animals and in man.

Pierce has clearly indicated the need to pay close attention to the problem of differentiation and its control in carcinogenesis (50). I am personally involved in the study of one biological system where differentiation of epithelial cells under biochemical control seems to be very closely related to transformation and carcinogenesis, namely, the respiratory epithelial cells from which bronchogenic carcinoma arises (51-56). Therefore, I am very responsive to this type of approach. In our choice of model studies in chemical carcinogenesis, we need to select tools that can be clearly analyzed and defined. We have to continue the exciting development and study of models based on a single cell population, which Dr. Ts'o has indicated as his preferred models (41); but I think it is also our function to try and relate those to larger orders of organization: tissues, organs, and whole organisms so that finally we can identify and learn to inhibit all the major steps that lead from the entry of a carcinogen into the human body, to its molecular activation and interaction in a target site, to the conversion of the target cells to a neoplastic state and to the final development of a cancer in man.

I think that I interpret the feelings of all the participants in expressing our very warm thanks to Dr. Ts'o and to Dr. DiPaolo for the organization of a most successful and useful symposium.

REFERENCES

1. B. Pullman, "Summary and Predictions: Chemical Aspects, " in Chemical Carcinogenesis (P.O.P. Ts'o and J.A. DiPaolo, eds.), Dekker, New York, 1974.
2. J.W. Cook, I. Hieger, E.L. Kennaway, and W.V. Mayneord, The production of cancer by pure hydrocarbons — Part I, Proc. Roy. Soc. London (Biol.), 111, 455 (1932); and G. Barry, J.W. Cook, G.A.D. Haslewood, C.L. Hewett, I. Hieger, and E.L. Kennaway, The production of cancer by pure hydrocarbons — Part III, Proc. Roy. Soc. London (Biol.), 117, 318 (1935).

3. C. Heidelberger, M. E. Baumann, L. Griesbach, A. Ghobar, and T. M. Vaughan, The carcinogenic activities of various derivatives of dibenzanthracene, Cancer Res., 22, 78 (1962).

4. B. L. Van Duuren, A. Sivak, L. Langseth, B. M. Goldschmidt, and A. Segal, "Initiators and Promoters in Tobacco Carcinogenesis, " in Toward a Less Harmful Cigarette (E. L. Wynder and D. Hoffman, eds.), National Cancer Institute Monograph No. 28, Washington, D. C., U. S. Government Printing Office, 1968.

5. W. Lijinsky, H. Garcia, and U. Saffiotti, Structure-activity relationships among some polynuclear hydrocarbons and their hydrogenated derivatives, J. Natl. Cancer Inst., 44, 641 (1970).

6. J. A. DiPaolo, P. J. Donovan, and R. L. Nelson, Transformation of Syrian hamster fetal cells in vitro by chemical carcinogens, Proc. Amer. Assoc. Cancer Res., 12, 65 (1971).

7. J. A. DiPaolo, "Quantitative Aspects of In Vitro Chemical Carcinogenesis, " in Chemical Carcinogenesis (P. O. P. Ts'o and J. A. DiPaolo, eds.), Dekker, New York, 1974.

8. International Agency for Research on Cancer, IARC Monographs on the Evaluation of Carcinogenic Risk of Chemicals to Man, Volume 1, 1972, Volume 2, "Some Inorganic and Organometallic Compounds, " 1973; Volume 3, "Some Polycyclic Aromatic Hydrocarbons and Heterocyclic Compounds, " 1973, World Health Organization, Lyon, France.

9. J. L. Hartwell, Survey of Compounds Which Have Been Tested for Carcinogenic Activity, U. S. Department of Health, Education, and Welfare, Public Health Service Publication No. 149, U. S. Government Printing Office, Washington, D. C., 1951.

10. P. Shubik and J. L. Hartwell, Survey of Compounds Which Have Been Tested for Carcinogenic Activity (Supplement 1), U. S. Department of Health, Education, and Welfare, Public Health Service Publication No. 149, U. S. Government Printing Office, Washington, D. C., 1957; Supplement 2 to the above (J. A. Peters, ed.), 1969.

11. U. S. Department of Health, Education, and Welfare, National Institutes of Health, National Cancer Institute, Survey of Compounds Which Have Been Tested for Carcinogenic Activity, U. S. Department of Health, Education, and Welfare, Public Health Service Publication No. 149, U. S. Government Printing Office, Washington, D. C., 1961-1967 Volume, 1973; 1968-1969 Volume, 1971; 1970-1971 Volume, in press.

12. J. A. Miller, "Current Thresholds of Research in Chemical Carcinogenesis, " in Chemical Carcinogenesis (P. O. P. Ts'o and J. A. DiPaolo, eds.), Dekker, New York, 1974.

13. P. Brookes, "DNA Reaction of Methylbenz[a]anthracene Derivatives in Relation to Carcinogenesis by These Compounds, " in Chemical Carcinogenesis (P. O. P. Ts'o and J. A. DiPaolo, eds.), Dekker, New York, 1974.

14. F. Wiebel, "Polycyclic Hydrocarbons and Flavones as Modulators of Benzo[a]pyrene Hydroxylase, " in Chemical Carcinogenesis (P. O. P. Ts'o and J. A. DiPaolo, eds.), Dekker, New York, 1974.
15. H. V. Gelboin, "The Regulation of Aryl Hydrocarbon Hydroxylase, " in Chemical Carcinogenesis (P. O. P. Ts'o and J. A. DiPaolo, eds.), Dekker, New York, 1974.
16. D. W. Nebert, "Aromatic Hydrocarbon-Produced Tumorigenesis and the Genetic Differences in Aryl Hydrocarbon Hydroxylase Induction, " in Chemical Carcinogenesis (P. O. P. Ts'o and J. A. DiPaolo, eds.), Dekker, New York, 1974.
17. A. H. Conney, "Factors Influencing Polycyclic Hydrocarbon Metabolism in Animals and Man, " in Chemical Carcinogenesis (P. O. P. Ts'o and J. A. DiPaolo, eds.), Dekker, New York, 1974.
18. R. T. Prehn, "The Role of Immunology in Carcinogenesis, " in Chemical Carcinogenesis (P. O. P. Ts'o and J. A. DiPaolo, eds.), Dekker, New York, 1974.
19. J. H. Coggin, "Phase Specific Autoantigens in Model Cancer Systems, " in Chemical Carcinogenesis (P. O. P. Ts'o and J. A. DiPaolo, eds.), Dekker, New York, 1974.
20. R. W. Baldwin, "Cell Antigen Changes during Chemical Carcinogenesis, " in Chemical Carcinogenesis (P. O. P. Ts'o and J. A. DiPaolo, eds.), Dekker, New York, 1974.
21. H. J. Rapp, "Immunotherapy of a Transplantable Hepatoma Induced in Guinea Pigs by Diethylnitrosamine, " in Chemical Carcinogenesis (P. O. P. Ts'o and J. A. DiPaolo, eds.), Dekker, New York, 1974.
22. C. Heidelberger, "Cell Culture Studies on the Mechanism of Hydrocarbon Oncogenesis, " in Chemical Carcinogenesis (P. O. P. Ts'o and J. A. DiPaolo, eds.), Dekker, New York, 1974.
23. E. D. Bergmann and B. Pullman (eds.), Physico-Chemical Mechanisms of Carcinogenesis, Academic, New York, 1969.
24. H. Katsuta, "Malignant Transformation of Rat Liver Parenchymal Cells by Chemical Carcinogens in Tissue Culture,"in Chemical Carcinogenesis (P. O. P. Ts'o and J. A. DiPaolo, eds.), Dekker, New York, 1974.
25. R. Bomford and I. B. Weinstein, Transformation of a rat epithelial-like cell line by murine sarcoma virus, J. Natl. Cancer Inst., 49, 379 (1972).
26. I. B. Weinstein, "Structural and Functional Changes in Nucleic Acids Modified by Chemical Carcinogens, " in Chemical Carcinogenesis (P. O. P. Ts'o and J. A. DiPaolo, eds.), Dekker, New York, 1974.
27. G. M. Williams, J. M. Elliott, and J. H. Weisburger, Carcinoma after malignant conversion in vitro of epithelial-like cells from rat liver by chemical carcinogens, Cancer Res., 33, 606 (1973).
28. D. Yohn, personal communication.

29. J. A. DiPaolo, R. L. Nelson, P. J. Donovan, and C. Evans, Host mediated in vivo-in vitro assay for chemical carcinogenesis, Arch. Pathol., 95, 380 (1973).

30. J. A. DiPaolo, P. J. Donovan, and R. L. Nelson, X-irradiation enhancement of transformation by benzo[a]pyrene in hamster embryo cells, Proc. Natl. Acad. Sci. U. S., 68, 1734 (1971).

31. J. A. DiPaolo, N. C. Popescu, and R. L. Nelson, Chromosomal banding patterns and in vitro transformation of Syrian hamster cells, Cancer Res., 33, 3250 (1973).

32. T. L. Dao, "Nature of Hormonal Influence in Carcinogenesis: Studies In Vivo and In Vitro, " in Chemical Carcinogenesis (P. O. P. Ts'o and J. A. DiPaolo, eds.), Dekker, New York, 1974.

33. H. A. Armelin and G. Sato, "Hormone Dependence Growth in Cell Culture, " in Chemical Carcinogenesis (P. O. P. Ts'o and J. A. DiPaolo, eds.), Dekker, New York, 1974.

34. R. W. Holley, Unifying hypothesis concerning the nature of cancer, Proc. Natl. Acad. Sci. U. S., 69, 2840 (1972).

35. J. P. Bader, Virus-induced transformation without cell division, Science, 180, 1069 (1973).

36. S. H. Yuspa, S. Del A. Eaton, D. L. Morgan, and R. R. Bates, The binding of 7, 12-dimethylbenz[a]anthracene to replicating and non-replicating DNA in cell culture, Chem.-Biol. Interactions, 1, 223 (1969).

37. F. T. Kao, "Cell Mutagenesis Studies Using Auxotrophic Markers as a Model System, " in Chemical Carcinogenesis (P. O. P. Ts'o and J. A. DiPaolo, eds.), Dekker, New York, 1974.

38. L. Mezger-Freed, "The Effect of Mutagen Treatment of Haploid Cell Lines on BUdR-Resistance, " in Chemical Carcinogenesis (P. O. P. Ts'o and J. A. DiPaolo, eds.), Dekker, New York, 1974.

39. M. Harris, "Cytogenetic Studies with Matched Polyploid Lines, " in Chemical Carcinogenesis (P. O. P. Ts'o and J. A. DiPaolo, eds.), Dekker, New York, 1974.

40. J. Bonner, "Molecular Events in Differentiation and De-differentiation, " in Chemical Carcinogenesis (P.O. P. Ts'o and J. A. DiPaolo, eds.), Dekker, New York, 1974.

41. P. O. P. Ts'o, W. J. Caspary, B. I. Cohen, J. C. Leavitt, S. A. Lesko, Jr., R. J. Lorentzen, and L. M. Schechtman, "Basic Mechanisms in Polycyclic Hydrocarbon Carcinogenesis, " in Chemical Carcinogenesis (P. O. P. Ts'o and J. A. DiPaolo, eds.), Dekker, New York, 1974.

42. R. B. Setlow, "The Magnitudes of DNA Repair, " presented orally at the World Symposium on Model Studies in Chemical Carcinogenesis, October 31-November 3, 1972.

43. J. Roberts, J. E. Sturrock, and K. N. Ward, "The Effects of Caffeine on Alkylation-Induced Toxicity and Mutagenicity in Chinese Hamster Cells, " in Chemical Carcinogenesis (P. O. P. Ts'o and J. A. DiPaolo, eds.), Dekker, New York, 1974.

44. J. L. Van Lancker, "DNA Repair and Its Restrictions, " in Chemical Carcinogenesis (P. O. P. Ts'o and J. A. DiPaolo, eds.), Dekker, New York, 1974.
45. B. C. Casto, "Enhancement of Viral Oncogenesis by Chemical Carcinogens, " in Chemical Carcinogenesis (P. O. P. Ts'o and J. A. DiPaolo, eds.), Dekker, New York, 1974.
46. A. Bendich, "Experimental Approaches to Problems in Carcinogenesis, " in Chemical Carcinogenesis (P. O. P. Ts'o and J. A. DiPaolo, eds.), Dekker, New York, 1974.
47. J. C. Leavitt, L. Schechtman, and P. O. P. Ts'o, "Studies on the Uptake of Foreign DNA by Mammalian Cells and the Biological Effects, " in Chemical Carcinogenesis (P. O. P. Ts'o and J. A. DiPaolo, eds.), Dekker, New York, 1974.
48. L. Sachs, "Mechanisms of Chemical Carcinogenesis and the Regulation of Malignancy, " presented orally at the World Symposium on Model Studies in Chemical Carcinogenesis, October 31- November 3, 1972.
49. J. P. Bader, "Temperature-Dependent Transformation of Cells by Rous Sarcoma Virus, " in Chemical Carcinogenesis (P. O. P. Ts'o and J. A. DiPaolo, eds.), Dekker, New York, 1974.
50. G. B. Pierce, "Cellular Heterogeneity of Cancers, " in Chemical Carcinogenesis (P. O. P. Ts'o and J. A. DiPaolo, eds.), Dekker, New York, 1974.
51. U. Saffiotti, F. Cefis, and L. H. Kolb, A method for the experimental induction of bronchogenic carcinoma, Cancer Res., 28, 104 (1968).
52. R. Montesano, U. Saffiotti, and P. Shubik, "The Role of Topical and Systemic Factors in Experimental Respiratory Carcinogenesis, " in Inhalation Carcinogenesis (M. G. Hanna, Jr., P. Nettesheim, and J. R. Gilbert, eds.), Atomic Energy Commission Symposium Series, No. 18 (CONF-691001), U. S. Atomic Energy Commission, Division of Technical Information Extension, Oak Ridge, Tennessee, 1970.
53. J. M. Smith, M. B. Sporn, D. M. Berkowitz, T. Kakefuda, E. Callan, and U. Saffiotti, Isolation of enzymatically active nuclei from epithelial cells of the trachea, Cancer Res., 31, 199 (1971).
54. C. C. Harris, M. B. Sporn, D. G. Kaufman, J. B. Smith, F. E. Jackson, and U. Saffiotti, Histogenesis of squamous metaplasia in the hamster tracheal epithelium caused by vitamin A deficiency or benzo[a]pyrene-ferric oxide, J. Natl. Cancer Inst., 48, 743 (1972).
55. D. G. Kaufman, M. S. Baker, C. C. Harris, J. M. Smith, H. Boren, M. B. Sporn, and U. Saffiotti, Coordinated biochemical and morphologic examination of hamster tracheal epithelium, J. Natl. Cancer Inst., 49, 783 (1972).

56. D. G. Kaufman, M. S. Baker, J. M. Smith, W. R. Henderson, C. C. Harris, M. B. Sporn, and U. Saffiotti, RNA metabolism in tracheal epithelium: Alteration in hamsters deficient in vitamin A, Science, 177, 1105 (1972).

AUTHOR INDEX

Numbers in parentheses are reference numbers and indicate that an author's work is referred to although his name is not cited in the text. Underlined numbers give the page on which the complete reference is listed.

Hageman, P., 77(89), 85
Hahn, G. M., 401(5), 423
Hakala, M. T., 575(9), 589
Hakomori, S., 669(20), 683
Hall, M. R., 588(25), 590
Hammer, E. J., 23(57), 24(56), 50
Hammond, W. G., 703(4), 709
Hamrick, M., 300(35), 304(35), 307
Hanafusa, H., 619(12, 17, 18), 621(16, 17, 18), 623(13, 27), 626(11), 629, 662(2), 666
Hanafusa, T., 619(12), 623(13, 27), 626(11), 628, 629
Hanawalt, P. C., 428(19, 20), 437
Hancock, R., 533, 540
Hanna, M. G., Jr., 706(12), 707(13), 709
Haran-Ghera, N., 624(14), 628, 632(6), 637
Hariharan, P. V., 427(2), 436
Harper, K. H., 98(26), 111
Harris, C. C., 65(19), 80, 740(54, 55, 56), 745 746
Harris, H., 337(42), 350, 469(21), 472, 517(23), 529
Harris, J. R., 695(13), 696(13), 698
Harris, M., 575(1, 7, 14, 17), 576(7, 17), 577(7, 17), 579(7), 586(7), 587(7), 589, 590, 738, 744
Harris, R. G., 517(27, 29), 529
Harrison, Y. E., 353(6, 7), 361(6, 7), 362(7), 363(7), 364(7), 365(7), 370
Hart, E. R., 64(18), 80
Hartley, J. W., 624(22, 28, 30), 629, 635(10, 11), 637
Hartline, E. J. H., 591(13), 601(13), 603
Hartwell, J. L., 64(15, 16), 79, 167(18), 175, 177(2), 178(7), 180(7), 180, 181, 730, 741

Harvey, D. A., 636(12), 638
Harvey, J. J., 607(31), 618
Harvey, R. G., 177(5), 181, 198(9), 215
Haslewood, G. A. D., 729(2), 741
Hatanaka, M., 664(9), 666
Hay, A. J., 337(47), 350
Hayaishi, O., 271(2), 285, 291(10), 305
Hayashi, S., 339(53), 350
Hayes, W., 565(4), 572
Hecker, E., 69(28), 80, 103(36, 37), 111
Heidelberger, C., 69(40, 43, 47, 48, 49, 50), 72(43, 61, 62, 63), 78(92), 81, 82, 83, 85, 87(8), 109, 115(2, 4, 12), 138(47), 139(49), 143, 144, 146, 149(1, 2), 150(12), 156, 157, 232(38), 235, 237(2, 3, 5, 7), 239(5, 7), 242(33), 243(2, 3, 27), 245, 247, 249(14), 253(29), 264(14), 267, 268, 271(11, 12, 13), 286, 294(17, 18), 306, 311(22), 313(22, 30), 249, 250, 360(42, 45), 373, 444(6), 453, 457(1, 2, 4, 5, 6), 458(7, 8, 9, 10, 11, 12, 13), 459(14-27), 460, 461, 608(10), 609(11), 616, 693(23, 24), 694(18), 696(18, 23, 24), 698, 729(3), 734, 737, 738, 742, 743
Hellström, I., 682(2), 689
Hellström, K. E., 686(2), 689
Helmkamp, G. K., 223(17), 233
Henderson, W. R., 740(56), 746
Heppner, G. H., 686(2), 689
Herberman, R. B., 697(29), 699
Herbst, A. L., 62(3), 79
Hershberg, E. B., 90(15), 110, 129(31), 145
Heston, W. E., 283(38), 288
Hewer, A., 69(41), 81, 241(29-32), 242(29), 247, 271(7), 285, 294(17), 306

MacDonald, J. C. , 360(34), <u>372</u>
Mackintosh, D. S. , 153(16),
154(16), <u>157</u>, 356(20), <u>371</u>
Macpherson, I. , 515(2), 525(2),
<u>527</u>
MacPowell, D. , 178(8), <u>181</u>
Magee, P. N. , 69(35), 73(69,
70), <u>81</u>, <u>83</u>, <u>84</u>, 353(2), <u>370</u>
Maggio, R. , 161(7), <u>174</u>
Mahboubi, E. , 63(8), <u>79</u>
Maher, V. M. , 66(24), <u>80</u>,
117(21), 128(21), 129(32),
<u>144</u>, <u>145</u>, 183(4), <u>194</u>,
232(39), <u>235</u>, 657(21), <u>659</u>
Maickel, R. P. , 358(25), <u>372</u>
Makino, S. , 464, <u>470</u>
Malfer, P. , 115(5), <u>143</u>
Malling, H. V. , 402(10), 416,
<u>423</u>, 545(23), 547(5, 24),
<u>551</u>(18, 19, 35), 553(20, 35, 36),
554(16), 559(21, 22, 35), <u>561,</u>
<u>562</u>, <u>563</u>, 576(20), 577(20),
<u>590</u>
Mallucci, L. , 137(41), <u>146</u>
Malmgren, R. A. , 449(21), <u>454</u>
Mangane, M. , 34(101, 102), <u>53</u>
Manning, G. , 183(7), <u>194</u>
Mantel, N. , 356(21), <u>371</u>
Marbaix, G. , 657(18), <u>659</u>
March, H. H. , III, 548(32), <u>563</u>
Marcoux, L. S. , 183(6), <u>194</u>
Margrave, J. L. , 180(18), <u>181</u>
Mark, J. , 138(46), <u>146</u>
Mark, L. C. , 254(31), <u>268</u>,
353(1), 361(1), 362(1), <u>370</u>
Markert, C. L. , 525(41), <u>530</u>
Marmur, J. , 227, <u>234</u>
Marquardt, H. , 69(43, 47, 48,
49), 72(43), <u>81</u>, 87(7, 8),
<u>109</u>, 237(2, 3), 243(2, 3),
<u>245</u>, 253(29), <u>268</u>, 271(11,
13), <u>286</u>, 360(42), <u>373</u>,
458(11), 459(15, 16, 17, 18,
19), <u>461</u>, <u>462</u>, 546(25), <u>562</u>
Marroquin, F. , 72(65), <u>83</u>

Marshak, M. I. , 575(8), <u>589</u>
Marshall, A. , 360(37), <u>373</u>
Martin, G. S. , 621(8, 23, 24),
<u>628</u>, <u>629</u>
Martin, M. , 20(27), <u>48</u>
Martin, M. A. , 653(23), <u>659</u>
Marushige, K. , 162, <u>174</u>, 531,
533, <u>540</u>
Maryak, J. M. , 77(85), <u>85</u>,
612(19), <u>617</u>
Marzullo, G. , 601(15), <u>603</u>
Mason, H. S. , 249(6), <u>267</u>,
271(1), <u>285</u>
Mason, W. S. , 620(21), 621(21),
625(40), <u>629</u>, <u>630</u>
Mathé, G. , 9, <u>46</u>
Matsushima, T. , 68(26), 72(66),
<u>80</u>, <u>83</u>
Matsuyama, A. , 103(33), <u>111</u>
Matsuyane, T. , 63(7), <u>79</u>
Matthaei, J. H. , 163(15), <u>175</u>
Matthews, E. J. , 337(50),
340(50), 343-347(67), <u>350</u>,
<u>351</u>
Mattocks, A. R. , 69(37, 38, 69),
<u>81</u>
Maurer, H. R. , 539(18), <u>541</u>
Mayfield, J. , 535(12), 538(17),
<u>540</u>, <u>541</u>
Mayneord, W. V. , 729(2), <u>741</u>
Mayyasi, S. A. , 635(9), <u>637</u>
McAuslan, B. R. , 339(51), <u>350</u>,
669(25), 679(25), <u>683</u>
McCafferty, D. E. , 360(40),
<u>373</u>
McCalla, D. R. , 69(34), <u>81</u>
McCarter, J. A. , 631(4), 632(7),
636(12), <u>637</u>, <u>638</u>
McCarthy, B. , 536, <u>541</u>
McCarty, K. S. , 339(56), <u>351</u>
McCutchan, J. H. , 642(12),
<u>659</u>
McFall, R. , 252(26), 253(26),
<u>268</u>
McFarland, V. W. , 679(11), <u>682</u>
McGowan, J. , 517(28), <u>529</u>

I

K